M000105694

Behavior Modification for Exceptional Children and Youth

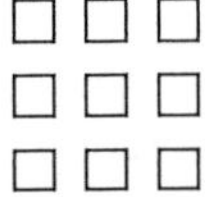

Behavior Modification for Exceptional Children and Youth

Marcia Datlow Smith, Ph.D.

Community Services for Autistic Adults and Children
Rockville, Maryland

Andover Medical Publishers
Boston London Oxford Singapore Sydney Toronto Wellington

Andover Medical Publishers is an imprint of Butterworth–Heinemann.

Recognizing the importance of preserving what has been written, it is the policy of Butterworth–Heinemann to have the books it publishes printed on acid-free paper, and we exert our best efforts to that end.

Efforts to produce this book were in part supported by Grant No. HO23C10149 from the U.S. Department of Education, Office of Special Education. However, the opinions expressed herein do not necessarily reflect the positition or policy of the U.S. Department of Education.

Library of Congress Cataloging-in-Publication Data

Smith, Marcia Datlow, 1951–
Behavior modification for exceptional children and youth / Marcia Datlow Smith.
p. cm.
Includes bibliographical references and index.
ISBN 1-56372-042-6 (ppc: alk. paper)
1. Problem children—Behavior modification. 2. Problem youth—Behavior modification. 3. Learning disabled children—Behavior modification. 4. Learning disabled youth—Behavior modification. 5. Mentally handicapped children—Behavior modification. 6. Mentally handicapped youth—Behavior modification. I. Title.
[DNLM: 1. Behavior Therapy—in adolescence. 2. Behavior Therapy—in infancy & childhood. 3. Child, Exceptional. WS 350.6 S655b]
RJ505.B4A57 1993
618.92—dc20
DNLM/DLC 92-11364

British Library Cataloguing in Publication Data

A catalogue record for this book is available from the British Library.

Butterworth–Heinemann
80 Montvale Avenue
Stoneham, MA 02180

10 9 8 7 6 5 4 3 2 1

Printed in the United States of America

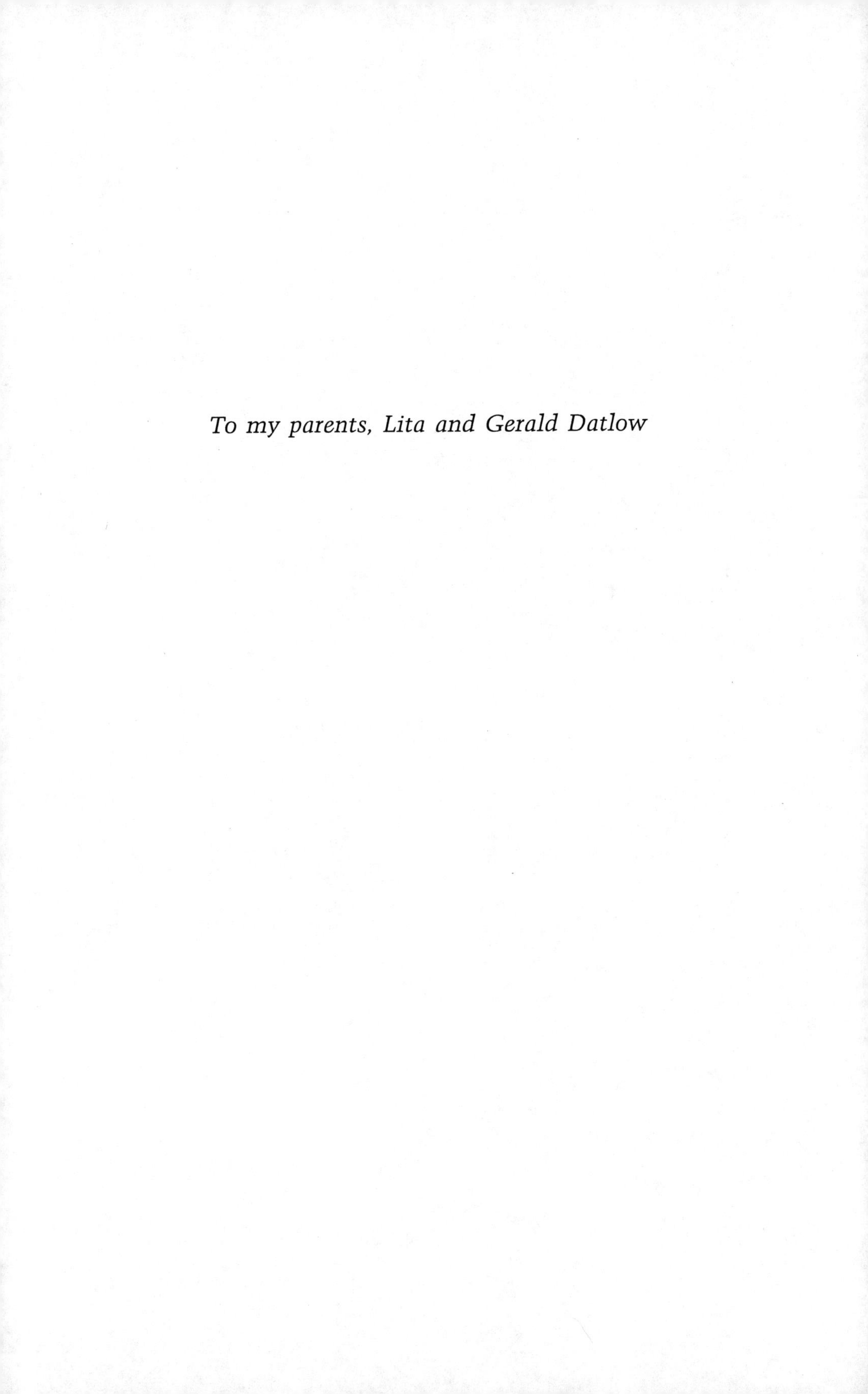

To my parents, Lita and Gerald Datlow

Contents

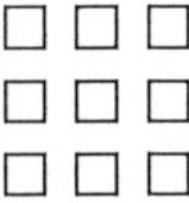

Contributing Authors

Myra Burgee
University of Maryland
College Park, Maryland

Glen Dunlap
Florida Mental Health Institute
University of South Florida
Tampa, Florida

V. Mark Durand
Department of Psychology
State University of New York at Albany
Albany, New York

Jolenea Ferro
Florida Mental Health Institute
University of South Florida
Tampa, Florida

James W. Halle
Department of Special Education
University of Illinois at Urbana-Champaign
Champaign, Illinois

Roger McIntire
Department of Psychology
University of Maryland
College Park, Maryland

Mark F. O'Reilly
Department of Special Education
The University of Western Autralia
Nedlands, Perth
Western Australia

Donald K. Pumroy
College of Education
University of Maryland
College Park, Maryland

Nancy R. Weiss
The Kennedy Institute
The Johns Hopkins University
Baltimore, Maryland

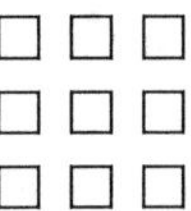

Preface

Behavior modification is a process that has been much maligned, often misused, usually misunderstood, occasionally banned, and seldom done well. However, when done well, behavior modification has made significant contributions to the functioning of children, youth, and adults in a variety of settings and circumstances. The group that has profited the most from behavior modification is children and youth who have special needs in the areas of learning, communication, and behavior.

Children with learning disabilities, who in the past were consigned to illiteracy, have profited from instructional procedures based on the principles of behavior. Children with social-skills problems or behavior problems, who in the past were excluded from social and educational opportunities, have benefited from interventions based on the principles of behavior. Children with the most severe disabilities, such as autism and profound mental retardation, who in the past spent nonproductive lives at home or in institutions, have been able to enjoy full participation in society as students, workers, and neighbors as a result of instruction and interventions based on the principles of behavior.

Unfortunately, many children and young adults with disorders of cognition, learning, communication, and behavior are limited in their progress by the knowledge gaps of those into whose care they are entrusted. A teacher, unknowledgeable about the principles of behavior, seeks to have a child expelled from the class—a child who could succeed given adequate use of behavior modification. A parent, unknowledgeable about the principles of behavior, seeks to send a child with a severe handicap to an institution for the mentally retarded—a child who could possibly make it at home given adequate use of behavior modification. An employer, unknowledgeable about the potential of workers with learning handicaps, seeks to fire the employee with a learning disability—an employee who could be productive given adequate use of behavior modification.

The purpose of this book is to provide the student with a broad knowledge of the principles of behavior and specific knowledge about the application of these principles to the learning and adjustment needs of children, youth, and adults with disabilities of learning and behavior. Chapter 1, the introduction, provides a brief history of behavior modification. Chapter 2 provides an overview of the first step in the behavior modification process, that of defining and measuring the behavior targeted for change. Chapter 3 describes the functional assessment and explains the basis for an understanding of much of human behavior and misbehavior. Chapters 4 through 8 cover the principles of behavior, their effects, and their influencing factors. Central themes of each of these chapters are the roles of these principles in behavior change and the practical relationships of these principles to the functional assessment. Chapter 9 covers punishment, its historical use in behavior change, and the dangers and disadvantages inherent in its use in applied settings. Chapter 10 covers self-management, the application of behavior modification to one's own behavior. Achieving behavior change across settings, people, and time has been a long-standing challenge in the field; Chapter 11 covers the technology of generalization and its limits. Chapters 12 and 13 cover the synthesis of behavioral principles into a behavior change plan. Chapter 14 covers the ethics of behavior modification, with a view toward promoting ethical and humane use of the principles of behavior.

The student progressing through this text is provided the opportunity to conduct a self-management plan; that is, the reader is encouraged to apply the principles of behavior to change a behavior of his or her own. Instructions for the self-management plan are at the end of pertinent chapters, beginning with Chapter 2. By applying the principles of behavior to one's own behavior, a student has the valuable opportunity of observing their effects and influences firsthand. In addition to the Self-Management Activities, most chapters include Self-Application questions which encourage the student to examine how the principles of behavior have operated in their lives.

Many of the readers of this book will eventually find themselves in positions of authority or influence over children, youth, or adults with and without learning or behavioral handicaps. When in that position, the reader of this book will be able to use behavior modification to assist these individuals in achieving their fullest potentials and taking their places in society as productive and valued students, employees, friends, and neighbors.

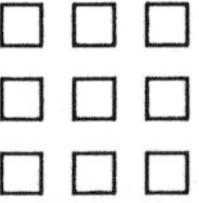

Acknowledgments

The bulk of the figures and illustrations for this book were drawn by Gerald Allex Datlow who graciously donated his time and talents to that effort.

Grateful acknowledgment is due to Lita Datlow and Timothy LaVallee for their editorial feedback; to Mark Durand, Nancy Ator, and Mary Alvord for their technical advice; to Ronald Belcher for his assistance; to Donald Pumroy and Roger McIntire for their foundational instruction; to Anne Donnellan and Gary LaVigna for years of assistance with the application of behavioral principles to persons with severe disabilities; to Christopher Huott for his assistance with the application of these principles to child management and athletics; to Susan Ingram, Cathy Fowler, and Karla Nabors for their support; and to Joe Bartell for his administrative assistance. Patricia Juhrs and Jane Salzano are gratefully acknowledged for their commitment to applied behavior analysis and for their support of the work from which most of the examples came. Special acknowledgment is due to Paul Wehman for his ongoing support and advice. Danielle and Jared also deserve special thanks and commendation for their independence and helpfulness during the writing of this book.

Behavior Modification for Exceptional Children and Youth

1

Introduction: Two Age-old Questions

Roger McIntire, Myra Burgee, and Donald Pumroy

The story of *behaviorism*, the study of behavior, is the story of two ancient questions. The first question is, Are we controlled primarily by the world that fate would have us encounter or are we controlled primarily by unseen forces and the will within us? The second question concerns how to study ourselves: Should we focus on what there is to see—what we do and what we say—or should we also speculate about what is going on inside the brain? The answers to these questions have not yet been fully discovered, but discovery continues of the numerous ways in which the world we encounter limits, influences, and even controls what we do.

In regard to the question about studying inside events, behaviorism resists the temptation to speculate on these events and focuses rather on what we do and say. This approach has produced many useful principles. Punishment, reinforcement, imitation, social signals, and even aspects of diet are among the many principles that can be effective when used in the careful ways described in this book.

There are aspects of human behavior that are not controlled by the present environment. Human behaviors, for example, result from the heredity, early experiences, and emotional states of a person. These influences are modified by the present environment but still have an influence of their own. When a precocious child plays the violin with a sensitivity and tone that can be described only as true beauty, how did she come to have such talent? Was she born with some advantages in dexterity, hearing, and perception? Was she helped by experiences with parents who cultivated her ability? Yes, and her day-to-day performance or even her willingness to perform at all comes under the influence of the here and now. As her talent matures, the influence of the present will become the dominating factor in her progress. Heredity is a given, and early experience cannot be changed, but ever-ongoing experiences continue to mold habits by plan or by accident.

How learning occurs and how the principles of behavior apply to learning have been a subject of science for several centuries. Principles of memory, reinforcement, conditioning, motivation, and emotion have all been investigated and have produced useful results for the professionals facing the problems of their clients.

Professionals Take Sides on the Questions

Principles of behavior immediately bring to mind individual control, power, and possible degradation of the client—the controlled and less powerful. The investigation and use of behavioral principles to control behavior have produced argument, fear, and denial by those who find the prospect of using behavioral principles to control behavior threatening. Those who find behavioral principles more promising than threatening sometimes have too much blind devotion to the founders of behaviorism or a narrow perception of the complexity of behavior.

Professionals with differing opinions on the correctness and usefulness of the principles of behavior even disagree on the current popularity of the field. Some professionals, pointing to the decline in animal experimentation and to studies showing the limited durability of some effects, claim that the area of behavioral principles is dead or at least seriously ill with a terminal disease of narrowness and inflexibility. Other professionals, pointing to the ever-expanding success of the behavioral approach in school and work settings with people with handicaps and disabilities and in the counseling of couples and families, say these principles are the success of twentieth-century psychology!

So, one extreme believes that the use of behavioral principles is outdated and of narrow and limited usefulness, while the other extreme believes that these principles constitute an invaluable technology of behavior change. Both extremes disregard issues that deflect or blur the focus that concerns their particular aspect of the controversy. Changes due to the application of behavioral principles are not likely to endure, for example, when the applications are ended and no similar influence occurs in the person's natural environment. Behaviors no longer reinforced will weaken, and old, less-controlled consequences will regain their previous advantages, having never lost their influence entirely. These prospects are often uncomfortable for the behaviorist because maintaining good behavior requires continuing good consequences. However, changes are being maintained, and the success of behavioral applications has been remarkable with exceptional children and youth, as well as with families, schools, and other institutions, if the applied principles are continuously attended. This fact can be comforting for the behaviorist!

Both sides of the controversy between professionals in regard to behavioral control would like to have a medicine for behavior—one dose and the job is done. For the most part, however, behavior is continually adjusting to a complex of needs, deprivations, and current consequences. Disorders are acquired from these influences and change only when the influences change; they change again when the demands regress. Unfortunately for both the detractors and the proponents of behavioral principles, changes in human behavior are achieved by hard work and maintained by hard work. Behaviorists are often confronted with apathetic parents, cynical teachers, or just lazy people not willing to make the effort to react consistently in a new way. The behaviorist often must wage war against the resistance to take action. Yet, the antibehaviorists are continually frustrated when confronted with these same resistances that will not change with mere talk. They too would like to get the process moving. The behaviorist has some ways to start. Some ethical questions need answers first. Although ethics will be a subject of a later chapter, the reader should be aware of the source of the unusual amount of ethical concern behaviorism generates.

Ethics of Treatment Using Behavioral Principles

Behavioral principles have attracted an unusual amount of concern about the ethics of the procedures. One reason for this concern is that, rather than leaving the whole process of change in the hands of the client, the behavioral approach is a procedure in constructing interventions that have determined objectives. The client may present these objectives, but in cases with clients with disabilities or with clients who are very young, the objectives are set out by the professional. Other therapeutic approaches have a similar intent but describe the procedure in a way that implies that the client is in control. The approach may, for example, have the objective of facilitating growth or development. These approaches intend to bring about changes in a client's behavior just as the objectives of the behaviorist do, but the cooperative, yet less specific, nature of the stated objectives makes it seem as if the ethical issues have been resolved.

Ethical questions seem more important with the behavioral approach because the objectives are specific and the approaches take control of at least some of the client's environment. The ethical question of who determines the objectives of treatment—particularly in cases of the young client and the client with disabilities—is made all the more complicated by other questions: What inconvenience or discomfort is justified? Whose values will be imposed? These problems are not unique to behavioral approaches but are highlighted because the professional employs specific procedures and objectives in an attempt to reach a particular outcome. So, as procedures and objectives are planned, applied behaviorism demands careful attention to the best interest of the client.

The behavioral approach to human problems emphasizes one additional aspect of the ethical issues in therapy: the scientific validation of the effectiveness of the procedures. Since behavior and its changes are observable and measurable events, a change can be confirmed by scientific observation. Evidence of effectiveness has been the central principle in the ethical debate. Many approaches to the treatment of human problems set out objectives that are not easily evaluated—better understanding, happiness, adjustment, and contentment. Without evidence of these improvements, the ethical issue arises that the therapist is engaged in false advertising, possibly relying on the client's tendency to believe the process is helpful because the client has gone to some effort and expense or the client would rather give the therapist more praise than fact. The behavioral approach sets an objective that is observable and puts the process to the test. If the therapy falls short, then the fairness—the ethics—of the charges can be debated.

History of the Two Kinds of Learning

There is a long history to the investigation and application of behavioral principles. The principles concern learning—changes in behavior due to practice and experience—and learning began with the first animals that made the slightest adjustment to their environments. The two kinds of learning, *respondent* and *operant*, have separate historical trends but have become closely associated in recent years because it is now known that they interact in the crafting of behavior and are at work, side by side, in each individual.

History of Classical (Respondent) Conditioning

The origins of the behavioral orientation in psychology can be traced back to I.P. Pavlov's pioneering laboratory experiments at the beginning of the twentieth century (Pavlov, 1927). Pavlov, a Russian physiologist, studied digestion by placing meat powder on a dog's tongue and then measuring the flow of saliva. Pavlov discovered that the dog salivated when he (Pavlov) merely walked into the room. In subsequent experiments, Pavlov rang a bell prior to placing meat powder on the dog's tongue, and this action resulted in a reflex salivation. Eventually, the bell alone elicited the salivary response. Pavlov concluded that learning had occurred and called this learning *conditioning* (i.e., existing reflex responses elicited by new stimuli). This type of learning became known as *classical conditioning* because of its importance in psychology's history (also referred to as *respondent conditioning*). All early applications of learning principles by psychologists were based on Pavlov's methods of classical/respondent conditioning. Classical-conditioning experiments were popular with scientists because these experiments permitted a high degree of control over the significant stimuli affecting behavior.

J.B. Watson, the founder of American behaviorism in 1913, applied Pavlov's respondent-conditioning principles to understanding maladaptive human behavior (Watson & Rayner, 1920). His assumption was that both maladaptive and adaptive behaviors operated under the same principles of learning. He held that all learning was the result of respondent conditioning and demonstrated the relationship between this conditioning and emotional disturbances.

In a famous experiment, Little Albert, an 11-month-old baby, was conditioned to fear furry objects. The experimenters first established that Albert showed a fear response to the sound of an iron bar struck immediately behind his head. This loud sound was then produced each time Albert was about to touch a white rat. After the fifth presentation of this procedure, Albert became conditioned to fear the rat when presented alone. Eventually, he showed the same fear response to other furry animals, demonstrating the principle of *stimulus generalization*.

Watson and Rayner then suggested several counterconditioning techniques that could be used to unlearn this fear response, such as repeatedly presenting the furry animals without striking the iron bar (*extinction*) and feeding candy when the feared object was present (*reconditioning*). Subsequently, Jones (1924) successfully treated children's phobias by using this suggested reconditioning-by-feeding technique where children were gradually exposed to a feared object while eating.

These early experiments led to the development of counterconditioning techniques, such as *reciprocal inhibition*, *assertive training*, and *systematic desensitization* (Wolpe, 1958). When developing the technique of systematic desensitization, Wolpe was also influenced by the readings of Salter's *Conditioned Reflex Therapy* (1949) and Edmund Jacobson's *Progressive Relaxation* (1938). Counterconditoning techniques have been successfully used to treat individuals with anxiety and phobic disorders. Early applications of these techniques resulted in reduction of fear of dogs (Lazarus & Abramovitz, 1962); fear of hospitals (Lazarus & Rachman, 1967); fear of buses (Obler & Terwilliger, 1970); and school phobias (Lazarus, Davison, & Polefka, 1965). Today, these techniques are the preferred methods for treating anxiety and phobic disorders by behavioral psychologists.

History of Operant Conditioning

The origins of *operant conditioning* can be traced back to Thorndike's laboratory experiments on reward learning (Thorndike, 1911). He developed a new experimental technique called the puzzle box, in which animals (usually cats) were placed in a box and learned to operate a latch in order to escape. From these experiments, Thorndike developed the principle of the Law of Effect (1911), which became known as *instrumental conditioning*. This principle states that when a satisfying event follows a response, the bond between the stimulus and the response is strengthened, and this in turn increases the probability of that response occurring in the future in the presence of the stimulus. The cat's response (operating the latch) will likely occur in the future because this response permits escape from the box (escape being a satisfying event). The bond between the response (opening the latch) and the stimulus (escaping) is strengthened. When an unpleasant event occurs, the reverse happens. So, for example, if the cat is given an electric shock upon operating the latch, the likelihood of the cat opening the latch in the future will decrease.

Thorndike referred to these conditions as satisfiers and annoyers respectively. The term *reinforcement* later replaced the term *satisfier* and was defined as a stimulus that increases the probability of a response when presented following that response. This term is more neutral than satisfier or reward because it does not imply that the event is pleasant or unpleasant but takes into account the fact that an event does not necessarily have to be pleasant in order to be reinforcing (e.g., negative attention from otherwise inattentive parents might reinforce a youngster's behaviors).

The principles and concepts of instrumental conditioning were most significantly developed by B.F. Skinner and his associates. Skinner referred to this type of learning as operant conditioning. This orientation was in contrast to the respondent-conditioning explanation of learning that behavioral psychologists followed at the time. Respondent conditioning holds that every response can be traced back to a stimulus and that learning is the result of the building of connections between stimuli and responses. Skinner was the first psychologist to break this tradition. He differentiated between two types of behavior, *respondent* and *emitted.*

"Respondent behavior is that which follows some identifiable stimulus and which is produced by it" (Skinner, 1938, p. 20). This behavior Skinner considered trivial, applying mostly to reflex responses (e.g., eye blink, knee reflex). He held that most behavior falls into the category of emitted behavior, as he believed that most learning is a function of what happens *after* behavior occurs. Skinner referred to behavior that occurs without any identifiable stimuli as *emitted behavior* and to the behaviors that are emitted as *operants* (1953). This new conceptualization of learning has proved significant, especially in educational settings.

In these settings, most learning is the result of operant rather than respondent conditioning (e.g., writing is used for communication). One reason for this is that during classical conditioning, the response remains the same throughout the learning process (dog salivates after the first and the last trials); during operant conditioning, however, the response changes as learning progresses. This phenomenon, referred to as *shaping*, is a central feature of operant conditioning. Most instances of learning occur through the process of shaping (e.g., learning to read and to write, learning appropriate classroom and social behaviors). Indeed, learning can be characterized as involving the gradual modification of responses.

From the 1930s through the 1950s, Skinner conducted numerous laboratory studies with animals that verified his operant principles. In his book *The Behavior of Organisms* (1938), Skinner summarizes his laboratory studies during the period 1930 to 1937, marking the official beginning of the science of behavior.

Classical and Operant Conditioning Applied

One of the earliest applications of behavioral principles with humans was reported by Fuller (1949), who conditioned an 18-year-old boy with profound mental retardation to move his arm (Fuller, 1949). In 1959, the publication of Ayllon and Michael's paper "The Psychiatric Nurse as a Behavioral Engineer" documented the effectiveness of using behavioral principles with patients with psychoses and mental retardation in a state hospital. Ferster (1961) and Ferster and DeMyer (1962) used behavioral principles to improve the functioning of children with autism. In 1965, Ullmann and Krasner's book, *Case Studies in Behavior Modification*, was very influential in the treatment of psychiatric disorders because it documented the effective use of operant principles in treating a broad range of psychiatric disorders, including anorexia, hysterical blindness, elective mutism, academic retardation, and encopresis.

Since these early applications of operant conditioning, the use of operant techniques by behaviorists has expanded to include work with normal individuals. Bijou, as the University of Washington, used principles of operant conditioning with preschoolers to improve academic work and peer interactions and to reduce regressed crawling (Bijou & Baer, 1961). Other examples of the expansion of operant principles include parent childbearing education (Pumroy, 1965), temper tantrum (Williams, 1959), weight control (Stuart, 1967), and education (Watson & Tharp, 1985; O'Leary & Becker, 1967, 1968). The use of operant principles in the educational setting has also proved particularly effective. Specifically, token reinforcement programs are effective in reducing disruptive behavior in children with a broad range of disabilities, including hyperactivity, autism, retardation, brain injury, and emotional disturbance (O'Leary & Drabman, 1971). O'Leary (1975) concluded that "token reinforcement programs are among the most effective procedures to be introduced into the educational setting within the past fifty years" (p. 175).

In summary, the history of respondent and operant conditioning is presented separately for explanatory purposes. Historically, psychologists have often drawn rigid lines between the two learning processes, espousing one or the other. However, these rigid distinctions may not be warranted. Often, learning is not purely operant or purely respondent. Liu (1964) explained that many laboratory experiments demonstrating operant conditioning also involve classical conditioning. For example, when the rat learns to press a bar to earn food, many events that are related to eating become conditioned as well, such as the click of the food dispenser. Also, classical-conditioning experiments have operant-conditioning components. After being classically conditioned to avoid shocks delivered after a signal, a dog may, for example, raise his paw in the absence of the signal when anticipating the shock, demonstrating that operant learning has occurred. Furthermore, respondent and operant techniques are compatible in practice and can be used in a complementary fashion. Early applications of both techniques together were reported by Obler and Terwilliger (1970), who provided reinforcers to children with neurological impairments. Children exhibiting a fear of buses were given reinforcers for gradually moving closer to a bus, after first looking at a picture of a bus, until achieving a tolerance for buses. Also, Lazaraus, Davison, and Polefka (1965) treated a school-phobic boy by using in vivo desensitization and rewards for attending school.

Finally, the presenting problem often determines the specific technique used. Operant conditioning techniques, for example, are often used when the concern is one of the management of behavior, while respondent conditioning techniques are used when the problem is anxiety related. Some problems involve both types of conditioning and therefore are best treated by using both approaches. From a behavioral perspective, problems are analyzed by examining what occurs prior to the behavior (stimulus) and what occurs after the behavior (consequences). This approach reflects the importance of examining the environmental factors that influence learning and maintain behavior. During the years that followed Pavlov's, Skinner's, and Thorndike's first contributions, Ferster (1961) and Ferster and DeMyer (1962) worked with children with autism; Homme (1965) and Baer, Wolf, and Risley (1968) began the long history of behavioral principles in classroom management; and Baer (1981) used the principles of punishment, escape, and avoidance with preschool children. The *Journal of Applied Behavior Analysis* (JABA) was first published in 1968.

The Continuing Controversy

Behaviorism has continued to be controversial because of Watson's initial exaggerated and extreme claims about predicting and controlling behavior. Watson, for example, in 1913, stated that if one could raise a dozen healthy, well-formed infants in his own special world, one could train any of these infants to become any type of specialist—doctor, lawyer, artist, merchant-chief, and yes, beggarman and thief—regardless of talents, penchants, tendencies, abilities, vocations, and race of ancestors (Watson 1913). This remark alienated many practitioners and has been used even today to denounce Watson and behaviorism. Recently, Skinner's *Beyond Freedom and Dignity* (1971), which asserts that individuals have no free will and that all behavior is determined by prior conditioning, has produced similar reactions. Skinner's *Walden Two* (1948) is a novel about a planned, ideal society in accordance with operant principles. Seen by many as a threat to human freedoms and compared to the philosophy of Mussolini, it contributed to the fear of many that behavioral principles would be misused. Most of Skinner's work was done with animal subjects and then generalized to human beings without taking into account the uniqueness of humans and thus giving the impression of a mechanistic view of human beings controlled by their environment in a simplistic way.

The cognitive revolution (1950s and 1960s) resulted in more criticism of behaviorism (Solso, 1988). Critics claimed that behaviorism failed to account for the diversity of human behavior: thinking, perception, imaging, problem solving, remembering, decision making, language development, and verbal behavior (Glover, Ronning, & Brunin, 1990). The cognitive movement was more acceptable than behaviorism because it gave individuals back the freedom and control that Skinner said they did not have. Many recent factors, however, have led to an increased acceptance of behaviorism. Behaviorism today is very different from Watson's 1920s psychology, where people were viewed as responding to distinct stimuli in a simple reflex manner. The notion of a stimulus followed by a simple reflex or response is called *S-R psychology*. Dollard and Miller (1950) developed a theory that integrates behaviorism and psychoanalysis by translating psychoanalytic concepts into behavioral terminology, and so broadened and expanded the applications of behavioral principles. Bandura provided an explanation of behavior in terms of a continuous reciprocal interaction between a person and the environment, which he termed *reciprocal determinism* (Bandura, 1977). A person responds to a situation in a determined way, and the response in turn results in certain effects that influence subsequent reactions in a lawful and determined way. These subsequent reactions may be seen as evidence of new interpretations of the environment by the subject. This position expands Dollard and Miller's writings on social learning and accepts the existence of causal cognitions—"Humans do not simply respond to stimuli; they interpret them" (Bandura, 1977). The recognition that both classical and respondent conditioning can occur as a result of observational learning (called *modeling effects*) instead of as a result of performing the response has produced many important applications.

Behavioral approaches have gained acceptance during the past several decades as research has supported their effectiveness. Masters, Burish, Hollon, and Rimm (1987), for example, provided a nonexhaustive list that reports the effective use of behavioral principles for a wide range of problems. The list mentions increases in prosocial verbal behavior, social interactions, sharing, praising, and social skills; and decreases in social disruption and reluctant speech. The list also includes successful treatment of self-control problems, such as decreases in hyperactivity, aggression, obesity, classroom disruption, and enuresis; and increases and improvement in family interaction, school performance and attendance, homework performance, and toilet training.

Cognitive-emotional problems have also been a focus, resulting in an elimination of school phobia, anxiety, depression, pain, and autistic-like behavior; and in an improvement in intelligence scores, creativity, and reading ability and comprehension. Behavioral interventions have benefited many populations, such as children with handicaps; normal children, adolescents, and adults; prisoners; children and adults with mental retardation, autism, and psychoses; and teachers.

Any problem that can be defined in behavioral, observable terms can be addressed using principles of behavior. In particular, behavioral principles have made significant contributions in the educational setting:

> Much of our current educational system reflects the influence of behaviorism. For instance, one readily can recognize the behavioral perspective in such familiar features of our educational system as instructional objectives, task analyses, and the use of positive reinforcement for achieving learning goals . . . [and these] have helped make education more effective, more accountable, and more humane. (Glover, Ronning, & Brunin, 1990, p. 4–5)

In terms of classroom management, "behavioral psychology gives educators a system by which to manipulate the school environment to maximize learning and minimize discipline" (Heitzman & Wiley, 1987, p. 41). Heitzman and Wiley explain that behavioral principles have been used effectively in special education and need to be used in regular education as well. Many universities now require prospective teachers to take courses in behavior modification and in classroom management.

Summary

Historically, behaviorism has been controversial because of what many called Watson's and Skinner's overbearing, dogmatic manner and religious zeal. Behaviorism has staying power because it has worked. Behavior is now viewed more broadly and includes covert behavior that can be clearly specified (Masters, 1987) as well as cognitive behavior modification and social learning theory, which are now referred to as *forms of behaviorism* (Cooper, Heron, & Heward, 1987). The cognitive movement has not discredited behaviorism but has offered a sophisticated version of behaviorism; differences between the two camps are mainly in vocabulary use and dealings with complex human phenomena.

The relatively recent change from the way native Americans were portrayed in the old John Wayne movies to how they were presented in the movie *Dances with Wolves* is noteworthy. In a similar manner, the history of behavioral principles with regard to helping people will vary depending upon who is doing the reporting. In other words, the history is in the eye of the beholder. Many individuals (Bijou, Lindsey, Wolpe, Ulrich, Ullman, O'Leary) involved in the early days of the behavioral revolution have written (or would write) histories different from the one in this book and would, perhaps, even disagree with parts of the book's presentation. This history is presented as the authors see it; they trust the reader will understand.

Several decades ago, following Watson's position, psychology was defined as the study of behavior, but part of the study focused on consciousness. The problem is still not resolved. Modern authors of introductory psychology texts define psychology as the study of behavior, thought, and emotions, or they sometimes state that psychology is the study of behavior, both overt and covert. The term *covert* refers to verbal material—usually subjects' talking to themselves or rehearsing and reviewing experiences. In one way, covert behavior is a misnomer in that to be a behavior it must, by definition, be overt. Nevertheless, covert behavior refers to vocalizations, loud enough to hear or not, that might guide complex behavior.

In any history, the perceptions of the people writing are different, and terms used by the authors of this book also differ. In the behavioral field, there are classical learning, operant and respondent conditioning, behavior modification, behavior analysis, and behavior therapy. *Classical learning,* a Pavlovian term, is essentially the same as Skinner's term *respondent. Instrumental learning* (Thorndike) is the same as Skinner's *operant.*

The term *behavior modification* was used in early studies to indicate the use of operant principles to change behavior. There was much opposition, and perhaps still is, to the term as it conveyed the concept of control or manipulation of a person's behavior. Such thinking did not set well with the general population. Behavior analysis is more neutral; at least it does imply doing nothing other than observing behavior. Note how the terms *behavior modification* and *behavior analysis* reflect the two questions that were posed at the beginning of this chapter. Analysis gives an explanation for the behavior, and modification tells how the environment changes behavior. The term *behavior therapy* has been used mostly to reflect the behavioral approach applied to the study of usually complex problems involving anxiety and fear and the individuals who are in treatment for such symptoms. For many people in the behavioral field, these three terms are used interchangeably. As the focus of this book is more on the use of operant principles, the term *behavior analysis/modifica-*

tion is used here to refer to the study of behavior controlled by consequences but broadened considerably to take into account the effects of antecedent stimuli and events and their relationships to consequences. The term *behavior therapy* most often refers to treatment that involves the respondent behavior of classical conditioning.

There are problems as to how to present the history of operant and respondent behavior and its application to treatment. This chapter dealt separately with the history of operant research and its application and with the history and application of respondent procedures, although there is overlap of the two kinds of learning and their applications. The contributions to these fields are, however, best organized by these terms. The authors are indebted to those who have made these contributions; their efforts will continue to help the suffering of many people in each of the settings reviewed.

Study Questions

1. Why do people sometimes feel threatened by behavior modification?
2. Why does behavior modification raise ethical questions that other treatment procedures do not raise?
3. Define *classical conditioning.*
4. What were Pavlov's, Watson's, Thorndike's, and Skinner's contributions to the study of human behavior?
5. Define *instrumental conditioning.*
6. Define *operant conditioning.*
7. What criticisms did the cognitive movement level against behaviorism?
8. Explain four contributions of behaviorism to human functioning.

References

Ayllon, T., & Michael, J. (1959). The psychiatric nurse as a behavior engineer. *Journal of Experimental Analysis of Behavior, 2,* 323–334.

Baer, D. M. (1981). A flight of behavior analysis. *The Behavior Analyst, 4,* 85–91.

Baer, D. M., Wolf, M. M., & Risley, T. R. (1968). Some current dimensions of applied behavior analysis. *Journal of Applied Behavior Analysis, 1,* 91–97.

Bandura, A. (1977). Self-efficacy: Toward a unifying theory of behavioral change. *Psychological Review, 84,* 191–215.

Bijou, S. W., & Baer, D. M. (1961). *Child development: A systematic and empirical theory.* New York: Appleton-Century-Crofts.

Cooper, J. O., Heron, T. E., & Heward, W. L. (1987). *Applied Behavior Analysis.* Columbus, OH: Merrill Publishing Company.

Dollard, J., & Miller, N. E. (1950). *Personality and psychotherapy: An analysis in terms of learning, thinking, and culture.* New York: McGraw-Hill.

Ferster, C. B. (1961). Positive reinforcement and behavioral deficits of autistic children. *Child Development, 32,* 437–456.

Ferster, C. B. & DeMyer, M. K. (1962). A method for the experimental analysis of the behavior of autistic children. *American Journal of Orthopsychiatry, 32,* 89–98.

Fuller, P. R. (1949). Operant conditioning of a vegetative organism. *American Journal of Psychology, 62,* 587–590.

Glover, J. A., Ronning, R. R., & Brunin, R. H. (1990). *Cognitive psychology for teachers.* New York: Macmillan.

Heitzman, A. J., & Wiley, E. G. (1987). School discipline—problems affecting solutions. *Pointer, 31*(4), 41.

Homme, L. E. (1965). Perspectives in psychology: XXIV. Control of coverants, the operants of the mind. *Psychology Record, 15,* 501–511.

Jacobson, E. (1938). *Progressive relaxation.* Chicago: University of Chicago Press.

Jones, M. C. (1924). Elimination of children's fears. *Journal of Experimental Psychology, 7,* 383–390.

Lazarus, A. A., & Abramovitz, A. (1962). The use of "emotive imagery" in the treatment of children's phobia. *Journal of Mental Science, 108,* 191–195.

Lazarus, A. A., Davison, G. C., & Polefka, D. (1965). Classical and operant factors in the treatment of school phobia. *Journal of Abnormal and Social Psychology, 70,* 225–229.

Lazarus, A. A., & Rachman, S. (1967). The use of systematic desensitization in psychotherapy. *South African Medical Journal, 31,* 934–937.

Liu, I. M. (1964). A theory of classical conditioning. *Psychological Review, 71,* 408–411.

Masters, J. C., Burish, T. G., Hollon, S. D., & Rimm, D. C. (1978). *Behavior therapy techniques and empirical findings* (3rd Edition). San Diego: Harcourt Brace Jovanovich.

Obler, M., & Terwilliger, R. F. (1970). Pilot study of the effectiveness of systematic desensitization with neurologically impaired children with phobic disorders. *Journal of Clinical and Consulting Psychology, 34,* 314–318.

O'Leary, K. D. (1975). *Behavior therapy: Application and outcome.* Englewood Cliffs, NJ: Prentice-Hall.

O'Leary, K. D., & Becker, W. C. (1967). Behavior modification of an adjustment class: A token reinforcement program. *Exceptional Children, 33,* 639–642.

O'Leary, K. D., & Becker, W. C. (1968). The effects of a teacher's reprimands on children's behavior. *Journal of School Psychology, 7,* 8–11.

O'Leary, K. D., & Drabman, R. S. (1971). Token reinforcement programs in the classroom: A review. *Journal of Abnormal Child Psychology, 1*(2), 127–138.

Pavlov, I. P. (1927). *Conditioned reflexes,* G. V. Anrep (Trans.). New York: Liveright.

Pumroy, D. K. (1965). *A new approach to treating parent-child problems.* Paper presented at the meeting of the American Psychological Association, Chicago, IL.

Salter, A. (1949). *Conditioned reflex therapy.* New York: Creative Age.

Skinner, B. F. (1938). *The behavior of organisms.* New York: Appleton-Century-Crofts.

Skinner, B. F. (1948). *Walden Two.* New York: Macmillan.

Skinner, B. F. (1953). *Science and human behavior.* New York: Macmillan.

Skinner, B. F. (1971). *Beyond freedom and dignity.* New York: Alfred A. Knopf.

Solso, R. L. (1988). *Cognitive psychology* (2nd Edition). Boston: Allyn and Bacon, Inc.

Stuart, R. B. (1967). Behavioral control of overeating. *Behaviour Research and Therapy, 5,* 357–365.

Thorndike, E. L. (1911). *Animal intelligence.* New York: Macmillan.

Watson, D. L., & Tharp, R. G. (1985). *Self-directed behavior: Self-modification for personal adjustment* (4th ed.). Monterey, CA: Brooks/Cole.

Watson, J. B., & Rayner, P. (1920). Conditioned emotional reactions. *Journal of Experimental Psychology, 3,* 1–14.

Ullmann, L. P., & Krasner, L., (Eds). (1965). *Case studies in behavior modification.* New York: Holt, Rinehart and Winston.

Williams, C. D. (1959). The elimination of tantrum behavior by extinction procedures. *Journal of Abnormal and Social Psychology, 59,* 269.

Wolpe, J. (1958). *Psychotherapy by reciprocal inhibition.* Stanford, CA: Stanford University Press.

2

Choosing and Measuring Behavior

Jane was an 8-year-old student who presented many challenges to her teachers. She often began her work but did not finish it. She muttered under her breath, yelled at other students, bit her classmates, and talked back to her teachers. She broke her pencils, ripped up her papers, and occasionally threw over her desk.

Changing Jane's behavior at first appeared overwhelming. However, the first step of the behavior modification process—choosing and measuring behavior—made order out of Jane's behavioral chaos. Choosing the behavior to be worked on, called the *target behavior,* allowed the teacher to establish priorities and go about the behavior modification process in an orderly fashion.

Jane's teachers decided to target the most disruptive behaviors first. They decided to help Jane with her biting and property destruction, since these were the most disruptive to Jane and to others. Simultaneously, they targeted task completion, a behavior necessary for Jane to make any progress in school. Once these behaviors were targeted, her teachers instituted a system to measure the frequency of the behavior and also to determine important facts about the circumstances under which the behavior occurred. These steps of targeting and measuring the behavior were essential in laying the groundwork for the development of the behavior modification plan.

This chapter covers the process and criteria for targeting behavior for change and the methods and reasons for measuring the targeted behaviors.

Choosing Target Behaviors

Choosing the target behavior is the first step of the behavior modification process. Target behaviors might be problem behaviors that the plan will seek to decrease in frequency, or they might be desirable behaviors that the plan will seek to increase in frequency. In either case, the target behavior must be both observable and measurable.

Choosing target behaviors involves the following:

1. choosing an observable behavior
2. choosing a measurable behavior
3. establishing priorities

Behavior Is Observable

The target behavior must be observable; that is, it must be readily seen or heard by any observer. Walking, running, sitting, standing, and talking are examples of observable behaviors. Yelling, screaming, kicking, hitting, pinching, and throwing are examples of observable behaviors. Beginning a task, working on a task, and completing a task are examples of observable behaviors. Asking for help, offering help, greeting others, and sharing supplies are also examples. All of these behaviors can be seen or heard by others.

States or conditions that are not observable do not qualify as target behaviors. How a person is feeling or thinking is not directly observable, and so these states would not be targeted for change. Feelings and thoughts describe what is going on inside an individual. So, feelings of happiness, sadness, insecurity, or anxiety would not qualify as target behaviors. These feelings are termed *inner states*, because they describe what is going on inside an individual.

Inner states, however, are often associated with observable behaviors. These observable behaviors should be targeted, not the inner state itself. For example, a young girl may have periods of sadness. It could be said that she is sad because she cries. Crying can be the target behavior, because it is observable. Sadness is simply the feeling that accompanies the behavior. To further illustrate, an adolescent boy may have feelings of anxiety, which are accompanied by refusal to do his assignments. Refusal to do assignments is clearly observable and can be targeted for change.

The behaviors targeted for Jane were all observable. Biting was clearly observable. Property destruction was also observable. When Jane ripped up her work, the behavior was obvious to any observer. Task completion, the third targeted behavior, was also observable. The tasks were assigned, and a check of her work revealed whether or not the task was completed. Although Jane may well have felt angry, sad, or excited when she engaged in the targeted behaviors, these feelings, or inner states, were not the targets of the behavior change plan. Rather, her observable behaviors were targeted.

Behavior Is Measurable

Throughout the behavior modification process, the targeted behavior must be measurable by direct observation by others. For example, work can be measured by the number of units completed. Accuracy can be determined by the percentage of units completed correctly. Asking for help can be measured by the number of times the behavior occurs. Property destruction can be measured, as well, by the number of times the behavior occurs. If a behavior is observable, it is generally true that it is also measurable.

At times, a behavior might be observable but difficult to measure because of practical considerations. The behavior of working on task is observable, but it might be impractical to measure because it would necessitate someone actually timing the person going on and off task. A more reasonable target behavior might be completing assigned tasks, since this is more easily measured. Inner states, such as feelings and thoughts, cannot be measured by others and so fail to meet this second criteria for qualifying as target behaviors.

Jane's target behaviors were measured easily. Property destruction was measured by the number of times it occurred, as was biting. Completing assigned tasks was measured and described as a percentage: the teacher computed the percentage of assigned tasks that Jane completed.

Establish Priorities

Behavior modification provides the technology for behavior change. However, behavior modification is a time-consuming and challenging process for both the individual whose behaviors are being changed and the behavior change agent. Therefore, it is important to establish priorities when targeting behaviors. Although an individual might have a large number of behaviors that are desirable to change, there may be only a small number that are at first practical to change. It is important to decide which behaviors are most necessary to change. As progress is made with these behaviors, others can be added.

Behaviors that deserve high priority are behaviors that jeopardize the health or welfare of the individual or the adjustment of the individual to the school, home, or work setting. Individuals with severe developmental disabilities might display self-injurious behaviors, such as head banging or self-scratching. These behaviors jeopardize the individual's health and so are priorities for change. Or, for example, a preschooler might have a willigness to talk to strangers, a behavior that poses a threat to the child's welfare. A college student may neglect to complete assignments, a behavior that poses a risk to the student's adjustment to college.

Measuring Behavior

Once the behavior is targeted, it must be measured. Measurement is the second step of the behavior change process, following definition of the target behavior. Measuring the behavior is a critical component of the process, and failure to measure can result in an ineffective plan and haphazard evaluation of success.

There are several purposes for measuring behavior. First, measurement gives an initial assessment of the severity of the problem. Rather than rely on subjective estimates of how often a behavior occurs, the behavior change agent can conduct a precise measurement. This initial measurement might even be a determining factor in deciding whether or not to proceed with a behavior change plan. Sometimes, after measuring the behavior, the decision is made that it does not occur often enough to constitute a problem.

If the target behavior is a skill, the initial measurement gives an indication of the level of performance. Performance on academic tasks, home-care tasks, self-care tasks, social tasks, motor tasks, and recreational and leisure tasks can be measured to determine an individual's initial skill level.

Measurement of the target behavior provides a means of evaluating the effectiveness of the behavior change plan. Initial measurement of a behavior, prior to implementation of a behavior change plan, is called the *baseline measurement.* Baseline is the period of time during which the behavior is measured in its natural state with no interventions. The baseline level of the behavior is then compared with the level of behavior during intervention. This comparison is used to assess the effectiveness of the behavior modification plan. Baseline measurement usually occurs over a time period long enough to get a stable picture of the range of the behavior; this period might be one week or one month. In cases of behaviors that are serious and have possibly destructive or harmful effects, it might be necessary to forego an extended baseline and begin intervention almost immediately in order to prevent injury or harm to the individual or others.

Measurement of the target behavior also provides information on the progress of the individual whose behavior is targeted for change. The amount and rate of progress can be evaluated by examination of the data that have been collected during baseline and throughout intervention. At the beginning of each school year, for example, the teacher might target individual goals for each student. Data collected throughout the year in the course of a behavior change plan provide an objective assessment of whether or not the student has met the planned goals and objectives.

Measurement of the targeted behaviors provides an objective basis on which to make decisions regarding the development of the behavior change plan and the effectiveness of that plan once it is implemented. Decisions to continue, change, or fade a behavior modification plan can then be based on quantitative data, rather than on subjective impressions.

There are several methods of measuring behavior. These methods provide information on different aspects of the target behavior or present different methods for measuring the same aspect. Measurement must include a precise measurement of the target behavior and a formal assessment of the circumstances under which the behavior occurs.

Measurement of the behavior itself can be done by assessing the frequency (how often the behavior occurs), the duration, and the effects of the behavior; or, in the case of skills, by assessing the steps of the task that the individual can complete. Circumstances can be evaluated by using assessment to determine the presence or absence of certain key circumstances that precede, occur concurrently with, or follow the behavior. The measurement method chosen will depend on which aspect of the behavior needs to be measured and on the resources of the setting.

Methods for Measuring Behavior

Tally

A tally consists of recording each instance of the behavior. It is a count of the number of times the behavior occurs, and it provides a measure of *frequency*. Tallies are practical if the teacher, caregiver, or other behavior change agent has time to observe and record each and every instance of the behavior. Often, in school, work, or home settings, a tally is impractical for behaviors of high frequency. For example, if a teacher has 30 students, it may be impossible for the teacher to record each instance of one student calling out of turn.

Time Block

Time block is a method in which the time period covered is divided into equal blocks of time, and for each block of time, the observer records whether or not the target behavior occurred. In Jane's case, for example, the teacher might divide the day into 30-minute blocks of time and for each of these time blocks, record whether or not Jane engaged in property destruction (See Figure 2.1).

The percentage of time blocks in which the behavior occurred is computed by dividing the number of blocks in which the behavior occurred by the total number of blocks and multiplying by 100% (See Figure 2.2).

In this example, Jane destroyed property in four of the eight half-hour time blocks. Her percentage is computed as shown in Figure 2.3

Jane destroyed property in 50% of the half-hour time blocks in the day.

Time block is not as precise as tally. However, it has the advantage of taking less time. The observer does not need to observe and record continuously. Instead, for each new time block, the observer records the first occurrence of the behavior, and does not need to observe or record again until the next time block begins.

The size of the time block depends on the resources of the setting and the

Student: ______________________ **Date:** ______________________

Target Behavior: ______________________ **Key: + = Behavior occurred**
- = No occurrence

9:00–9:15			
9:15–9:30			
9:30–9:45			
9:45–10:00			
10:00–10:15			
10:15–10:30			
10:30–10:45			
10:45–11:00			
11:00–11:15			
11:15–11:30			
11:30–11:45			
11:45–12:00			
12:00–12:15			
12:15–12:30			
12:30–12:45			
12:45–1:00			
1:00–1:15			
1:15–1:30			
1:30–1:45			
1:45–2:00			
2:00–2:15			
2:15–2:30			
2:30–2:45			
2:45–3:00			

Figure 2.1 Time block data sheet.

$$\frac{\text{No. of blocks with behavior}}{\text{Total no. of blocks}} \times 100\% = \begin{array}{c}\text{\% of blocks in which}\\ \text{behavior occurred}\end{array}$$

Figure 2.2 Formula for computing the percentage of time blocks in which a targeted behavior occurred.

$$\frac{4}{8} \times 100\% = 50\%$$

Figure 2.3 Percentage of time blocks in which Jane destroyed property.

frequency of the behavior. Time blocks in research settings are often very short, e.g., 10 seconds. Short time blocks (such as 30-second time blocks) might be impractical in school, home, or work settings, whereas a 15-minute, 30-minute, or 60-minute time block might be more feasible. In some cases, it might be desirable to use the whole day as the size of the time block. If, for example, Martin has problems with wetting his pants at school, Martin's teacher might simply record whether he wet that day, without counting each individual incident. The time block must be short enough to provide reasonable baseline information but long enough to be practical.

Duration

Duration measures involve timing the target behavior. Measuring the length of time a runner takes to run a mile is an obvious example of a duration measure. Another example is a teacher measuring the length of time a student takes to complete a set of math problems. When the target behavior involves an undesirable behavior that lasts over time, such as prolonged screaming, the parent or teacher might time the duration of the episode. Duration is the measurement of choice when behavior takes place over a period of time and when that period of time is of practical interest.

Accuracy

Measures of accuracy focus on the correctness of the behavior when compared with some standard. Accuracy is often examined in terms of a percentage, that is, the percent of the steps or portions of a task that were performed correctly (See Figure 2.4).

$$\frac{\text{No. of steps done correctly}}{\text{Total no. of steps}} \times 100\% = \%\text{ of steps correct}$$

Figure 2.4 Formula for computing the percentage of steps performed correctly.

Toothbrushing might be broken down into 15 steps and the learner observed to determine how many of the 15 steps are performed correctly. Assembling a product might be broken down into 20 steps and the worker observed to determine how many of the 20 steps are performed correctly. A multi-step math problem might be graded in terms of the number of steps executed correctly. Accuracy can also be measured by computing the percentage of trials performed correctly. The number of basketballs that the player shoots in the baskets, for example, or the number of math problems completed accurately can be examined as a percentage of the total number of problems.

Instructional skills and physical skills are often examined in terms of their accuracy. Social skills can also be measured in this way. A preschool teacher, for example, might be interested in the percentage of times a student says "thank you" when handed juice. A parent might be interested in the percentage of times a child says "please" when making a request. A job coach of an adult worker with mental retardation might be interested in the percentage of times the worker asks for help when having difficulty with a task.

Permanent Products

These procedures focus on the trace, or aftereffect, of the behavior rather than on direct observation of the behavior. These procedures are also called *behavioral trace procedures* or *outcome recording*. A completed math test is an example of a permanent product. The behavior is not measured by observing the student actually complete the math problems but by scoring the product of his work, the math test. The work of a factory worker might be examined by counting the lamps he has assembled. Those lamps are the products of his daily work behavior. In cases of self-injury, the marks on the body left by the self-injury are behavioral traces of the actual behavior of self-injury.

Progress toward academic goals is assessed by examining classwork, homework, tests, and term papers. Progress toward vocational goals is assessed by examining the products of the worker's efforts, such as the objects that are manufactured, the reports that are generated, or other tasks that are accomplished.

Behavior modification plans that focus on more undesirable behaviors might also use permanent product measures. Nail biters might count the number of torn nails, weight watchers the number of lost pounds, and hair twirlers the size of the bald spot. Parents and instructors of individuals with developmental disabilities and behavior problems might measure the number of bruises from self-injury or the amount of property that has been destroyed during behavioral outbursts.

Permanent products allow for data collection when direct observation of the behavior is not possible or feasible. In the case of students or workers, it is not always possible nor desirable to have a teacher or supervisor directly observing an individual at work. Examining the products of the work is adequate and allows for more independence on the part of the student or worker. Individuals with behavior problems might engage in the behavior in private, and caretakers can measure only the effects of the behavior. An example of this is a young boy who scratches his skin only at night when unobserved by his parents.

Methods for Measuring the Circumstances of Behavior

Measuring aspects of the behavior itself, such as frequency, duration, or aftereffects is important in planning and evaluating a behavior modification plan. It is just as important to have some measure of the context within which the behavior occurs. The immediate context can be assessed by examining the events that directly precede the behavior, known as **antecedents**, and the events that follow the behavior, known as **consequences**. It might also be desirable to assess those events that happen some time prior to the behavior and may run concurrently with the behavior. These events are known as **setting events**.

Antecedents are of interest because of their possible role in triggering the behavior. A common antecedent to a person awakening in the morning is the sound of an alarm clock blaring. A common antecedent to a car coming to a halt on a highway is a red traffic light. Common events in the school environment that routinely precede and trigger behavior are instructions from teachers to begin assignments, a fire alarm signaling time to evacuate, and bells ringing that signal a change of class. Antecedents to certain problem behaviors might be criticism from an instructor, failure on a task, or an insult from a peer.

Setting events can precede the behavior by several hours or more, indirectly triggering certain behaviors. A situation in which a child is kept awake all night by a sick sibling, for example, creates the physiological setting event of fatigue. When the child goes to school fatigued, he is more likely to have academic and behavioral problems that day. Other physiological setting events include illness, hunger, and the presence or absence of drugs or caffeine in one's body.

Setting events can be ongoing factors in a person's environment, such as the amount of structure; the amount of attention from adults or from peers; the amount or difficulty of tasks; the amount of space, light, or noise; and the weather conditions. Aspects of the instructional environment, including the manner and amount of instruction, can also serve as setting events that affect behaviors.

Consequences are of interest because of the possible role they play in the probability that the behavior will recur. Common consequences for superior work are raises, good grades, and other forms of commendation. Immediate consequences for inferior work might be criticism, lectures, and warnings; other consequences are poor grades, poor job evaulations, and perhaps expulsion from school or termination from work.

Antecedents, setting events, and consequences can all be assessed as part of the behavior modification plan. There are several methods for assessing these circumstances.

Diary

A diary approach involves observing an individual over a period of time and keeping a diary of the individual's circumstances and behaviors during that time period. An extended example of the diary method is in *One Boy's Day*, (Barker & Wright, 1951), in which the authors describe the behaviors of a boy they trailed for a full day. The diary method has the advantage of providing a complete description of the behavior and its context. The disadvantages of this method are that it is time consuming and may contain much irrelevant information.

Structured Diary

A structured diary is a modified diary approach. It involves recording information on certain selected aspects of the circumstances and the behaviors. Use of a structured diary in behavior modification plans most commonly includes recording the following information about occurrences of the target behavior: date, time, antecedents, behavior, and consequences. The structured diary as used in behavior modificaiton is often called an *ABC chart* (Antecedents-Behavior-Consequences chart as shown in Figure 2.5).

The recording of antecedents includes a brief descripton of the events preceding a behavior and of the people involved. The behavior is described, and a brief description of it is recorded. The recording of consequences includes a description of those events or responses that occurred immediately following the behavior.

Cindy, for example, may have thrown over her desk at school immediately after the teacher criticized her math paper. After she threw over the desk, she was sent to the principal's office, where she was lectured about her behavior,

Date	Time	Antecedents	Behavior	Consequences

Figure 2.5 An ABC Chart.

Date	Time	Antecedents	Behavior	Consequences
1/15/92	10:30 am	Mrs. Jones pointed out some errors in Cindy's math paper	Cindy yelled and threw over her desk	Cindy was sent to the principal's office, reprimanded, and spent the afternoon helping the secretary

Figure 2.6 A filled-in ABC chart describing the student's incident.

and then she spent the afternoon helping the secretary collate papers. The incident would be recorded as follows on an ABC form (see Figure 2.6). The use of the ABC chart is discussed in more detail in Chapter 3.

Setting Events

Information can be collected on setting events in a simple checklist fashion. The checklist can include those events that might possibly serve as setting events for the targeted behavior. Assessment of setting events is discussed in more detail in Chapter 3.

Time Sampling

It may be inconvenient or unnecessary to take data continuously. In either case, it might be possible to use any data collection procedure discussed above on a time sampling basis. Time sampling involves designating certain periods of time during which data will be collected and collecting it only during those time periods. Time periods can be chosen randomly or assigned, with the condition that the time chosen be generally representative of the whole time period of interest.

The case of Angela provides a good example of the use of time sampling. Angela was a young girl with mental retardation and communication problems. A behavior that was targeted for change was her screeching, which she did often. Her teacher did not have time to record each and every incident of screeching all week long. So, data on Angela's behavior will be collected on a time sample basis; that is, data will be collected on screeching every Tuesday and Thursday. These days are fairly representative of the whole week, so data collected during these days should give a fair picture of the frequency of the behavior.

Any type of data collection can be done on a time sample basis. Angela's teacher, for example, could decide to use either a time block or a tally every Tuesday and Thursday or could collect duration data on the length of the screeching episodes.

Choosing Data Collection Procedures

Data collection procedures must be chosen carefully. Since data collection can be time consuming, it is important to choose methods that give the necessary information and are practical. If the target behavior is a misbehavior, two types of information are critical: information on the quantity of the behavior, in terms of either frequency or duration, and information on the circumstances of the behavior. If the target behavior is a skill, information is then needed on the learner's performance of the targeted skill. Typically, a combination of methods is used. Some general considerations in choosing data collection procedures are as follows:

1. The tally method is best when it is possible and practical to count every incident of the behavior's occurrence.
2. The time block is best when the behavior occurs too often to count every incident.
3. Duration data is good when the length of time is important. Under some circumstances, duration might be impractical. A teacher with 25 students, for example, may not be able to time the duration of one student's episodes of refusing to work. On the other hand, a teacher with three students might have no trouble collecting duration data on refusals.
4. Accuracy data may be needed when a specific skill is targeted, especially an academic, a vocational, or a motor skill.
5. Permanent product data may be used as an adjunct to another data collection method or it may be the only method feasible.
6. Any behavior modification plan that involves a misbehavior must include data on the context of the behavior. A structured diary is a convenient method for collecting data on circumstances. Additional assessment tools for the context of behavior are discussed in Chapter 3.

Targeting Additional Behaviors

After data collection, it might be clear that additional behaviors must be targeted. This information typically is derived from an analysis of the circumstances under which the behavior occurs. It might become obvious that the learning or strengthening of a new behavior is necessary to treat the original targeted behavior. If this is the case, additional behaviors may be added after initial data collection.

Carr and Durand (1985) carried out a series of experiments that demonstrated targeting replacement behaviors for misbehavior. Four children prone to tantrums, self-injury, and aggression served as subjects in the study. The researchers did assessments to determine the context of these behavior problems. Since the misbehavior often occurred either when the children were having difficulty with a task or when there was a lack of adult attention, the behaviors targteted for change were asking for assistance when having difficulty with a task and soliciting of adult attention.

Smith and Coleman (1986) did a study on a young man with autism who worked at a printing company where he often had tantrums. The original target behavior was the tantrum behavior, which consisted of jumping and screaming. After initial data collection, it became apparent that he often had tantrums when he was having difficulty with a task. Therefore, an additional behavior was targeted for change: the asking for assistance when having difficulty with his work.

Additional target behaviors for change can be added once progress is made on priority behaviors. In Jane's case, for example, if progress is made on property destruction and aggression, the teachers can target her behavior of yelling.

Graphing Data

Raw data are data as collected on data sheets but not processed or analyzed in any way. For example, the time block data sheets, as filled in by a teacher or parent, constitute raw data. Filled-out ABC forms are also raw data.

Certain data, such as ABC data, are quite useful as raw data. The actual write-up of the incident provides valuable information that might be lost if processed in any way. However, frequency data, time block data, or duration data are most practical when summarized on a graph. A graph provides a summary and picture of the course of a behavior over time and across treatment or intervention conditions.

Behavioral data are typically graphed with time on the *x-axis* and frequency on the *y-axis*. Time can be noted in minutes, hours, days, weeks, months, or any other units. Frequency can be noted in terms of the total number or of the mean number of incidents. The y-axis can also represent the percentage of time blocks in which a behavior did or did not occur.

Several graphs of Jane's behavior follow. (Figures 2–7 through 2–9.)

Baseline data might fluctuate from day to day, week to week, or month to month. A graph of baseline data can provide a representation of the behavior that allows the behavior analyst to see these fluctuations that occur over time. The graph provides depiction of the range of behavior, as well as the variability. Figure 2.7, for example, shows that the baseline range of Jane's biting is from 2 to 10 incidents per week; Figure 2.8 shows the variability in Jane's yelling. This behavior fluctuates from days with no screaming to days in which screaming occurred during 90% of the 15-minute time blocks.

A graph that summarizes baseline data and treatment data provides a visual representation of the effectiveness of the behavior modification plan. An effective plan will result in obvious increases in the frequency of desirable behavior, as a graph will show. Likewise, the frequency of misbehavior will obviously decline as a result of effective intervention, and a summary graph will note this decline. A graph that reveals no change in the behavior signals that something is amiss with either the intervention plan or its implementation.

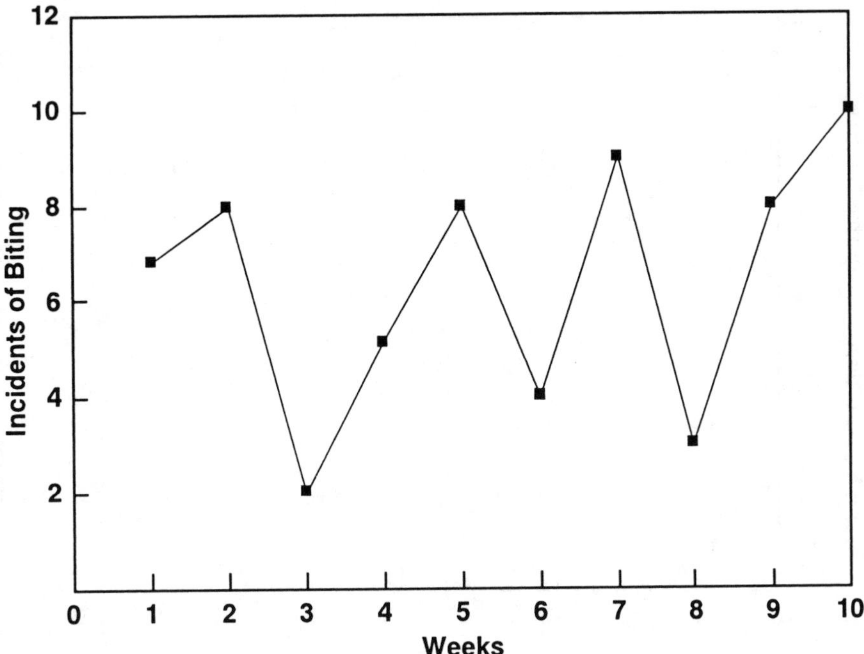

Figure 2.7 The total number of incidents of biting each week.

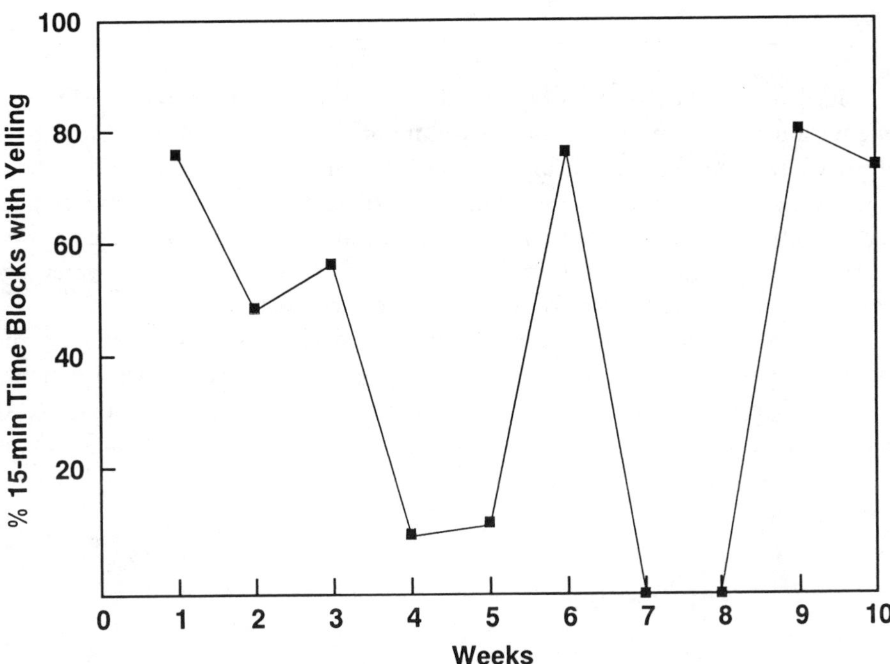

Figure 2.8 The percentage of 15-minute time blocks in which yelling occurred each week.

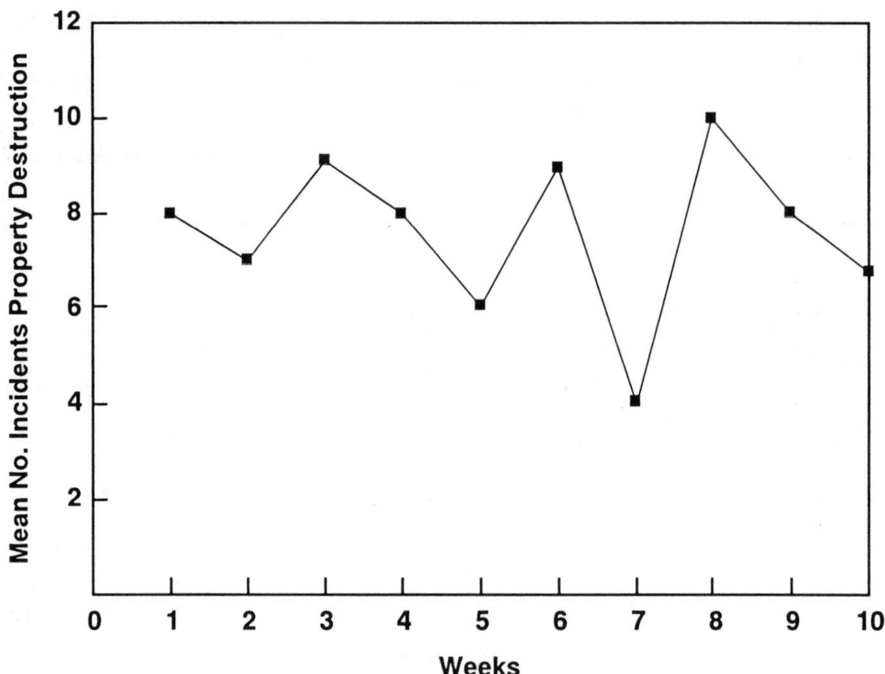

Figure 2.9 The mean number of incidents of property destruction each week.

Figure 2.10 shows Jane's biting behavior during baseline and after implementation of her treatment plan. Baseline and treatment are separated by a dotted line. The decrease in biting is clearly depicted.

Figure 2.11 shows the percentage of words a student spelled correctly on her weekly spelling tests, both during baseline and intervention. It is clear that the intervention had no positive effect on her spelling accuracy, as the percentage remained around 50% throughout both baseline and intervention.

Decisions about continuing a behavior modification plan, changing the plan, or terminating the plan are all based on data. Clear graphs provide a visual representation of the data, which in turn allows for good decision making based on that data. So, quantitative data should always be graphed and graphed in such a way as to be useful during decision making related to the behavior modification plan.

Applications

Case 1

James was a 10-year-old student with a severe learning disability and an educational diagnosis of emotional impairment. He attended the neigh-

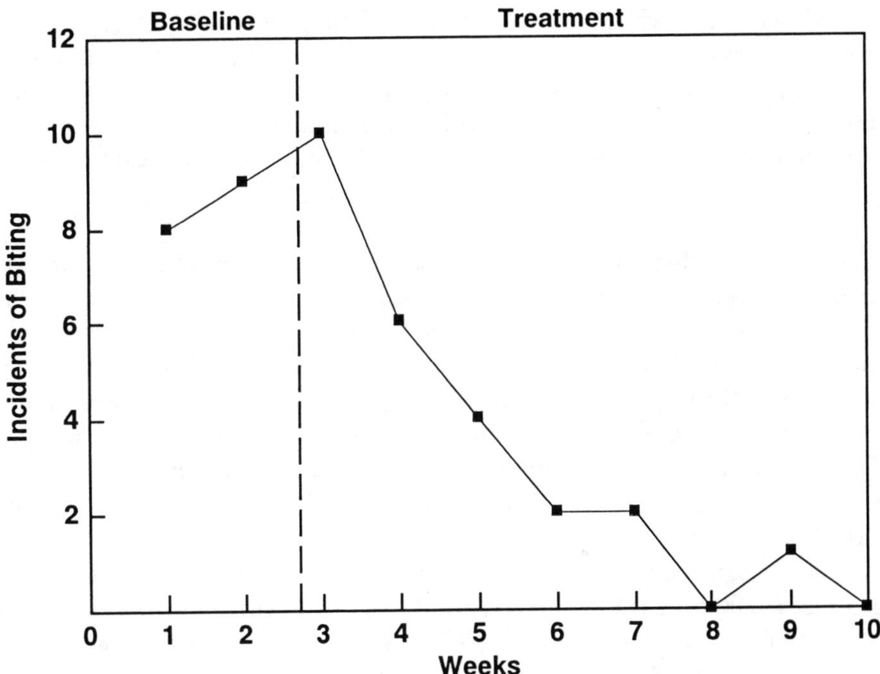

Figure 2.10 The number of incidents of biting each week during baseline and treatment.

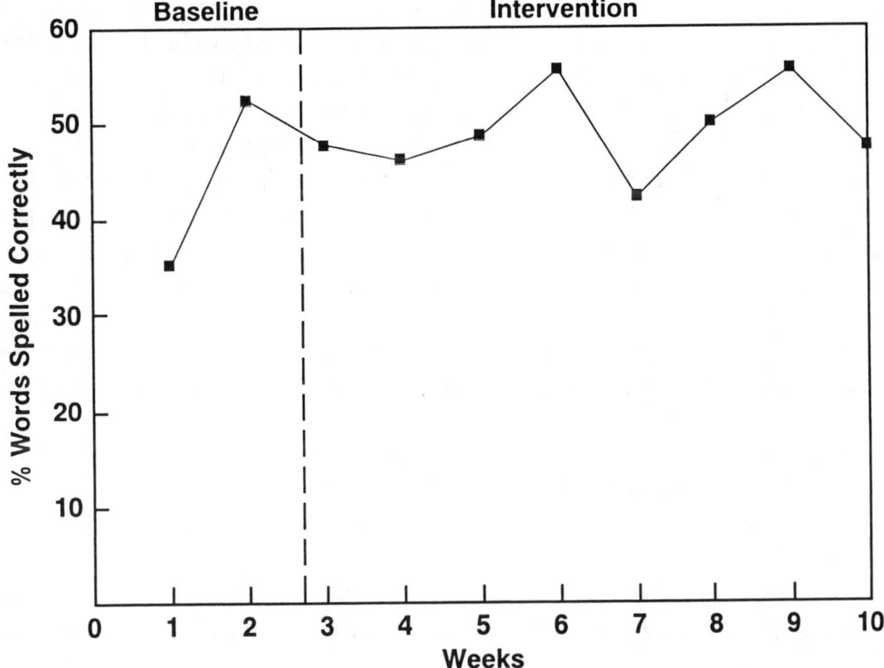

Figure 2.11 The percentage of words spelled correctly each week during baseline and intervention.

borhood elementary school. He was in a regular fifth-grade class and provided with the part-time assistance of a special aide to help him with his school work and his social behaviors. James had several social problems of concern, including talking aloud to himself, laughing aloud, nail biting, skin picking, and refusing to complete assigned tasks. Occasionally, he hit other students and threatened to hit the teacher.

First, the teacher and the aide needed to target the behaviors for change. James had several behaviors that were in need of change, but the decision was made to prioritize and choose those behaviors that were most critical to change. James's teachers decided to target hitting others, skin picking, and task completion. Hitting others and skin picking posed a threat to the health and welfare of James and other students, and task completion was critical for school adjustment. The remaining behaviors of talking to himself, laughing aloud, and nail biting were not initially targeted for change and could be worked on later.

Second, data collection procedures were chosen. Hitting others, which occurred about three times weekly, would be documented on ABC forms. A setting event checklist would also be filled out for each incident of aggression. Skin picking occurred frequently, and sometimes out of sight of teachers; since the teachers could not observe the actual behavior, the decision was to use a behavioral trace procedure. Twice daily, once in the morning and once at the end of the school day, the teachers would check James's hands to determine whether there were any fresh wounds since the previous check. Then, the percentage of checks that showed clear skin would be computed. If skin picking were observed, ABC data would be collected on a sample basis for those incidents that the teacher observed in which blood was drawn.

Task completion data would be taken from permanent product data. The teacher would record daily the number of tasks completed and compute the percentage of tasks completed. Accuracy data, or the percentage of items completed correctly, would be computed as a routine part of the record keeping in the classroom.

A graphing method was then determined. The number of incidents of aggression would be graphed across weeks, as shown in the graph set-up in Figure 2.12.

The percentage of checks that showed clear skin would also be graphed each week, as shown in Figure 2.13.

The percentage of tasks completed each week would be graphed as shown in Figure 2.14.

Data collection for James allowed James's teacher to collect information on the frequency of aggression, the effects of skin picking, and the percentage

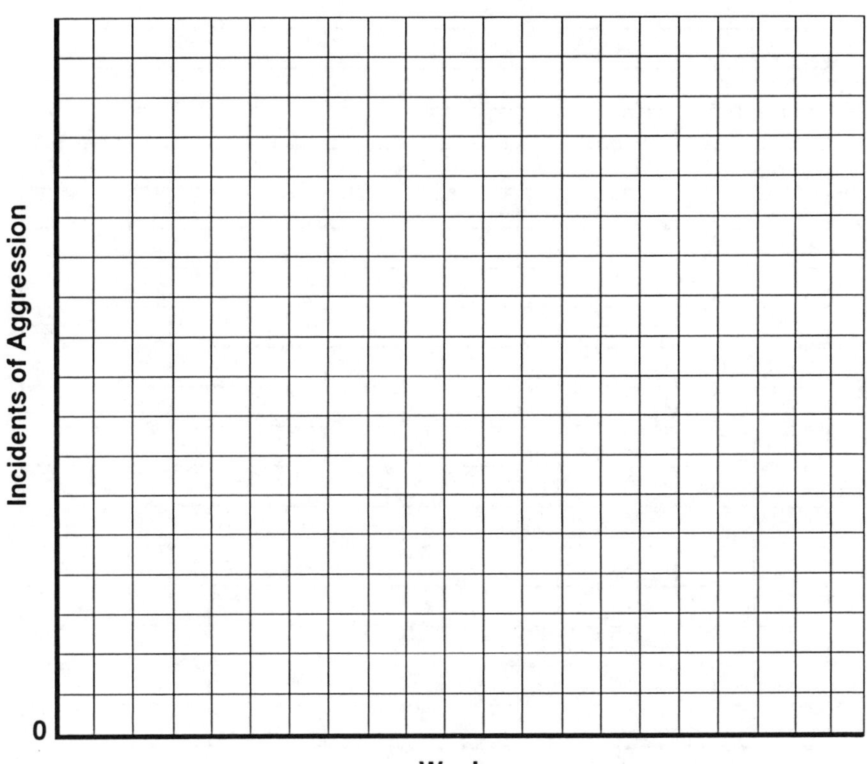

Figure 2.12 A graph set up to represent the number of incidents of aggression each week.

of assignments completed. Additionally, data on the circumstances of aggression and skin picking were collected. These data provided information on the quantity and on the circumstances of the behavior. Graphs allowed a visual representation of the quantity of James's behavior across baseline and intervention conditions.

Case 2

Joanne was a 14-year-old girl with mental retardation and autism, who lived at home with her parents and attended preschool in the mornings. She had no verbal skills and had behavior problems that included breaking her toys, pushing other children, spitting, banging her head on the floor, and screaming. It was difficult to keep her engaged in productive activities for more than a few minutes, as she preferred to engage in self-stimulation, such as picking at lint, watching records spin, and running through the house.

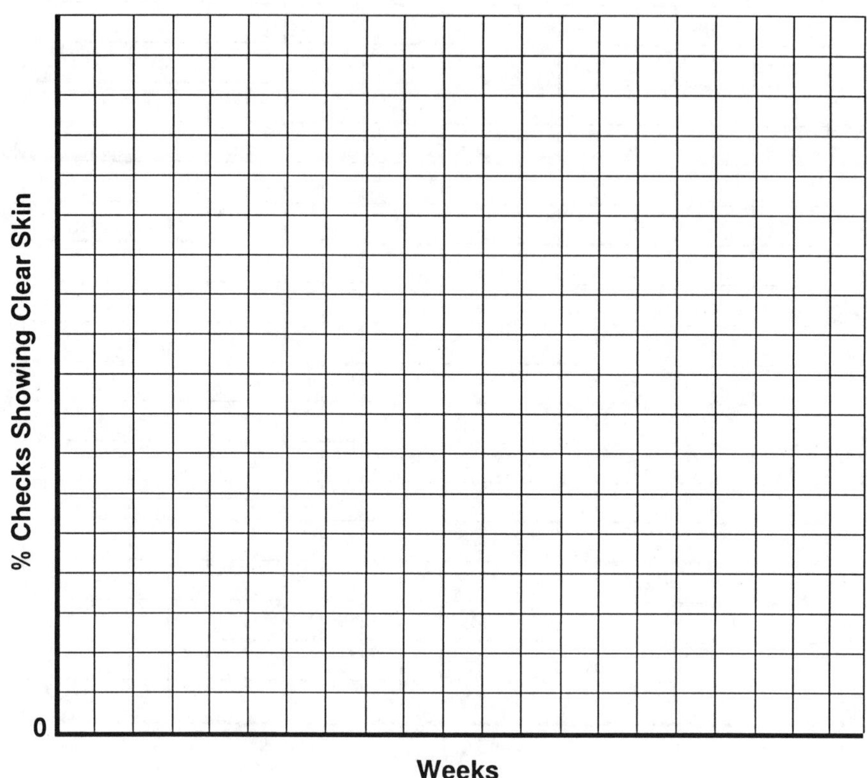

Figure 2.13 A graph set up to represent the percentage of checks showing clear skin each week.

First, it was necessary to target priority behaviors for change. Property destruction, pushing other children, and head banging were targeted because of the intensity of their destructive and harmful effects. At school, participation in tasks for a minimum of five minutes was also targeted. Screaming and spitting, although certainly undesirable behaviors, were not formally targeted for change due to the severity of the destructive behaviors.

Second, it was necessary to choose data collection procedures. ABC data were collected for all incidents of property destruction, aggression, and self-injury. Participation in tasks for a minimum of 5 minutes was taken as time block data, on 15-minute time blocks, on a time sample basis, twice weekly; that is, two mornings per week, with the mornings divided into 15-minute time blocks. For each 15-minute time block, the teacher recorded whether or not Joanne engaged in an activity for at least 5 minutes.

Graphs were set up for each targeted behavior. Property destruction, aggression, and self-injury were graphed separately. Participation in tasks was

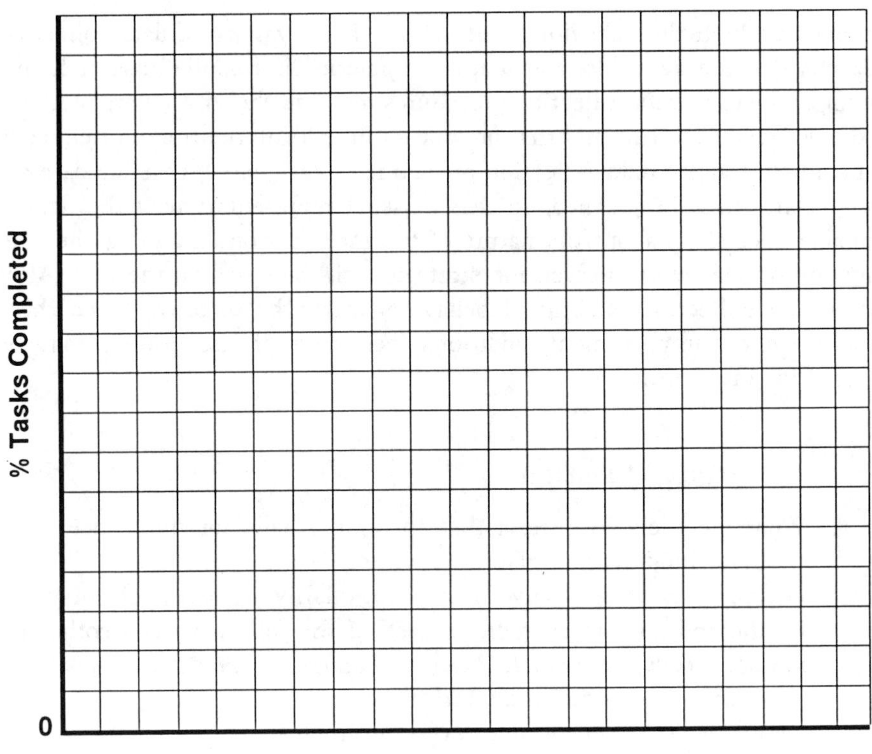

Figure 2.14 A graph set up to represent the percentage of tasks completed each week.

graphed as the percentage of 15-minute time blocks measured per week in which Joanne engaged in an activity for at least 5 minutes.

Joanne's teacher and parents decided to take these data and maintain the graphs for a two-week baseline period and, then, throughout intervention. These graphs provided a visual representation of the frequency of Joanne's behavior and the effects of intervention.

Summary

The formal process of behavior change begins with targeting the behavior to be changed. The behavior targeted must be observable and measurable. In practical terms, the behavior must be important, and if the individual has several areas of behavioral need, it might be necessary to prioritize behaviors for change. Once the behavior is targeted for change, a data collection method is chosen. It is important to obtain quantitative data on the behavior, and in many cases it is just as critical to obtain information on the circumstances and context in which the behavior occurs. There are a variety of data collection methods that are available, and many are practical for applied use at home, school, and work. Data collection procedures must be chosen that are practical in the designated setting and that provide sufficient information on frequency and context. Once a data collection procedure is designated, baseline data are taken. Data must be graphed, so that a visual representation of the data is available. Decisions about the nature of the intervention and about the continuation or change of intervention strategies will be based on the data. After initial data collection, additional behaviors might be targeted. Once these behaviors show improvement, additional behaviors of less priority may be targeted for intervention.

Study Questions

1. What are the two criteria that the target behavior must meet in a behavior modification plan?
2. Define *inner states*. Why do they not qualify as target behaviors?
3. Define and give an example of each of the following data collection methods: *tally, time block, duration, behavioral trace procedures, time sampling, diary*, and *structured diary*.
4. Define *setting events*. Give several examples.
5. Why is it desirable to graph data?

Exercises

1. Bill is a 13-year-old boy with mental retardation and severe behavior problems. His problems include self-injury (hitting himself in the head), aggression toward other people (hitting, kicking, biting), screaming, refusal to follow directions, talking back to teachers, spitting, frequent demands for food, and nail biting. What behaviors might be prioritized and targeted for change in a behavior modification plan? Explain your choices.

2. Alice is a 7-year-old girl. Her teacher has targeted the following behaviors for change: grabbing food from other students and screaming. What data collection procedures might be used for Alice? Explain your choices.

3. Norman is a 15-year-old boy. At home, he refuses to do chores and often talks back to his parents. What data collection procedures might be used for measuring these two behaviors?

4. Beth is a 5-year-old girl. Her mother is trying to teach her to say "thank you." What type of data might her mother take on this behavior? Explain your choice.

5. Set up graphs for the targeted behaviors for Alice, Norman, and Beth.

SELF-MANAGEMENT PROJECT

1. Choose a behavior of your own to target for change. You will do a self-management project with your chosen behavior; that is, you will apply the principles of behavior to change your own behavior, as directed from selected chapters in this book. Choose a behavior that is observable and measurable and that you would like to work on throughout this course.
2. Select methods for collecting data on your behavior.
3. Begin to take data on your behavior. Take data as baseline data until you begin to implement strategies.
4. Set up graphs for the behavior you choose.

References

Barker, R. G., & Wright, H. F. (1951). *One boy's day*. New York: Harper and Row.

Carr, E. G., & Durand, V. M. (1985). Reducing behavior problems through functional communication training. *Journal of Applied Behavior Analysis, 18,* 111–126.

Smith, M. (1986). Managing the aggressive and self-injurious behavior of adults disabled by autism in the community. *The Journal of the Association for Persons with Severe Handicaps, 10,* 228–232.

Smith, M., & Coleman, D. (1986). Managing the behavior of adults with autism in the job setting. *Journal of Autism & Developmental Disorders, 16,* 145–153.

3

Functional Assessment and Functional Analysis

V. Mark Durand

Kevin was 16 years old but looked as if he could be 21. He had spent the last four years in and out of adolescent psychiatric hospitals for reasons that included truancy from school, running away from home, and chronic drug abuse. His last admittance was for digging up graves at a local cemetary and using the skulls for satanic rituals. During his latest stay at the hospital, he threatened to kill his parents, several members of the teaching staff, and his therapist.

Martha was 6 years old and had been given the diagnosis of autism. She did not speak and had no formal means of communicating with her parents or teachers. Her mother described her as a loving child who enjoyed spinning toys for extended periods of time. Martha would, for no apparent reason, scream and slap herself in the face. The screaming and face slapping continued for 30 to 60 minutes at a time and happened several times a day.

The problem behaviors these two children display represent typical challenges facing parents and professionals in the field of special education. What can be done to get Kevin to stop threatening people? How can Martha be helped to stop her tantrums? Increasingly, the professionals who work in this field realize that they cannot effectively help children such as Kevin and Martha without at least some idea as to why they behave in the ways they do. Before asking how to prevent children and youth from engaging in behavior problems or how to modify any behavior, it is important to understand some of the factors that influence these behaviors.

This chapter focuses on understanding the behaviors of students through the use of the *functional assessment*. The various ways knowledge about the presumed causes and maintaining factors of behaviors is gathered through functional analyses and related assessments are examined, and their strengths and weaknesses are discussed. A major theme throughout this chapter suggests that there is not one preferred method for assessing behavior. Rather, the method of analysis depends on considerations such as the frequency of the target behavior, its severity, and the accessibility of the factors hypothesized to be influencing it.

Factors Maintaining Behavior

Before beginning a discussion of how to assess behavior, it is important to identify the types of influences that are important in this assessment. These influences (or *maintaining variables*) are those events that contribute to the continued presence of a behavior. For example, a young girl named Julia may continue to scream at home because her parents spend time with her during these outbursts (e.g., they sit beside her and try to calm her). One of the variables maintaining her screaming may be the positive social attention she receives from her parents.

There may be any number of influences on behavior. Julia might start screaming because a favorite toy is taken away. She might be ill and in some pain and have no other way of telling her parents about the discomfort. She may have had a bad night's sleep and, therefore, be irritable. Suppose all of these factors play some part in her screaming. How does one begin to figure out which things to look for as possibly influencing Julia's screaming (and the behavior problems of other children)?

A behavioral view of this problem emphasizes the *antecedents* and *consequences* of behavior. What happened before Julia began screaming (antecedents) and what happened afterward (consequences) are important to an understanding of the behavior itself. An antecedent to Julia's screaming might be her mother's walking away from her to answer a ringing telephone. A consequence of her continued screaming might be her mother's leaving the phone to comfort her. One assumption made from a behavioral perspective is that these immediate antecedents and consequences are probably very important in explaining why children continue to misbehave. Why Julia began these screaming episodes several years ago may never be known, but a look at the current antecedents and consequences of this behavior may provide ideas as to why they continue to occur.

In addition to looking at immediate antecedents and consequences (sometimes called *stimulus events*), professionals have also tried to assess the influence of more distant factors. Although a bad night's sleep, for example, is not the first thing that happened just before Julia's tantrum, it certainly could have affected her screaming. Complex conditions (such as sleeping habits, illness, diet) that are either concurrent with behavior problems or more distant in time are often called *setting events*. The next section describes some stimulus events and setting events that have been demonstrated to affect behavior. This information is followed by a description of assessment techniques.

Stimulus Events

Positive Reinforcement

Sometimes positive consequences follow instances of behavior problems (e.g., Julia's mother calming her), and such consequences can increase the likelihood that the behavior problem will occur again in the future. Obviously, no one wants to encourage children to misbehave. However, despite the best intentions of parents, teachers, and others, sometimes the way they react to these problems actually serves to positively reinforce the very behavior they want to reduce.

Several research studies have documented this type of influence on behavior. Solomon and Wahler (1973), for example, conducted a study in which they looked at the behavior of sixth-grade boys who were disruptive in their classroom. They found that the boys' classmates paid attention to them only when they were disruptive; when these disruptive boys were well behaved, their peers ignored them. Peer attention may thus have served to reinforce the continued disruptive behavior of the boys. In a study by Lovaas and colleagues, empathic statements (e.g., "I don't think you are bad.") were made to a 9-year-old girl, diagnosed with schizophrenia and autism, each time she hit herself (Lovaas, Freitag, Gold, & Kassorla, 1965). This presumably humanistic treatment actually resulted in an increase in her self-injurious behavior. This outcome suggests that adult attention may have reinforced her behavior. Withdrawing this attention (i.e., extinction) each time she hit herself decreased the frequency of this behavior.

This work describes how positive social events (e.g., peer and adult attention) can serve to reinforce problem behavior. Some behaviors also are intrinsically reinforcing; that is, some behaviors continue to occur independently of environmental influences—they reinforce themselves. For example, some people love to jump out of airplanes (skydive). Attention from others may be partly responsible, but these people report that the major reason they continue to skydive is because it feels great to do it. The sensory feedback involved is sufficient to reinforce skydiving and to increase the likelihood that they will jump again.

Researchers have also investigated the role that these sensory influences play in behavior problems. Rincover, Newsom, and Carr (1979) studied the compulsive behavior of two children with developmental disabilities. Both of these children engaged in frequent light-switching rituals: they insisted on turning lights on and off numerous times in each room they entered. The researchers found that light switching stopped for one student when the switch itself was deactivated and no longer controlled the overhead light. The second student stopped light switching when the switch was modified so that it no longer made any sound when used. The visual (for the first student) and auditory (for the second student) feedback provided by the light switching appeared to be responsible for these compulsive rituals. The first child seemed to switch lights on and off because it looked good to have the lights go on and off, and the second child performed the behavior because it sounded good to hear the switch clicking. The positive reinforcement was the sensory feedback from light switching.

Negative Reinforcement

Although positive reinforcement involves following a behavior with some desirable, or positive, outcome, negative reinforcement consists of removing something undesirable, or negative, following a behavior. For example, if a mother nags her son to make his bed, the child may consider this behavior as something negative. If, however, the boy starts to yell and to protest his mother's behavior, and she then stops trying to get him to make his bed, the mother has negatively reinforced her son for screaming by removing something negative (i.e., her nagging him to make his bed). He will likely scream and protest the next time his mother asks him to make his bed, because she might give in again.

A good deal of research has focused on the role of negative reinforcement in the maintenance of children's problem behavior. Among the best research in this area is the work by Gerald Patterson at the University of Oregon. Patterson has studied the *coercive family process* and how this process can lead to ever-increasing levels of aggression in children (Patterson, 1982). Using the previous example, the mother will probably risk her son's screaming and insist that her son make his bed at some later time. However, the son has learned that, in these situations, he should not give up but, rather, escalate his outbursts. If screaming alone doesn't work (i.e., his mother does not give up her demand), he can break something or hit his mother. Over time, the child learns not only to be non-compliant but also to escalate to more serious behaviors in order to get the parent to back down. Patterson suggests that this escalation pattern can result in children who are severely aggressive.

For both types of stimulus events just described (positive and negative reinforcement), well-intentioned parents, teachers, and peers can inadvertently contribute to behavior problems by how they react to them. For example, a teacher may stop working with a student who is disruptive in an effort to admonish the student, yet this outcome may be exactly what the student wants (i.e., to stop working). A father may yell at his child in a supermarket for whining, but this attention from the parent may outweigh any negative aspects of the father's behavior from the child's point of view. Obviously, knowing why the child is misbehaving in the first place can help to determine how parents and teachers should respond to these concerns.

Setting Events

As has been seen, it is often possible to explain why a student misbehaves by looking at the immediate antecedents and consequences (stimulus events) of the behavior. Yet, sometimes life isn't so simple, and other factors play a role in the continued presence of a behavior problem. As mentioned previously, setting events are complex conditions that happen concurrently with problem behaviors or are more distant in time. A setting event might be a chronic earache that makes a student irritable. Another example of a setting event might be a high level of noise in a shopping mall that contributes to a student's hand biting. There are three types of setting events—physiological, social, and environmental.

Physiological Events

It is common for parents, teachers, and other professionals to attribute behavior problems to physiological causes. Illnesses, injuries, and other biological problems are often blamed for problem behavior. Gillberg and Steffenburg (1987), for example, found that behavior problems in children with autism became more serious after puberty, presumably because of hormonal changes. Another study found that decreasing the caffeine in coffee consumed by a group of individuals with mental retardation led to a decrease in aggression (Podboy & Mallery, 1977). Unfortunately, however, these types of studies are rare in the field, given the difficulties inherent in studying these types of influences (e.g., someone cannot deliberately be made ill to study the effect of illness on problem behavior).

Social Events

How social setting events affect problem behavior is just beginning to be understood. Gardner, Cole, Davidson, and Karan (1986), for example, found that the aggressive behavior of a certain young man was affected by a variety of setting events. The researchers observed that aggressive outbursts from this person were more likely to occur following visits with his brother and in the presence of a particular teacher. They concluded that these types of setting events interacted with his responses to the stimulus events occurring during the day (e.g., corrective feedback, prompts); in other words, he was more likely to become aggressive following corrective feedback on those days following a visit with his brother. This type of work highlights the complexity of human behavior and its relationship to both stimulus (e.g., corrective feedback) and setting (e.g., visits with a sibling) events.

Environmental Events

A variety of environmental events have been correlated with problem behavior. The wearing of certain clothing, for example, has been observed to decrease self-injurious behavior in some individuals (Rojahn, Mulick, McCoy, & Schroeder, 1978). Physical relocation has been studied in the context of deinstitutionalization, and a variety of studies have shown generally positive effects with individuals displaying severe disabilities (e.g., Singer, Close, Irvin, Gersten, & Sailor, 1984). Thus, moving people from a large institutional setting with many unrelated people living together to a home-like environment with family grouping can result in a reduction in problem behavior.

An Integration of Stimulus and Setting Events

Most setting events do not have direct effects on problem behavior. Instead, such conditions as illness, sleep disorders, group density, staffing patterns, and temperature affect the salience of the stimulus events. Being tired, for example, will not make a person severely self-injurious; however, being both tired and asked to respond to heavy demands may promote self-injury. Similarly, having an earache will not make someone aggressive; yet, being ignored when in pain might make a person more likely to hit someone.

Figure 3.1 shows how these influences might interact by illustrating stealing. Mike stole CDs. Why? Looking at some of the setting events of his behavior, it is discovered that his father abandoned the family when Mike was 7 years old and that Mike's family moved constantly because of financial problems (i.e., Mike had a disrupted family life). He reported that he felt bad about himself and had few friends. Although Mike's disrupted family life as a setting event did not cause him to steal, this situation interacted with episodes of his friends teasing him and calling him a wimp (a stimulus event for stealing). Perhaps if Mike felt better about himself and if his family life was more stable, the teasing would not have greatly affected him. However, the combination of the two types of antecedents resulted in his taking a CD from a record store.

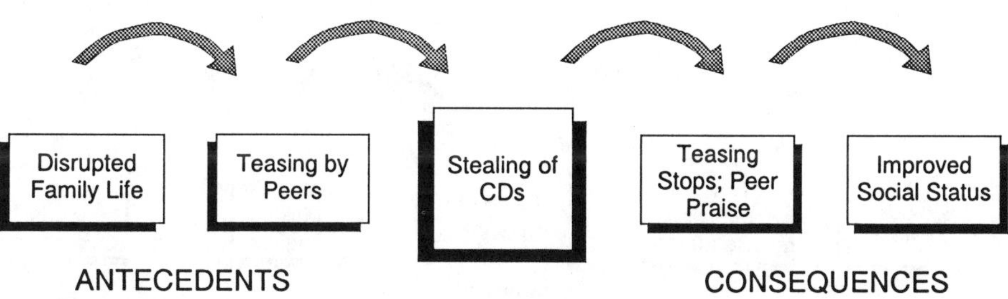

Figure 3.1 The sequence of antecedents and consequences involved in the maintenance of Mike's theft of CDs.

What were the consequences for Mike following the theft of the CD? The teasing stopped (negative reinforcement), and then his peers provided approval for his bravado (positive reinforcement). This type of reaction from his peers probably resulted in his improved social status among other youngsters who steal. The reinforcement he received for stealing will increase the likelihood that he will steal again, especially if his family life remains unstable and any additional peer pressure is applied. Unless someone intervenes in this cycle, Mike can be expected to steal again and/or to engage in other behaviors to gain peer approval.

In another example, Denise is an 8-year-old girl with a diagnosis of severe mental retardation. She bites her hand in school. Why? Figure 3.2 shows that one setting event might involve her not getting enough sleep at night. Obviously, this will make her irritable but by itself should not make her bite her hand. Suppose, though, that her teacher asks her to do something that might be difficult for her to do (e.g., spreading peanut butter on bread), and she bites her hand. Her teacher will possibly stop asking her to spread the peanut butter, which would negatively reinforce her hand biting. In the long run, Denise's teacher might place fewer demands on her to avoid hand biting. In Denise's case, unless something occurs to break this cycle, she will continue to bite her hand to escape demands, and her teacher will stop challenging her with new work.

It is hoped that readers will be convinced at this point that it is important to understand why a student engages in a behavior problem. Some of the possible stimulus and setting events contributing to these behaviors have already been explored. A look at different methods for conducting an assessment of the functions of behavior problems follows. The goal is to discover what factors play a role in each student's behavior.

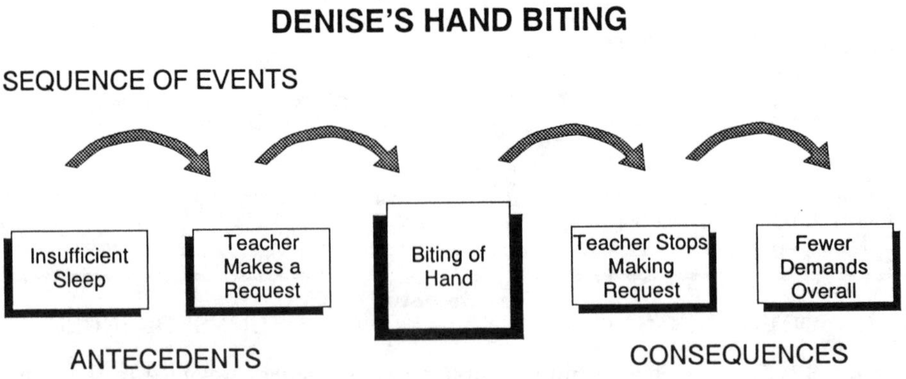

DENISE'S HAND BITING

SEQUENCE OF EVENTS

Insufficient Sleep

Teacher Makes a Request

Biting of Hand

Teacher Stops Making Request

Fewer Demands Overall

ANTECEDENTS

CONSEQUENCES

Figure 3.2 The sequence of antecedents and consequences involved in the maintenance of Denise's hand biting.

Functional Assessment

An essential question to answer when making an assessment is, "Why is this person engaging in this behavior in this setting at this time?" A functional assessment is designed to answer this question. It is important to point out that sometimes the terms *functional assessment* and *functional analysis* are used interchangeably. However, these terms have different meanings and should not be confused. A functional analysis is one type of functional assessment and has been the focus of much attention from behaviorally oriented researchers.

Functional analysis refers to "a believable demonstration of the events that can be responsible for the occurrence or non-occurrence of that behavior" (Baer, Wolf, & Risley, 1968, pp. 93–94). In the strictest sense, a functional analysis involves the manipulation of those events that are thought to influence the behavior of interest and the observation of any change in that behavior. For example, if it were thought that teacher attention influenced a student's classroom behavior, a functional analysis would involve a systematic increase and decrease in teacher attention and an observation of the student's behavior under these different classroom conditions. Using this example, it could be said that a functional analysis of the role of teacher attention on the student's classroom behavior has been performed.

Functional assessment, by contrast, includes functional analysis in addition to a number of other techniques designed to gather information about the function of a behavior that do not directly manipulate or change aspects of the environment. For example, observing a youngster throughout a day, looking for antecedents and consequences of a problem behavior, would be a form of functional assessment. Because parts of the day were not changed and things simply observed as they happened, it would not be considered a functional analysis.

Functional Analysis or Other Functional Assessments?

When should a functional analysis be performed? When should other functional assessment methods be used? When should these methods be combined? There are a number of factors that will determine how the function of behaviors will be assessed. One issue is *accessibility to manipulation.* There are certain influences that currently cannot be manipulated or changed in order to perform a functional analysis. Such things as some illnesses, a disrupted family life, and chromosomal aberrations can affect behavior problems, but they cannot be turned on and off in order to assess their influence. In these instances, other functional assessment techniques are useful.

Another concern involves the *ethics* of conducting a functional analysis. There are other influences that could be manipulated but may not be desirable to change if they will result in an increase in behavior problems. In many instances, deliberately increasing a severe behavior problem in order to assess it (e.g., increasing adult attention or otherwise reinforcing problem behavior) can be questioned on ethical grounds. In these cases, assessment that does not involve manipulation and subsequent increases in problem behavior is recommended.

In general, as with any other type of assessment, it is usually recommended that multiple methods of assessment be used. No one method is ever correct 100% of the time, so it is best to use two or more methods to improve accuracy. Therefore, if a functional analysis can be performed, it is wise to use one or more of the other functional assessment methods to back up or validate the functional analysis. In a way, doing this is like getting a second opinion from another physician after a medical diagnosis. An additional assessment method can serve as a second opinion on the function of the behavior problem.

Until recently, there have been few specific guidelines for conducting a functional assessment. This section reviews a variety of different assessment methodologies that are designed to gather information about behavior problems. Specifically, the goal of these assessments is to generate hypotheses about the variables maintaining these behaviors. Methods designed to assess stimulus events and setting events are reviewed together. Table 3.1 lists these methods along with their advantages and disadvantages.

Functional Analysis

As mentioned previously, a functional analysis involves the manipulation of various antecedents and/or consequences that are thought to influence a student's problem behavior. As students are placed in different situations, their reactions are observed and measured to determine what, if any, effects these changes have on their problem behaviors. With this kind of objective observation, direct influences on a student's behavior should be seen directly.

Antecedent Changes

To conduct a functional analysis on the role of an influence such as adult attention on a student's behavior, the following could be done. After identifying and defining the behavior to be studied (i.e., after developing an operational definition), observe the student in a variety of situations that differ in only one respect—in this case, the amount of adult attention provided. Give the student some activity or task to work on and systematically vary the

Table 3.1 Methods for Functional Assessment

Procedure	*Advantages*	*Disadvantages*
Functional analysis	Possibility of sampling a wide range of influences; concurrent reporting of events; experimental demonstration of influence	Ethical concerns surrounding increasing behavior problems; difficult to conduct in some settings; can be time consuming and labor intensive
Clinical intuition	Possibility of sampling a wide range of influences; ease of use	Lacks demonstrated reliability and validity; no specific guidelines to assist in identifying influences; retrospective reporting of events
Structured interviews	Possibility of sampling a wide range of influences; ease of use; specific guidelines to assist in identifying influences	Retrospective reporting of events; lack of reliabilty and validity data
Rating scales (e.g., Motivation Assessment Scale, Setting Events Checklist)	Ease of use; some have demonstrated reliability and validity; specific guidelines to assist in identifying influences	Some scales lack demonstrated reliability and validity; retrospective reporting of events
Recorded reviews (e.g., daily logs, incident reports, previous interventions)	Can assess history of successes and failures; ease of use	Sample of influences limited to history of assessment and intervention and to thoroughness of documentation; lack of reliability and validity data; no specific guidelines to assist in identifying influences; retrospective reporting of events
Formal observations (e.g., ABC charts, scatter plot)	Ease of use; possibility of sampling a wide range of influences; concurrent reporting of events	Limited guidelines for assessing influences; some methods lack reliability and validity data

Adapted from Durand, V. M. (1990). *Severe behavior problems: A functional communication training approach*. New York: Guilford Press. Reprinted with permission.

amount of attention provided during the activity. For example, work one-on-one with the student for 10 minutes, providing uninterrupted and constant attention. Next, give the student the same task for an additional 10 minutes but work with the student only half the time, breaking up the session by spending part of the time working with another student. Finally, give the student the task and expect independent work (i.e., no attention) for 10 minutes.

In order to insure reliable results, this sequence would probably be repeated several times over several days and at different times of the day. This procedure would help to rule out alternative explanations of the student's behavior, such as having a particularly good or bad day. During each of these 10-minute sessions, record the student's behavior; later, compare the results from the different conditions. If the student reliably misbehaved during one of these settings and was well behaved in other settings, then it is possible to begin to generate some hypotheses about what might be influencing this student's behavior.

Say, for example, that the student rarely misbehaved when someone was working with him one-on-one. However, during any time when someone was not working directly with this student, the problem behavior was frequent. One hypothesis, or guess, based on this information is that the student is misbehaving to get positive reinforcement in the form of adult attention. In the past, this student may have learned that his misbehavior resulted in people attending to him (e.g., walking over to him to tell him to stop), and, as discussed previously, this could have reinforced his continued misbehavior.

The same type of assessment could be performed to look at other influences. One way to assess the role of negative reinforcement, for example, is to change the level of difficulty of the task on which the student is working. The amount of attention would be kept the same (e.g., one-on-one attention), but there would be a 10-minute session in which the task is easy, a session in which the task is moderately difficult, and a session in which the task is very difficult. If the student displayed misbehavior mostly during the more difficult tasks and was relatively well behaved when easy tasks were provided, the assumption could be made that the behavior problems may have been used in the past to escape from unpleasant tasks (i.e., negative reinforcement).

Important information is taken from situations in which the student is disruptive as well as from situations in which the student is well behaved. Sometimes valuable assessment information is found by looking at when the student is well behaved. For example, sometimes teachers report that a student is disruptive all day; however, one may find that if no demands are placed on the student (e.g., no work is required and no rules are in place), this student does well. This might indicate that the student is disruptive to escape even minor requests (e.g., requests to sit down) and suggests that negative reinforcement is involved in the student's problem behavior. It is equally important to determine the situations that lead to improvements in behavior as well as those that seem to create problems.

Consequence Changes

Several examples of the use of antecedents to perform a functional analysis have just been described. Changing the amount of adult attention or the difficulty of the tasks are antecedent manipulations. Another method that has been used to conduct a functional analysis is the use of consequences. This method involves using the influence as a consequence for the behavior (e.g., following a behavior with adult attention) and observing whether or not the behavior increases as a result.

Another way to assess the role of attention, for example, would be to follow every instance of misbehavior with attention from an adult. Every instance of screaming could be responded to by something like, "Stop that! Don't yell in the classroom." If the screaming increased, one interpretation is that the student screamed to get adult attention. Using the negative reinforcement example, the difficult task could be removed every time the student screamed. If the screaming increased under these conditions, it could be said that negative reinforcement may play a role, and the student may be screaming to escape from difficult tasks.

There are several problems with using consequences as part of a functional analysis. One concern, already mentioned briefly, involves ethics. Changes in both antecedents and consequences will result in increases in the problem behavior under certain circumstances (e.g., with decreased attention or when attention is a consequence). However, an additional consideration specific to the use of consequences is the possibility of increasing the future probability of the behavior; in other words, if attention follows screaming, and screaming increases, then attention is a reinforcer. If screaming is reinforced during the functional analysis (e.g., by repeated use of attention as a consequence), will this adversely affect the behavior outside of the functional analysis? Is the problem made worse by doing this kind of assessment? This question has not yet been answered and should be addressed when considering the use of consequences in a functional analysis.

An additional concern when using consequences involves problems with interpreting the results of this assessment. Are we looking at why the student has been misbehaving up to this point, or are we seeing the effects of reinforcing the problem behavior? Suppose, for example, a person regularly gets a Diet Pepsi from a certain machine near her home. Several times a day, on the way to and from her home, she puts money in the machine and receives a soda. Suppose also that a friend wants to find out why this person buys soda from this particular machine and decides to do a functional analysis. One hypothesis the friend considers is the role of social attention in the selection of the machine.

In order to test this attention hypothesis, the friend recruits several attractive adults to hang around the machine and to talk to this person buying a soda (providing attention as a consequence). They are present every day for two weeks, but only talk to the person on alternate days. The friend observes that during the days when these people are present and talk to this person buying a Diet Pepsi, she visits the soda machine more often. The friend decides, based on this functional analysis, that the person has been regularly visiting this machine in the past because of the adult attention she has received.

An alternative explanation for this behavior could be made, however. The person may have previously used this machine because it reliably provided Diet Pepsi and was conveniently located near her home. Her increased use during certain days, though, would be attributed to the attention she received. She was reinforced for using the machine more, but that did not explain why she used it in the first place.

Similar functional analyses can be conducted on students and their problem behaviors. Suppose a student's aggressive behavior increases if it is attended to. Does this necessarily mean that he has been hitting people because he gets attention, or does it simply mean that attention is a reinforcer that can increase the probability of aggression happening more often? Obviously, interpreting the results from this type of assessment should be done carefully. One solution to this concern regarding interpretation involves using additional assessment techniques to support or validate the functional analysis. Some of these other functional assessment methods and their uses are looked at next.

Clinical Intuition

Perhaps the most common method of assessing the variables maintaining problem behavior is *guessing*. Guessing (or *clinical intuition*) typically occurs at an interdisciplinary team meeting where several persons familiar with the student in question hypothesize about the relative influence of numerous variables on the student's behavior, based solely on their own, usually unsystematic, recollections. Clinical intuition is mentioned here with a warning: it is important to get information from the people who know the student best. Historical information (e.g., how and under what circumstances the student misbehaved in the past) is also invaluable. However, because more formal methods of collecting this information exist (some of which have demonstrated reliability and validity data), it is recommended that the people involved with the decision-making process look to these additional, and perhaps more valid, methods for assessing behavior problems.

Structured Interviews

One recently proposed additional method for assessing past instances of behavior problems is the use of structured interviews. The interview described by O'Neill and colleagues, for example, involves questioning teachers, parents, and other concerned persons about the nature of the behavior problems and their possible controlling variables (O'Neill, Horner, Albin, Storey, & Sprague, 1990). These questions should concern the respective roles of such things as medication, sleep patterns, eating routines, and daily activities on the behaviors of interest. This approach has advantages over less formal questioning techniques because of the structured nature of the questions. With a variety of influences surveyed each time with each individual, important influences are less likely to be overlooked.

An important limitation of the proposed structured interviews that is common to most of the assessment strategies reviewed here is that there is no demonstrated reliability or validity. Would the same answers and conclusions be made if two individuals (e.g., a teacher and an aide) were interviewed separately? Will the conclusions made from the interview predict how the student will behave later (e.g., scream if a toy is taken away)? Such interviews may be reliable and valid, but to date there have been no such demonstrations. Therefore, persons using such interviews should be cautious about the conclusions drawn from them. Again, one safeguard is to use multiple forms of assessment to strengthen the inferences made about why a student is misbehaving.

Rating Scales

In an effort to provide an alternative assessment method, several rating scales have recently been developed to assess the function of problem behavior (e.g., Donnellan, Mirenda, Mesaros, & Fassbender, 1984; Durand & Crimmins, 1988). These scales, designed to be completed by teachers, clinicians, and parents, ask questions about the variables that may be influencing behavior problems. One of these scales, the Motivation Assessment Scale (MAS), asks questions about how students would behave in situations involving difficult tasks, unstructured settings, denial of reinforcers, and reduced adult attention (Durand & Crimmins, 1988). One question asks, "Does the behavior occur following a request to perform a difficult task?" This question is designed to discover whether negative reinforcement (escape from difficult tasks) is involved in the continued presence of the problem behavior.

Since students sometimes use the same behavior for different reasons in different settings, it is important to complete separate scales for these separate settings. For example, a boy could slap himself in the face at home to get his mother's attention. At school, however, he may do the same thing (face slapping) to escape school work. The assessment, therefore, should be conducted in different situations (e.g., at home and at school). This procedure is important for rating scales such as the MAS as well as for all the other forms of functional assessment.

One of the few devices specifically designed to assess setting events is the *setting events checklist*, developed by Gardner and his associates (Gardner, Cole, Davidson, & Karan, 1986). It asks questions about such things as previous negative interactions (e.g., Did the person with problem behavior just have an argument with someone?), medication changes, or illnesses; and, as mentioned previously, is unique in its attempt to assess more global influences on behavior problems. Several studies have been conducted with this device that suggest that it can improve the predictability of assessing behaviors such as aggression.

One of the problems of using rating scales and checklists is that they rely on retrospective information. Teachers and others are asked to recall what happened in various past situations, and their memory of events may sometimes be inaccurate. What is gained in ease of use (these scales take only a few minutes to complete) can sometimes be offset with inexact information. However, these scales take only a few minutes to complete, and, therefore, make good complements to other assessment methods.

Record Reviews

Another method of assessing behavior problems is the review of available records. A variety of routine records are maintained by most programs and may be of some help in assessment. *Daily logs* are narratives about important events of the day, and may, for example, serve as sources of informal information about the relationship between specific incidents and locations or times of the day. Additional records to review that may provide information about serious behavior problems are official *incident reports* (see Meyer & Evans, 1989). These documents are required by many schools and programs and usually contain descriptions of serious incidents (e.g., where a student is injured) and the circumstances surrounding them.

Behaviors that have been problems for some time will likely have been the targets of several previous treatment attempts, and this information can sometimes be found in existing records. Knowing that a certain treatment made a behavior problem worse, for example, may be very helpful. If a former teacher had previously removed a child from the classroom for screaming, and if screaming got worse during this time, it may be that screaming was this child's way of escaping from demands (i.e., it was maintained by negative reinforcement). Knowing what worked and what did not work in the past can sometimes tell a great deal about why the student misbehaved in the first place. Of course, reviews of records are helpful only so far as records are accurate, and accuracy is sometimes hard to assess.

Formal Observations

Direct observation of behavior is perhaps the most traditional means of collecting information about the function of behavior problems. In this approach, teachers, parents, and others observe and record instances of the problem behavior along with such information as important antecedents and consequences. One of the more common methods of observation is the *ABC chart* (Bijou, Peterson, & Ault, 1968). Using this format, a person records each time the problem behavior occurs, what happened immediately before it, and what happened immediately afterward. Figure 3.3 shows a typical chart format.

Using this chart, Nancy's teacher (Mrs. Parker) recorded each time that Nancy was aggressive in class. She not only wrote down that Nancy was aggressive but described the specific behavior (e.g., pinching). This information is helpful because Nancy might possibly pinch her teacher for one reason (e.g., negative reinforcement) but kick other students for a different reason (e.g., positive reinforcement). Any obvious patterns of antecedents or consequences are looked for in these records. In Nancy's case, she seemed to be aggressive during times when demands were placed on her (e.g., when asked to sit down, told to go back to work). Her teacher seemed to respond to her aggression by removing these demands (e.g., she sent her out of the room, walked away). If this pattern of antecedents and consequences were relatively stable over several days, one might suspect that Nancy used her aggression to escape from demands and, in fact, was successful with this teacher.

An alternative direct-observation procedure involves recording when during the day the problem behavior occurs. This procedure is easier to complete than the ABC chart, because it does not require recalling and writing down antecedents and consequences. One example of this approach is called a *scatter plot* (Touchette, MacDonald, & Langer, 1985). Figure 3.4 shows a sample scatter plot for a boy named William.

The numbers at the top of the sheet correspond to days, and the times of day are on the side. Column number one shows William's data for October 15th, column two shows his data for October 16th, etc. In this example, William's parents and his teachers recorded times during the day when William slapped his face, and they shaded in the time periods when this behavior occurred. Although on a day-to-day basis, there might not seem to be any order to William's face slapping, looking across several weeks of information, a pattern does seem to emerge. Most of the problem times seem to be during meal times. It may be, for example, that William was hungry and that face slapping

ABC Chart

Name: *Nancy* Rater: *Mrs. Parker* Date: *November 3rd*

Antecedent	Behavior	Consequence
I asked her to sit down.	*She pinched me.*	*I walked away from her.*
I told her to go back to work.	*She kicked another student.*	*I sent her out of the room.*
I was working with her on her math.	*She scratched my arm.*	*I sent her to the principal's office*
She came back into the room from the principal's office.	*She slapped another student.*	*I sent her back to the principal's office.*

Figure 3.3 A sample ABC chart completed for Nancy's aggressive behaviors.

Scatter Plot

Name: *William* Behavior: *Face slapping* Starting date: *October 15*

Day/Time	1	2	3	4	5	6	7	8	9	10	11	12	13	14	15	16	17	18
7:00 am																		
7:30																		
8:00																		
8:30																		
9:00																		
9:30																		
10:00																		
10:30																		
11:00																		
11:30																		
12:00																		
12:30																		
1:00 pm																		
1:30																		
2:00																		
2:30																		
3:00																		
3:30																		
4:00																		
4:30																		
5:00																		
5:30																		
6:00																		
6:30																		
7:00																		
7:30																		
8:00																		
8:30																		
9:00																		

Figure 3.4 A sample scatter plot completed for William's face slapping.

was his way of getting more food during these times (positive reinforcement). More information is needed to confirm this possibility, but seeing this pattern provides a start.

Despite the widespread use of direct observation as an assessment procedure, however, direct observation sometimes provides little useful information about the function of behavior. Because there are so many things that could influence a student's problem behavior, it is sometimes difficult to identify them by observing day-to-day activities. ABC charts and scatter plots help structure these observations, but, again, it is useful to combine these procedures with information from other methods.

Applications

As has been seen, there are a number of methods for assessing the function of behavior problems. It may be helpful to look at two cases in which several of these methods have been applied, to see how the information is collected and used.

Case 1

Dan was a 17-year-old young man, diagnosed with Down syndrome, who had an interest in music. Intelligence-testing placed his cognitive abilities in the moderate mental retardation range, although his reading ability exceeded expectations for someone with these scores. Dan was referred for evaluation because of problems related to one of his vocational placements. It was reported that he was frequently uncooperative and would refuse to work on some of the jobs assigned to him.

Dan's sheltered workshop was the place where these problems were reported. Dan was required to spend two days each week in this setting in order to prepare for a job in the community. The sheltered workshop activities involved doing such things as stuffing envelopes and reshelving groceries in a mock grocery store created in the building. Information from an administration of the Motivation Assessment Scale suggested that negative reinforcement was involved in Dan's problem behavior. Further assessment using an ABC chart suggested that often when Dan was asked to work on a new task, he would either get up and walk away or push the materials on the floor. No problems were reported during break times. The staff at the workshop expressed concern that Dan was not ready for a job in the community because of his behavior problems at the shop.

Fortunately, Dan's day included times when he was required to work, and observations made during these times allowed for a comparison with times when he was not at work. Dan, for example, worked several hours each week at a local supermarket, and observations made at the supermarket indicated that when he was asked to do jobs similar to those at the workshop (e.g., reshelving), noncompliance was not a problem. He would complete the task efficiently and without disruption.

One conclusion from these observations was that Dan was disruptive to escape work in the sheltered workshop. However, the observations at the supermarket suggested that he was not trying to escape all work but may have been trying to escape tasks he found demeaning (e.g., reshelving fabricated grocery shelves). This information was important because it led to the recommendation to *not* treat his noncompliance at the sheltered workshop, per se. Instead, the suggestions were that he be encouraged to expand his hours at the supermarket and that he be assisted in acquiring additional skills on the job. The treatment involved removing Dan from the sheltered workshop and replacing the time he would have spent there with genuine work activities.

Case 2

James was a 12-year-old boy diagnosed with autism and severe mental retardation. At the time he was referred for an assessment, he was the favorite child of the staff at a local group home and attended school in his neighborhood. People at the home were concerned about James because he had no formal means of communicating to other people and because he would sometimes scream, cry, and violently hit his head with his fist.

The staff at his group home and his teachers at school had been collecting information about his tantrums on ABC charts for several years, but no obvious pattern of behavior emerged from them. A review of his records showed a great number of incident reports describing serious behavioral episodes but no indication as to what set off these problems. A setting events checklist was given to the staff, indicating that James's occasional sleepless nights might have contributed to his behavior problems during the day. The Motivation Assessment Scale suggested that both escape from tasks (negative reinforcement) and getting access to things he wanted (positive reinforcement) might also be involved in his tantrums.

A functional analysis was done to see how escape from tasks might influence James's problem behaviors. An abbreviated assessment was set up in his classroom. At first, his teacher was instructed to go into the classroom while James was there but not to talk to him or go near any of the work materials. James was observed for about 5 minutes during this situation, and he had no tantrums. Next, his teacher was asked to go over to her desk and pick up some work but not to give it to James. Again, he was observed for about 5 minutes, during which time he had a tantrum.

Later in the day, after James had calmed down, these two situations were repeated, and his behavior was monitored. These observations were conducted in a similar manner for three days. What became clear after this functional analysis was that James was well behaved as long as the teacher did not even approach the work on her desk. However, if she picked up some of the classwork—even if it was not meant for him—James would frequently have a tantrum. These tantrums were also more likely to occur on the day following a bad night's sleep.

One interpretation of these events was that James could not discriminate between classwork meant for him and for others, especially when he was tired. He simply saw the work materials and had a tantrum in an effort to avoid the work. The teachers and staff had not realized this before. In their minds, when they were about to work with someone else, James would begin screaming out of the blue.

As a result of these assessments, several things were tried with James. First, the staff was instructed in how to set up nighttime routines for James and in how to react to his occasional tantrums at bedtime. These efforts were made to assure James a better night's sleep and make him less irritable and more alert during the day. In addition, James was taught to point to a picture to request a break from work while he was at school. This form of communication training was tried with James because the teachers felt that he did not have an appropriate way to tell them when he had worked too long and needed a rest. It was thought that if he had some control over the pacing of his classwork, he would not need to tantrum to escape or avoid it. After several weeks of these efforts, James's tantrums were almost completely eliminated, and he seemed happier at school and at home.

Conclusions

Assessing the function of behavior is essential for designing appropriate intervention strategies. Previously, workers in the field attempted to reduce behaviors by using a series of strategies on a trial-and-error basis. Fortunately, a number of methods for collecting information on the function of behavior are now available that can be completed in a reasonable amount of time and that can complement each other. As has been seen, an understanding of why someone behaves in a certain way makes knowing what to do about this behavior much easier.

Study Questions

1. What is the relationship of antecedents and consequences to a problem behavior?
2. What is the difference between a *functional analysis* and a *functional assessment*?

3. Describe at least two reasons why someone may not be able to perform a functional analysis.
4. What kind of information does one get from a *scatter plot*?
5. Explain why a person needs to know why a behavior problem is occurring in order to design an intervention.
6. What two ethical concerns are raised when one considers performing a functional analysis?

Exercises

1. A mother nags her daughter to clean up her room. The daughter reacts to this nagging by crying, screaming, and throwing toys around the house. The mother eventually gives in and stops making the request. The daughter then stops her tantrums. Is the daughter likely to have a tantrum the next time her mother makes a similar request? Why or why not?

2. Billy is a fourth-grade boy. He is frequently out of his seat during math class. His teacher often stops class to lecture him and occasionally sends him to the principal's office. What might be the functions of his out-of-seat behavior?

3. Cynthia is a 10-year-old girl with mental retardation and the behavior problem of frequent, loud screaming. How might a functional analysis of her screaming behavior be conducted? How might a functional assessment of her screaming behavior be conducted?

4. Earl is a 4-year-old boy with a language delay and severe behavior problems. Some mornings when he arrives at nursery school he is cooperative and willing to follow instructions. Other mornings, he comes in and sulks, cries, and refuses to participate. What setting events might affect his morning behavior at nursery school?

References

Baer, D. M., Wolf, M. M., & Risley, T. R. (1968). Some current dimensions of applied behavior analysis. *Journal of Applied Behavioral Analysis, 1*, 91–97.

Donnellan, A. M., Mirenda, P. L., Mesaros, R. A., & Fassbender, L. L. (1984). Analyzing the communicative functions of aberrant behavior. *Journal of The Association for Persons with Severe Handicaps, 9*, 201–212.

Durand, V. M. (1990). *Severe behavior problems: A functional communication training approach.* New York: Guilford Press.

Durand, V. M., & Crimmins, D. B. (1988). Identifying the variables maintaining self-injurious behavior. *Journal of Autism and Developmental Disorcers, 18,* 99–117.

Gardner, W. I., Cole, C. L., Davidson, D. P., & Karan, O. C. (1986). Reducing aggression in individuals with developmental disabilities: An expanded stimulus control, assessment, and intervention model. *Education and Training of the Mentally Retarded, 21,* 3–12.

Gillberg, C., & Steffenburg, S. (1987). Outcome and prognostic factors in infantile autism and similar conditions: A population-based study of 46 cases followed through puberty. *Journal of Autism and Developmental Disorders, 17,* 273–287.

Lovaas, O. I., Freitag, G., Gold, V. J., & Kassorla, I. C. (1965). Experimental studies in childhood schizophrenia: Analysis of self-destructive behavior. *Journal of Experimental Child Psychology, 2,* 67–84.

Meyer, L. H., & Evans, I. M. (1989). *Nonaversive intervention for behavior problems: A manual for home and community.* Baltimore: Brookes.

O'Neill, R. E., Horner, R. H., Albin, R. W., Storey, K., & Sprague, J. R. (1990). *Functional analysis of problem behavior: A practical assessment guide.* Sycamore, IL: Sycamore Publishing Company.

Patterson, G. R. (1982). *Coercive family process.* Eugene, OR: Castalia.

Podboy, J. W., & Mallery, W. A. (1977). Caffeine reduction and behavior change in the severely retarded. *Mental Retardation, 15,* 40.

Rincover, A., Newsom, C. D., & Carr, E. G. (1979). Using sensory extinction procedures in the treatment of compulsivelike behavior of developmentally disabled children. *Journal of Consulting and Clinical Psychology, 47,* 695–701.

Rojahn, J., Mulick, J. A., McCoy, D., & Schroeder, S. R. (1978). Setting effects, adaptive clothing, and the modification of head banging and self-restraint in two profoundly retarded adults. *Behavior Analysis and Modification, 2,* 185–196.

Singer, G. H. S., Close, D. W., Irvin, L. K., Gersten, R., & Sailor, W. (1984). An alternative to the institution for young people with severely handicapping conditions in a rural community. *Journal of The Association for the Severely Handicapped, 9,* 251–261.

Solomon, R. W., & Wahler, R. G. (1973). Peer reinforcement control of classroom problem behavior. *Journal of Applied Behavior Analysis, 6,* 49–56.

Touchette, P. E., MacDonald, R. F., & Langer, S. N. (1985). A scatter plot for identifying stimulus control of problem behavior. *Journal of Applied Behavior Analysis, 18,* 343–351.

4 Strengthening Behavior through Positive Reinforcement

Linda was a 16-year-old student who had moderate mental retardation. As part of a work-study program, Linda had a part-time job in the stock room of a clothing store. Her job involved hanging shirts and pants on hangers so that they could be sent out onto the floor for sale. Linda worked extremely slowly. Her work-study teacher felt that she was capable of working much more quickly, and she was in danger of losing her job.

Linda earned a fair wage, but she was paid only every two weeks. Linda appeared to need a more immediate payoff for her efforts. Her teacher, Ms. Adams, put her on a salary schedule under which she received small rewards for each set of 20 pants that she hung, as long as they were hung within a 30-minute period. Her rewards were short breaks, small snacks or drinks, or short chats with her supervisor. So, Linda earned small rewards for working at a certain desirable rate of speed. Under this system, Linda's productivity increased to satisfactory levels. Linda appeared to enjoy her job more, and the employer felt she had become a valuable employee.

Linda's job was almost lost through low productivity. A simple reinforcement system, with reinforcers that appeared natural at the work place, strengthened Linda's work behavior. She transformed into a valued employee. This chapter explores the process of reinforcement—and its use in strengthening behaviors.

Reinforcement Defined

Behavior is lawful, operating under the law of reinforcement. *Reinforcement* is a process by which behavior is strengthened by its consequences. There are two types of reinforcement: *positive reinforcement* and *negative reinforcement*. Positive reinforcement is a process that describes the strengthening of behavior through the contingent delivery of a stimulus. Negative reinforcement is a process that describes the strengthening of behavior through the contingent removal of a stimulus.

If a target behavior is followed by the presentation of a stimulus that increases the likelihood that the behavior will occur again, the process of positive reinforcement has occurred. Bill, for example, puts 75 cents in a soda machine, presses a button, and receives a soda. Each day when Bill passes the machine, he repeats the behavior of putting coins in the machine, and each time the consequence is a soda. Bill's behavior of putting coins in the soda machine has been strengthened through the process of positive reinforcement.

If a target behavior is followed by the removal of an aversive stimulus, resulting in an increased probability of the target behavior, the process of negative reinforcement has occurred. Jim, for example, awakens each morning to the sound of a shrill alarm clock. He has learned to terminate the sound by pressing the OFF button. Jim's pressing of the OFF button has been strengthened by the resulting termination of the shrill sound. His behavior has been negatively reinforced and will likely recur each morning when the alarm clock produces the shrill sound.

The process of positive reinforcement is said to occur only if the probability of the behavior occurring in the future is increased as a result of the contingent application of a given stimulus, referred to as a *positive reinforcer*. The process of negative reinforcement is said to occur only if the probability of the behavior recurring is increased as the result of the contingent removal of a given stimulus, referred to as a *negative reinforcer*. Thus, a teacher, parent, or trainer can attempt to arrange a reinforcing situation, but whether the situation is reinforcing depends entirely on the reinforcer's effects on the frequency of the target behavior.

A behavior that is strengthened through reinforcement is termed an *operant behavior*. Its naturally occurring level, prior to increases due to reinforcement, is termed its *operant level*. The process of modifying the frequency of behaviors through reinforcement is called *operant conditioning*.

Types of Reinforcers

Positive reinforcers are events or stimuli that reinforce behavior by their presentation. These events are normally considered desirable, such as food, drink, and favorite activities. Negative reinforcers are events that reinforce behavior by their removal. These events are normally considered aversive, with an individual behaving in a certain way in order to remove them. Examples of negative reinforcers are shrill sounds, bad tastes, and stimuli causing pain upon touch.

Primary, or *unconditioned, reinforcers* are reinforcers that are considered essential for life, such as food and drink. Primary reinforcers reinforce behavior without being associated with other stimuli. *Secondary*, or *conditioned, reinforcers* are stimuli that become reinforcing through association with other established reinforcers. Milk, for example, functions as a primary reinforcer for baby Jo almost immediately following her birth. The sound of her mother's voice may be a conditioned reinforcer, acquiring its reinforcing properties through association with the milk fed to baby Jo. For 5-year-old Billy, candy is a primary reinforcer. Nickels became a conditioned reinforcer for Billy through their association with the candy he was able to purchase with them.

Generalized reinforcers are conditioned reinforcers that have acquired reinforcing properties through association with a wide variety of established reinforcers. Money is an example of a generalized reinforcer. Its reinforcing value has been established through association with a wide range of other reinforcers.

Conditioned and generalized reinforcers maintain their effectiveness through at least occasional pairing with the reinforcer on which they are based. For example, Mr. Jones initially allowed his students to earn pennies and trade the pennies for chocolates. Money lost its value for this class of 7-year-old children with developmental disabilities when he stopped allowing these children to trade their pennies for candy. The conditioned reinforcer can also lose its effectiveness if the reinforcer on which it is based loses its reinforcing value. If Mr. Jones continued to allow his students to trade pennies for candy, but many of the students began bringing candy to school in their lunches, Mr. Jones's candy would become less reinforcing for them.

A wide variety of primary, conditioned, and generalized reinforcers have typically been established for individuals, and other events and activities continue to acquire reinforcing value as the individual grows older. In addition to food and drink, physical contact and social interactions serve as reinforcers. The relative reinforcing value of these primary reinforcers will vary across individuals. Teacher attention, for example, may serve as a powerful social reinforcer for one student, whereas the same teacher attention may have no effect on another student's behavior.

An early study in applied behavior analysis demonstrated the value of teacher attention as a reinforcer. Hall, Lund, and Jackson (1968) increased the time that first- and third-grade students engaged in good study behavior by providing teacher attention contingent on good study behavior. When teacher attention was no longer provided as a reinforcer, good study behavior declined. In another study, Wolber, Carne, Collins-Montgomery, and Nelson (1987) taught toothbrushing to a man with mental retardation. They compared the effectiveness of social attention alone, such as praise, with the effectiveness of social attention plus tangible reinforcers such as favorite foods. The use of social plus tangible reinforcers was more effective than social reinforcers alone in promoting the acquisition of toothbrushing skills.

Activities also serve as reinforcers. The Premack Principle, described by Premack (1959), states that high-rate behaviors can serve as reinforcers for low-rate behaviors. Playing outside, for example, is a high-probability behavior for Billy; cleaning his room is low-probability behavior. Playing outside functions as a reinforcer for Billy's behavior of cleaning his room. He is more likely to keep his room clean when this behavior is reinforced by the opportunity to play outside.

Osborne (1969) did a study demonstrating that free time functioned as a reinforcer for in-seat behavior of school children. Osborne provided free time from school work as a reinforcer for six girls, aged 11 through 13 years, in a school for children without hearing. When free time was used as a reinforcer for the girls' remaining in their seats, the number of times they left their seats declined.

An innovative use of technology as a reinforcer was demonstrated in a study by Salend and Santora (1985). Five students with mental retardation or learning disabilities served as participants in this study that investigated the use of access to computers as a positive reinforcer. With computer access serving as a reinforcer, the students came to class with required work materials and completed assignments.

Sensory stimuli, too, serve as positive reinforcers. Music, lotions, perfumes, colognes, water beds, and pulsating shower heads are a few of the stimuli available that produce sensory stimulation that can reinforce behavior. Some sensory stimuli, such as addictive drugs, can be so reinforcing that they render most other events relatively useless as reinforcers.

Classroom teachers typically use activity reinforcers and social reinforcers to strengthen desirable behaviors in their students. Good grades are conditioned reinforcers that achieve their reinforcing value through association with social reinforcers (e.g., parental praise), with activity reinforcers (e.g., special trips), and in some cases, with generalized reinforcer (e.g., money).

Teachers who work with students with such severe disabilities as profound mental retardation, autism, and other developmental disorders may use a wider variety of reinforcers to strengthen behavior. They may use primary reinforcers such as favorite foods and drinks as well as physical reinforcers such as back-pats and handshakes, social reinforcers such as praise, and activity reinforcers such as extra recess. They may also use sensory reinforcers such as lotions and music as well as conditioned and generalized reinforcers such as tokens, gold stars, and checkmarks, which the student can trade later for primary or activity reinforcers.

Effects of Reinforcement

Strengthening

The primary effect of reinforcement is that the target behavior increases in frequency. The future likelihood of the behavior occurring is increased as a result of the reinforcement process. This increase in rate is referred to as *strengthening*. Two examples of strengthening follow.

Danny was a fourth-grade boy. During the first marking period of fourth grade, he brought home three A's and three B's. Danny's parents rewarded him with $10 for each A he earned. With this money, a generalized reinforcer, Danny purchased a baseball card. The following grading period Danny received five A's and one B. His behavior of achieving A's was strengthened by the positive reinforcer of money.

Sammy was a 10-year-old boy who had been given the educational diagnosis of emotional impairment. He often refused to do his classwork. His teacher decided to give him five minutes extra at recess for each completed paper he handed in. He began doing all of his assignments because this behavior was strengthened by the positive reinforcer of extra time at recess.

Order of Responding

A second effect of reinforcement is a change in the order of responding. During the strengthening process, a specific order of responding becomes established and is maintained. Linda's performance of hanging pants initially consisted of repetitive, nonefficient motions. For example, she would pick up several hangers, and holding them in one hand, then pick up several pairs of pants and another several hangers, and so forth. Finally, with great difficulty, she would hang the pants on the hangers. Once the reinforcement procedure began, she quickly became efficient at picking up one hanger and one pair of pants and hanging the pants on the hanger before picking up the next hanger and pair of pants. She quickly became dependable at performing this task with this set order of steps. Her initial behavior was replaced by an orderly and efficient system.

Decrease in Variability

Another effect of reinforcement is a change in the variability of response. Prior to reinforcement, there may be some variability in the manner in which a reponse is made. Once the reinforcement process is implemented, however, the variability is reduced and the responses become more similar.

Linda's case provides an illustration. Initially, Linda's manner of placing pants on hangers was variable: one pair would be hung on straight, the next pair would be askew, a third pair would straddle the hanger. As a result of providing reinforcers for hanging pants, her responses became more similar, and eventually she was hanging all the pants in the same way.

Satiation

An outcome of the reinforcement process may be *satiation*, the process through which the reinforcer loses its value as a reinforcer as a result of repeated presentations. Satiation can occur either directly, through an individual's overuse of a certain reinforcer in the reinforcement process, or indirectly, by the individual's having other access to the reinforcer in the environment. For example, candy remained a reinforcer for Mr. Jones's students when it was given to them only several times a week. When Mr. Jones used candy as a reinforcer for every correct response, by the end of the first hour each child had earned at least ten pieces of candy, and satiation prevailed. The children tired of the candy, and so candy lost its power to reinforce.

Reinforcers used repeatedly are likely to result in satiation. Generalized reinforcers such as money, however, are less likely to result in satiation than more specific reinforcers such as popcorn, because money allows access to a wide range of reinforcers. When positive reinforcement is used to strengthen and maintain behavior, it may be necessary either to vary the reinforcers used or to restrict access to particular reinforcers, in order to avoid satiation. Restriction of access is discussed as an ethical issue in Chapter 14.

Termination

If the positive reinforcement procedure is terminated, the target behavior will possibly decrease in frequency. In many cases, however, behaviors will continue once the reinforcement is stopped because other events will begin to serve as reinforcers. A student praised frequently for his initial attempts at reading, for example, may no longer require praise once he becomes a good reader because the stories in books are reinforcing.

Individuals with severe developmental disabilities might have an ongoing need for formal reinforcement schedules, since there may be no adequate substitutions in the environment if their reinforcement schedules are terminated. Johnny, for example, has profound mental retardation. He is nonverbal and does not understand the meaning of a paycheck from his part-time job stocking items at a local department store. He is rewarded for his work with short hourly breaks and snacks or favorite drinks. If Johnny's job coach eliminates the reinforcement schedule, Johnny's work behavior will likely decline in frequency, since Johnny's paycheck has no meaning for him and is only provided every two weeks.

Individuals without disabilities may also undergo these same behavioral declines once reinforcement is terminated. For example, a manager of a bankrupt store may quit his job after only one day of earning no salary.

Schedules of Reinforcement

Target responses can be reinforced either every time they occur or occasionally, according to specific schedules. These schedules are called *schedules of reinforcement*. Different schedules of reinforcement have different characteristic effects on target behaviors.

Continuous Reinforcement

If every occurrence of a response is reinforced, the schedule is referred to as a *continuous reinforcement schedule (CRF)*. Many behaviors are reinforced and maintained by continuous reinforcement schedules. For example, if each time Doris makes a pitcher of juice she gets a glass of juice and a cookie, her behavior is said to be on a continuous reinforcement schedule. If each time Bill puts 75 cents into a soda machine and presses a button he receives a soda, his behavior is on a continuous reinforcement schedule. More examples of this schedule follow. Every time a student completes a paper, it is graded (presuming grades are reinforcing). Every time a restaurant customer orders a meal, food is served. Each time one turns on a light switch, a light comes on. Every time the front door key is placed in the lock and turned, the front door opens. Each time a caller picks up the telephone receiver, a dial tone is heard (signaling the phone is ready to use).

Carol's case provides a good example of the use of a CRF. Carol was a young woman with autism who worked part-time unpacking boxes of socks at a warehouse, with the help of a job coach. After being shown how to take the socks out of a box, Carol stood staring at the box. Occasionally, she would reach down and take out a pair of socks, then return to staring. To improve her performance, her job coach put unpacking boxes on a continuous schedule of reinforcement, with praise and handshakes serving as reinforcers for Carol. Each time Carol unpacked a pair of socks, her job coach praised her and shook her hand. This CRF schedule helped strengthen Carol's behavior of unpacking socks.

CRF schedules are valuable when an individual is first learning a behavior. This schedule can rapidly increase the frequency of the behavior. However, there are several disadvantages to the long-term use of CRF schedules. For one, the individual may quickly satiate, particularly if the responses are of short duration and occur frequently, so that many reinforcers are delivered in a relatively short period of time. In Carol's case, then, if handshakes and praise are provided each time she unpacks a pair of socks and if her rate of unpacking increases, handshakes and praise may lose their reinforcing value.

A second disadvantage of the CRF schedule is that behaviors that have been reinforced on these schedules tend to decrease rapidly once reinforcers are no longer provided. Putting coins into a soda machine is a good example. This behavior is normally reinforced on a CRF schedule; so, if a person puts coins into a soda machine and a soda does not come out, the coin-putting behavior will extinguish very rapidly. In fact, it is unlikely that this person will put any more money into this machine.

A third disadvantage of the CRF schedule is that it is difficult to carry out in many classroom, home, and work settings. A CRF schedule may require the instructor or parent to observe the person continuously and act almost continuously in response to that person performing the targeted behavior. Such close monitoring and reinforcing are often impractical in applied settings.

Intermittent Reinforcement

Initial use of a CRF is more practical if it is quickly replaced by an *intermittent schedule of reinforcement*, which reinforces some but not all occurrences of a response. In many cases, an intermittent schedule of reinforcement is sufficient from the outset. If a teacher, for example, calls on Elinor only occasionally instead of every time she raises her hand, Elinor's hand raising is on an intermittent schedule of reinforcement. If Sally usually calls her friend when she arrives home from school and sometimes her friend is not home to answer the telephone, Sally's telephoning is on an intermittent schedule of reinforcement.

These schedules of reinforcement are often the schedules of choice for changing behavior for reasons of their convenience and their effect on behavior. Each of the several types of intermittent schedules of reinforcement has its own characteristic effect on behavior. There are two types of simple schedules of reinforcement: *ratio schedules* and *interval schedules*. Ratio schedules deliver reinforcers contingent on the number of responses. Interval schedules deliver reinforcers based on the amount of time between responses.

Ratio Schedules

Ratio schedules can be fixed or variable, with *ratio* referring to the proportion of reinforcers to responses. A fixed ratio schedule (FR) involves a fixed reinforcer-to-response ratio. Examples of fixed ratio schedules are plentiful. If a boy receives $1 for every 10 envelopes he addresses, he is on an

FR 10 schedule. If a girl receives a star for every 5 math problems she completes, she is on an FR 5 schedule. If workers are paid by the number of units of work they complete, they are on fixed ratio schedules of reinforcement and so are students who are allowed to engage in preferred recreational activities following the completion of set units of work.

Variable ratio schedules specify an average reinforcer-to-response ratio. If a slot machine provides a payoff on the average of every 50 plays, a player of this machine is reinforced on a VR 50 schedule. If a worker manufactures computer cables and her supervisor gives her a break after approximately every 30 cables she completes, she is working on a VR 30 schedule.

Ratio schedules typically produce rapid rates of behavior while the person is responding. However, the fixed ratio schedule can also result in a short period of time following delivery of a reinforcer during which an individual does not respond. This interval of no responding is called a *post-reinforcement pause.* If the worker's behavior of making computer cables is reinforced on an FR 30 schedule, she can be expected to take a short pause in her work between sets of 30, following delivery of the reinforcer. Variable ratio schedules typically produce very high and constant rates of behavior.

A danger of arranging a ratio schedule is having the required number of responses too high. If this number is too high, the schedule is too thin, and the behavior will not increase in frequency. Simon's case presents a good example of this problem. Simon's teacher told him that for every 500 math problems he completed, he could jump on the trampoline. This requirement was too high for Simon, and his math behavior was not strengthened.

Interval Schedules

Interval schedules allow for the delivery of a reinforcer for every response that occurs following a specified period of time. These schedules can be fixed or variable. A fixed interval (FI) schedule provides a reinforcer following responses made after a fixed amount of time. For example, an FI 5-minute schedule provides a reinforcer for the first response that occurs after a 5-minute interval. A variable interval schedule provides a reinforcer following responses made after intervals of time that are of some specified average length, the exact length of which varies from interval to interval. A VI 15-minute schedule, for example, provides a reinforcer for the first response that occurs after intervals averaging 15 minutes in length. However, any given interval might not be exactly 15 minutes. In another example, if a laboratory rat is reinforced for lever-pressing on an FI 1-minute schedule, its first response after 1 minute results in the delivery of food pellets; if the rat's lever-pressing is placed on a VI 1-minute schedule, the intervals between availability of these reinforcers will vary but average 1 minute.

Fixed interval schedules typically generate low rates of the target behavior early in the interval, with increasing rates of the target behavior as the end of the interval approaches. For example, if her teacher gives math quizzes every 5 days and Louise needs to study about 30 minutes to get an A on a quiz, Louise typically will study for 30 minutes directly before the quiz is given. Her study behavior, then, is fairly low at the beginning of the week, but as the end of the 5-day interval approaches, it increases, peaking about 30 minutes before her quiz. Reinforcement of Louise's study behavior approximates an FI 5-day schedule.

Variable interval schedules produce more consistent responding throughout the interval than do fixed interval schedules. Typically, response rates are lower under interval schedules than under ratio schedules. However, behavior under interval schedules can be more stable than under ratio schedules. Under a ratio schedule, particularly if the ratio is too high, the responding can drop off due to the infrequency of reinforcement. Under an interval schedule, the mere passage of time provides the opportunity for reinforcement, even if some responses are omitted. Thus, rate declines from insufficient reinforcement are less of a danger on interval schedules.

Differential Schedules

Differential schedules of reinforcement specifically reinforce one pattern of behavior as distinct from other patterns. One such schedule, *Differential Reinforcement of High Rates of Behavior (DRH)*, provides reinforcers for high rates of performance of a target behavior. Ellen, for example, is a 15-year-old girl with mental retardation who completes her math assignments very slowly. If she completes math problems at the high rate of 5 problems within a 30-minute period, she is provided with a reinforcer; if she does not, she is not given a reinforcer. In another example, to get a reinforcer, Jackie must hang at least 30 pairs of pants within a 30-minute period.

Smith and Coleman (1986) used a DRH schedule to increase the rate of work-related behaviors in a man with autism who worked in a printing company under the supervision of a job coach. The man was working initially at 60% of the rate of his nonhandicapped co-workers. Under a DRH schedule that used visual feedback and praise as reinforcers, the man's production rate increased from 60% to 100% of that of nonhandicapped workers.

Differential Reinforcement of Low Rates of Behavior (DRL) are used to encourage responding at a specified low rate of behavior. For example, Belinda is a fourth-grade student who rarely raises her hand in class to answer a question. The teacher wants Belinda to volunteer to answer a question occasionally, but she does not want Belinda to raise her hand continually. Her hand raising should occur at the low rate of once an hour. So, if Belinda raises her hand once each hour, she is called on and praised, but if she raises her hand more often, she is not called on.

Shaping

Shaping is the process of reinforcing successive approximations of a desired behavior until the goal behavior is performed. Shaping is often used when teaching new, complex behaviors. Initially, approximations of the desired behavior are reinforced. Gradually, reinforcement is provided for closer approximations of the goal behavior and not provided for cruder approximations. Finally, only accurate performance of the goal behavior is reinforced.

Shaping is often used with young children to reinforce successive approximations of a desired behavior until the goal behavior is performed. Shaping is often used when teaching new, complex behaviors. Initially, approximations of the desired behavior are reinforced. Gradually, reinforcement is provided for closer approximations of the goal behavior and not provided for cruder approximations. Finally, only accurate performance of the goal behavior is reinforced.

Shaping is often used with young children to reinforce language development. If, for example, the parents of an 8-month-old baby gleefully clap and rush to get a bottle when the baby says "ba," this sound is reinforced. When the child occasionally begins to say "bot," the parents begin to get the bottle in response to this sound and no longer reinforce "ba." As the child begins to utter "bottle," only this word is reinforced. The word bottle is shaped through reinforcing successive approximations.

Handwriting is often reinforced through shaping. Young children are asked to copy a circle, for example. At first, any mark they make on the paper is reinforced; but as the marks begin to approximate a circle, only those approximations are reinforced. Finally, when circles are drawn correctly, only the correct circle is reinforced. Letter formation is reinforced through this same process of reinforcing successive approximations of the desired response.

Positive Reinforcement and the Functions of Behavior

Functional assessment plays an important role in decision making regarding the use of positive reinforcement in a behavior change plan. The functional assessment can reveal the need to use or to not use positive reinforcement, the type of reinforcer to use, and the schedule under which to deliver the reinforcer.

The functional assessment of a targeted misbehavior reveals the functions that the misbehavior serves. If a misbehavior fulfills certain critical functions for an individual, then the individual might not be sufficiently motivated to learn or to use a more acceptable behavior. It would then be necessary to include a reinforcement schedule for acceptable behavior as part of the behavior change plan. The functional assessment may suggest the need for a positive reinforcement schedule. Brigit's care provides an example of the use of the functional assessment to suggest the need for positive reinforcement.

Brigit was a 6-year-old girl with mild mental retardation and a language disability. She had a high frequency of screaming and grabbing for food. The functional assessment revealed that when Brigit screamed for food or grabbed for food, her parents typically gave her food. Since her screaming and grabbing served the function of obtaining food, there was no need for Brigit to learn to ask for food politely. The functional assessment suggested that a behavior change plan needed to include a component in which a more acceptable behavior, such as asking politely, was strengthened with a schedule of positive reinforcement.

The functional assessment also helps to identify reinforcing events. Randomly choosing such events can prove ineffective, for what is reinforcing for one individual may not be reinforcing for another. A functional assessment is a useful source of information about potential reinforcers.

In cases of targeted misbehavior, a variety of events may function as reinforcers that maintain that misbehavior. The functional assessment identifies these events that function as reinforcers. The events can then be scheduled as reinforcers to strengthen a targeted desirable behavior. If the events functioned as reinforcers for misbehavior, they might well function as reinforcers for more positive behavior.

A functional assessment suggested that Brigit's parents inadvertently used food to reinforce her screaming and grabbing behavior. This information was used to construct a schedule of positive reinforcement, using food as a reinforcer, to strengthen the behavior of asking politely for food.

In another case, Larry was a 5-year-old child who often had temper tantrums at home. He also was uncooperative in many necessary activities, such as dressing himself, putting away his toys, and eating meals with his family. Although Larry's behavior modification plan needed to address the elimination of tantrum behavior, it was also necessary to strengthen cooperative behavior. Strengthening of Larry's cooperative behavior required a schedule of reinforcement, and identification of possible reinforcers was undertaken through a functional assessment of his misbehavior.

A functional assessment of his temper tantrums revealed that several events served as reinforcers. When Larry had a tantrum, he was often held, spoken to soothingly, and given favorite snacks or a special toy to play with, in order to calm him.

Part of Larry's behavior change plan involved scheduling positive reinforcement for cooperation with his tasks and activities. It was necessary to identify possible reinforcers. This identification was performed through a functional assessment of his tantrum behavior. The events that functioned as reinforcers for tantrums were scheduled as reinforcers for cooperative behavior. Larry's task completion behavior was put on a continuous schedule of reinforcement: each time he completed a task cooperatively, he was provided with praise and hugs and offered a favorite snack or the opportunity to play with a special toy.

A functional assessment of the targeted desirable behavior itself might also be useful in order to identify possible reinforcers. Some individuals display a certain desirable behavior but only infrequently. The goal of the behavior change plan might be to increase the frequency of the desirable behavior. A functional assessment of that behavior can reveal the events that are serving as reinforcers. If necessary, more dense scheduling of those same reinforcers is arranged in order to increase the frequency of the desirable behavior.

An example of a situation in which an increase in the density of reinforcement is needed follows. Johnny occasionally completed his homework, and his teacher wanted to increase the frequency with which Johnny accomplished this task. A functional assessment of homework completion revealed that about once every two weeks when Johnny did his homework, his teacher praised him (homework completion was on a VI 2-week schedule of reinforcement). On other occasions, nothing was said to Johnny when he handed in homework. It appeared that the teacher's praise was maintaining his behavior but at a low rate. So, it was necessary to increase the density of the reinforcement schedule to achieve higher rates of homework completion. The teacher then began praising Johnny at least twice a week for handing in his homework (VI 2-day schedule), in order to strengthen his homework-completion behavior. The density of reinforcement was thus increased from a VI 2-week schedule to a VI 2-day schedule of positive reinforcement.

The functional assessment might also suggest that the type of schedule of reinforcement must be changed. Johnny's teacher may have decided to change the reinforcement schedule from a variable interval schedule to a DRH specifically to reinforce higher rates of the behavior. So, instead of praising Johnny every two weeks for completing one homework assignment, she may have decided to praise him every four days if he completed at least three assignments within that 4-day period. The schedule would be changed from a VI 2-week schedule to a DRH.

Positive Reinforcement to Strengthen Behavior

Positive reinforcement is a valuable and powerful tool for strengthening behavior within the context of a behavior modification plan. The effective use of positive reinforcement is dependent on numerous factors.

It is worthwhile to examine these factors prior to implementing strategies based on positive reinforcement.

Identification of Need

Not all behavior change plans require the formal use of positive reinforcement. If a goal of the plan is to strengthen a desirable behavior, then positive reinforcement may or may not be indicated. Prior to implementing a strategy based on positive reinforcement, it is important to assess the need for such a strategy. If the need is motivational, positive reinforcement is appropriate. If the need is primarily instructional, a formal schedule of positive reinforcement may not be necessary.

Some individuals do not display a desired behavior because the behavior is not in their repertoire. In these cases, it is necessary to teach the individual how to perform the behavior. Instructional issues, rather than motivational issues, may be of paramount importance. Larry, for example, was a fifth-grade student whose teacher was concerned about his poor handwriting. Initially, she felt that he was not trying to write well. So, she tried various positive reinforcers to improve his handwriting, including praise, stars, and even small pieces of candy; but, Johnny's handwriting remained generally poor. Upon closer examination, she noted that he was actually forming the letters incorrectly—his poor handwriting was not a motivational but an instructional issue. Good letter formation was not in his behavioral repertoire, and he needed to be taught how to form many letters. So, he was given extra instruction on letter formation, and his handwriting improved.

Another example concerns Gloria, a 16-year-old girl with a learning disability. She had difficulty ironing, and often refused to iron clothes. Gloria's problem, like Larry's, was instructional. She did not need a schedule of reinforcement for ironing clothes; rather, she needed to be taught how to iron clothes. Once she was given appropriate instruction on how to iron, she began to cooperate in performing the task.

It may also be necessary to strengthen behavior in cases where a behavior is in an individual's repertoire but information on when the behavior is to be performed is not. Again, the issue may be one of instruction or of rearranging environmental cues, rather than of motivation. For example, Fred is a 3-year-old boy who knows how to say "please" when asking for candy. However, he does not use the word when making any other requests. The behavior is thus in his repertoire, but he has not yet learned when the behavior needs to be performed.

The functional assessment and other assessments might reveal that an individual is capable of performing a desired behavior, understands the conditions under which the behavior should be performed, but chooses not to perform the behavior. This failure to perform the desired behavior may be a motivational issue, and a schedule of positive reinforcement may be necessary in order to strengthen the behavior.

Janet, for example, was an 18-year-old girl with moderate mental retardation. She attended school in the morning and had a job at the local library each afternoon. Her job involved sorting books for shelving. Janet's productivity was extremely low: she would sort one book approximately every five minutes. She knew how to sort the books and when she was supposed to sort them; however, she chose not to sort them. A schedule of positive reinforcement was needed in order to increase the frequency of book sorting.

Allan was six-year-old boy with a language delay. He spoke only a few words and did not use these words often. Allan frequently did not respond to instructions or to training that did not include the use of positive reinforcers. The strengthening of verbal behavior in Allan required the use of instructional strategies combined with positive reinforcement.

Types of Reinforcers

Decisions must be made regarding the selection of events to serve as positive reinforcers. These decisions must be based on some assessment of events that are reinforcing for the individual whose behavior is to be strengthened. There are a variety of ways to choose reinforcers.

Functional Assessment

The functional assessment might suggest events that currently function as reinforcers. These same events are used as reinforcers to strengthen desired behaviors. If, for example, Bobby's teacher completed a functional assessment of his pushing behavior and noted that Bobby often pushed other children to gain access to a favorite toy, access to that toy could be expected to function as a positive reinforcer in strengthening more desirable behavior.

Reinforcement Inventory

Reinforcement inventories provide listings of numerous types of reinforcers. Social, activity, and food reinforcers are generally included on the inventory. These inventories are filled out either by the individual or by teachers, parents, or other people who know the individual well.

Observation

Observation of the individual often reveals potential reinforcers. Noting the events that an individual chooses during naturally occurring situations can suggest possible reinforcers. For example, Ellen is a 10-year-old girl with a developmental disability. She needs a schedule of positive reinforcement in order to strengthen task-related behaviors. Her teacher has noted that during free time Ellen often chooses specific activities and play materials and that at lunchtime, snack time, and birthday parties she chooses certain foods. These activities and foods that Ellen often chooses are possible reinforcers to use in strengthening task-related behaviors.

Sampling

Providing an individual choices from a variety of events helps determine potential positive reinforcers. Sam's teacher, for example, typically used only praise as a reinforcer. However, Sam, a 6-year-old boy with language delays and severe behavior problems, appeared to need more concrete reinforcers. He expressed little interest in the activities available in the classroom. So, his teacher purchased a variety of snack foods and assembled an assortment of games and toys. She provided Sam with short periods of access to these items in order to determine which ones he preferred.

Effects

An event is not conclusively called a positive reinforcer unless it increases the frequency of the behavior it follows. A method for selecting reinforcers is to use a variety of events to consequate behavior and note which ones serve to increase the frequency of the target behavior. As the schedule of reinforcement is implemented, it may be necessary to change reinforcers based on the effects of these events on the target behaviors.

Natural

It is best to use events that are naturally occurring in the environment. If praise, feedback, and grades suffice to maintain good classroom performance, then they should not be embellished. If hugs, praise, and smiles suffice to maintain cooperative behavior at home, then there is no need to use other reinforcers. However, if conventionally available or natural reinforcers are not effective in strengthening desired behavior, more contrived reinforcement schedules may be necessary. The use of food, activities, social events, and sensory stimuli might be unnecessary for students with average or above average learning ability, but these events might be indispensable for very young children and for children and youth with developmental disabilities or other cognitive or behavioral handicaps.

Choosing the Schedule of Reinforcement

It is important to choose the schedule of reinforcement prior to its implementation. When choosing the schedule, there are a number of factors to consider.

Frequency of Target Behavior

If the frequency of the target behavior is low or nonexistent, it may be necessary to use a fairly dense schedule of reinforcement, such as a continuous schedule of reinforcement. If the frequency is moderate, but less than acceptable, an intermittent schedule of reinforcement might be sufficient.

Potency of Reinforcers

If the reinforcers are powerful, an intermittent schedule of reinforcement might suffice. Leonard's father, for example, paid Leonard $150 to cut the grass on a VR 5 schedule, so approximately every 5 times Leonard cut the grass, he was given $150. The potency of this reinforcer was sufficiently strong to keep the grass cutting behavior at an acceptable level. In another example, Gary's father paid Gary $10 for cutting the grass, and the money was delivered on an FR 1 schedule. Each time Gary cut the grass, he expected the $10. Gary's reinforcer was less potent than Leonard's, and so it needed to be delivered more often.

Practicality

Issues of practicality play a role in the selection of a reinforcement schedule. Social behaviors, for example, usually cannot be practically reinforced each time they occur. Sharing materials, asking or offering assistance, and working quietly are all behaviors that may occur in an ongoing manner and cannot be easily reinforced following each distinct occurrence. These types of behaviors might best be reinforced on interval schedules. For example, Gene might be put on a VI 1-hour schedule for working quietly, with his teacher praising him the first time after approximately each hour that she sees him working quietly. On the other hand, Alma, who works in a factory making computer cables, might have work reinforced on an FR1 schedule, under which she is paid $1 for each computer cable she makes, because it is easy to count each cable that she produces.

Reducing the Density

The density of reinforcement is the frequency with which the target behavior is reinforced. Initially, it may be necessary to use a continuous schedule of reinforcement or a fairly dense interval schedule in order to achieve desired frequency goals. However, it may then be possible to reduce the density, or thin the reinforcement schedule. If this thinning is accomplished abruptly, a reduction in the frequency of the desired behavior can be expected.

Reductions in frequency should be gradual. An FR 1 should not be abruptly thinned to an FR 10. For example, if Louis, a 3-year-old child who has been given a smile and a hug each time he picked a book off the floor and put it on the shelf, has his FR 1 schedule abruptly switched to an FR 20, he might wander away from the pile of books on the floor long before picking up the 20th book. If Louise, who is typically paid each week for her work in the student store, has her weekly paycheck abruptly switched to a monthly paycheck, she might look elsewhere for employment.

Satiation

If an individual undergoes satiation while performing a task, the effect is the same as extinction of that task. *Extinction* is a process in which the behavior declines in frequency due to a severing of the connection between the behavior and its reinforcer (see Chapter 5). If as a result of satiation, a consequence loses its reinforcing value, the behavior is, in effect, on extinction. Satiation can often be avoided, or compensated for, by careful observation and planning. One method for avoiding satiation is by the use of a generalized reinforcer, such as money, which can then be used to obtain any of a variety of other reinforcers.

Generalized reinforcers such as money, however, are often not practical or useful in certain settings or with certain individuals. In classrom or home settings or for individuals needing more immediate, concrete reinforcement, it is often helpful to provide a variety of reinforcers. For example, Jenny, an 8-year-old girl with mental retardation, has her cooperative, on-task behavior reinforced on a VI 15-minute schedule, using a variety of reinforcers. For any given interval, the reinforcer may be food, drink, music, or one of a variety of activities or toys that Jenny enjoys. To avoid satiation, these reinforcers are not repeated within each hour, and novel reinforcers are introduced each week.

Satiation can also be avoided through varying the reinforcers or through the use of *reinforcer menus*, which are lists of available reinforcers from which the individual can choose. For example, Arnold, a 15-year-old boy with mental retardation who works part-time, has his productivity reinforced on a DRH schedule and receives access to a reinforcement menu for maintaining designated production rates. The reinforcement menu includes several activities from which Arnold can choose, such as lunch at a favorite restaurant, a trip to an ice cream parlor, and rental of a movie.

If a behavior is strengthened, and a reduction in frequency is then observed, it may be that satiation has occurred. If satiation is a possibility, it is necessary to use other events as reinforcers.

Applications

Case 1

Daryl was a 9-year-old boy with profound mental retardation and no verbal language. He often refused to participate in gross motor activities in his physical education class. He did occasionally cooperate in playing ball and in doing calisthenics, so the teacher determined that these behaviors were in his repertoire. Since motivation seemed to be the primary issue in Daryl's behavior, a schedule of positive reinforcement was implemented. Initially, Daryl's calisthenics were reinforced on an FR 1 schedule: after each set of jumping jacks, Daryl was provided with praise and a small treat. Gradually, over several weeks, the FR 1 schedule was increased to a VR 20 schedule, with Daryl becoming an active participant in the class. After two months, the schedule was thinned even further to a VI 1-week schedule. About once each week, the instructor would provide a handshake and praise when Daryl was exercising.

Case 2

Kevin was a 16-year-old boy with severe autism and profound mental retardation, who was employed part-time at a clothing store. His job was to price items with the help of a job coach, but Kevin refused to participate. He just stood in place, flicking his fingers. So, a VI 15-minute schedule of reinforcement was used, in which a special food, drink, hand lotion or cologne was provided for working. Within one week, Kevin was working steadily. Attempts to thin his reinforcement schedule failed, with Kevin returning to self-stimulation and refusal to work. Kevin was able to maintain adequate production goals only as long as his behavior was reinforced on a VI 15-minute schedule.

Case 3

Eileen was a 17-year-old girl with a communication disorder and mild mental retardation. She was often uncooperative at home, refusing to participate in any household chores. Eileen's mother made a list of the chores that Eileen needed to complete each evening, and she received a check for each chore completed. If she completed all of her chores within the week, she was presented with a reinforcement menu on Saturday. This menu included a variety of special activities from which Eileen could choose, such as going to the movies, going skating, and going out to eat. Under this reinforcement schedule, Eileen's cooperative behavior improved significantly. After several months, however, she again began refusing to participate in household chores. It appeared that satiation had occurred, since her reinforcement menu had not been changed in months. Eileen's cooperative behavior returned when other choices of favorite activities were added to her reinforcement menu.

Case 4

Jim was a 15-year-old boy who often failed to complete his homework assignments and complained about having to cut the grass. Jim's homework completion behavior was put on a schedule of negative reinforcement, in which he was allowed to avoid cutting the grass on the weekend if he completed all of his homework assignments for the week. So, Jim began to complete all of his homework in order to avoid cutting the grass. Jim's homework completion behavior was strengthened through negative reinforcement.

Summary

Reinforcement is the process of strengthening behavior by its consequences. In positive reinforcement, the frequency of a behavior is increased by following the behavior with some desired event. In negative reinforcement, the frequency of a behavior is increased by following the behavior with the removal of some aversive event.

Positive reinforcers can be stimuli that meet basic needs, such as food and drink, as well as social events, activities, and sensory experiences. An event or stimulus is a reinforcer only if it strengthens the behavior it follows. The choice of reinforcers to use is based on information derived from the functional assessment, from reinforcement inventories, and from observation of the effects of specific stimuli on the performance rate of behavior.

Reinforcement schedules are valuable components of behavior change plans when motivation is an issue. Decisions to use reinforcement schedules and which schedules to use are based on a functional assessment as well as on the frequency of the target behavior, the potency of available reinforcers, and practicality.

Reinforcement schedules describe the pattern for delivery of the reinforcer. Ratio schedules allow for the delivery of reinforcers contingent on units of behavior. Interval schedules allow for the delivery of reinforcers contingent on behavior that occurs following the passage of time. Ratio and interval schedules are either fixed or variable.

Shaping is a process of providing positive reinforcement for successive approximations of a goal behavior. It is a valuable tool in the teaching of new behaviors.

Study Questions

1. Define *positive reinforcement.* Give an example.
2. Define *negative reinforcement.* Give an example.
3. What is the main effect of positive reinforcement? Discuss two additional effects.
4. Give an example of each of the following basic schedules of reinforcement: *fixed ratio, variable ratio, fixed interval, variable interval.*
5. What role does the functional assessment play in designing a positive reinforcement plan?
6. List three methods for choosing reinforcers.

7. List two ways to avoid satiation.
8. Define *shaping*. Give an example of its application.

Exercises

1. Bert is a six-year-old boy who usually refuses to put away his toys when he has finished playing. Discuss how to plan a reinforcement procedure to strengthen the behavior of putting away toys. Explain how to choose reinforcers.

2. Mildred is a 15-year-old girl with mild mental retardation. She recently got a part-time job filling orders in a warehouse. Her current rate is two orders each half hour. Her employer would like her to be filling 15 orders each half hour. Describe a reinforcement schedule that might be effective. Explain how reinforcers might be chosen.

3. Ernie has been on a reinforcement schedule for six months for completing his assignments in school. He receives praise and a handshake for each assignment he completes. Recently, he has not been completing his assignments. He is given ample instruction, but the problem appears to be motivational. What might his teacher do to encourage assignment completion?

4. Linda is a 3-year-old child who has been on a schedule of continuous reinforcement for using the toilet. Describe a plan for thinning the reinforcement schedule.

5. Betty makes many errors in her math homework. What should be assessed before implementing a schedule of positive reinforcement?

Self-Application

1. List items and objects in your environment that function as reinforcers for you.
2. Consider your own study behavior. What reinforcers maintain that behavior? On what schedule of reinforcement is your study behavior?
3. Do you have any behavior in your repertoire that is reinforced on a fixed ratio schedule? If so, what is the behavior, and how does the schedule operate?
4. Give an example of an item or activity in your life that has functioned as a reinforcer and has then undergone satiation.
5. Give two examples of items that function as generalized reinforcers for you.

6. Give two examples of items or events that function as conditioned reinforcers for you. With what primary or previously conditioned reinforcers were these reinforcers intially paired?
7. Identify a behavior in your repertoire that was previously weak but became stronger as a result of positive reinforcement. Describe the reinforcement process applied to that behavior.
8. Identify a behavior in your repertoire that was acquired through shaping. Describe the process applied to that behavior.

SELF-MANAGEMENT PROJECT

1. How might positive reinforcement be used to achieve the goals of your self-management project?
2. If positive reinforcement seems like it would be a useful procedure, answer the following questions:
    - What behavior will you reinforce?
    - What schedule of reinforcement will you use?
    - What positive reinforcers will you use?
    - Will satiation be a problem? If so, how will you avoid this?

References

Charlop, M. H., Kurtz, P. F., & Casey, F. G. (1990). Using aberrant behaviors as reinforcers for autistic children. *Journal of Applied Behavior Analysis, 23,* 163–181.

Hall, R. V., Lund, D., & Jackson, D. (1968). Effects of teacher attention on study behavior. *Journal of Applied Behavior Analysis, 1,* 1–12.

Osborne, J. G. (1969). Free time as a reinforcer in the management of classroom behavior. *Journal of Applied Behavior Analysis, 2,* 113–118.

Premack, D. (1959). Toward empirical behavioral laws: I. Positive Reinforcement. *Psychology Review, 66,* 219–233.

Salend, S. J., & Santora, D. (1985). Employing access to the computer as a reinforcer for secondary students. *Behavioral Disorders, 11,* 30–34.

Smith, M., & Coleman, D. (1986). Managing the behavior of adults with autism in the job setting. *Journal of Autism and Developmental Disorders, 16,* 145–153.

Wolber, G., Carne, W., Collins-Montgomery, P., & Nelson, A. (1987). Tangible reinforcement plus social reinforcement versus social reinforcement alone in acquisition of toothbrushing skills. *Mental Retardation, 25,* 275–279.

5 Extinction

Ellen was a 5-year-old girl in kindergarten at East Lake Elementary School. If the teacher gave her a task she did not like, she was likely to cry. If she wanted another child's materials and could not have them, she cried. Whenever Ellen cried, her teacher, Mrs. James, would rush to her side, give her a hug, find out her problem, and then help her with a solution. If Ellen cried about her work, Mrs. James would help her with her work. If she cried because she was having difficulty with another child, Mrs. James would settle the matter, often in Ellen's favor. By November of her kindergarten year, Ellen was crying several times each week.

In December of that year, Mrs. James moved out of the area, and a new teacher, Mrs. Howard, took over. Mrs. Howard provided Ellen with ample assistance with her work, but if Ellen cried, Mrs. Howard just looked over to see that no one was in danger and then busied herself elsewhere in the room. When Ellen's crying was no longer responded to by her teacher, it initially became louder, and on several occasions Ellen cried for over 15 minutes. Gradually, over a period of several weeks, however, Ellen's crying became less and less frequent, and by the end of January, Ellen was as cheerful as the rest of her classmates.

Ellen's crying was eliminated in school by a process known as extinction. This chapter explores the process of extinction—its definition, its effects and side effects, and its use in behavior modification.

Extinction Defined

Extinction—one law under which behavior operates—is a process in which the connection between a behavior and its reinforcing consequences is severed. As a result, the previously reinforced behavior decreases in frequency to operant levels (the level that existed prior to reinforcement).

Although other conditions can result in declines in the rate of a behavior, such as satiation and fatigue, extinction has several specific properties, which must be present in order to conclude that it is the reason for the decline in responding. First, the response, or target behavior, must have been previously reinforced. In Ellen's case, crying was the response, and it had been previously reinforced by attention, escape from a task, and meeting of demands. Second, the previously contingent reinforcers must be withheld; and, in Ellen's case, the teacher withheld these reinforcers. Third, a decline in the frequency of the target behavior to operant levels must occur. Ellen's crying eventually did decrease to zero in the school setting.

Extinction, as with all laws of behavior, does not just operate with special populations. It is a process to which all behaviors are subject. For example, Margaret sent a greeting card to her friend Betty at a certain address in Iowa each year and always received a response from her friend until her last card, which came back stamped "Addressee Unknown." When Margaret's behavior of mailing cards to Betty at that address was no longer reinforced by a response from her friend, it was put on extinction. Margaret never again mailed cards to that address.

In another example illustrating extinction, Jackie and John enjoyed eating at a certain restaurant on Avalon Place. They would typically drive to Avalon Place, approach the restaurant, find it open, go in, and eat. One day they arrived at the restaurant and found a sign on the door indicating that the restaurant was no longer in business. In its place was a jewelry store. Never again did Jackie and John drive to Avalon Place. Their behavior of going to that location, previously reinforced with a meal, was no longer reinforced by food, and the effects of extinction were immediate.

Alan, in yet another example, enjoyed dating Martha. After dating her several times, he found that when he attempted to arrange the next date, she was busy. He tried several times more, and after a series of rejections, he eventually stopped calling Martha. Alan's behavior of asking Martha for a date, previously reinforced by acceptances, was placed on extinction, and he eventually stopped calling her.

Williams (1959) provided a demonstration of extinction of the bedtime tantrum behavior of a 2-year-old child. A functional assessment revealed that after putting the child to bed, he would scream and cry. Upon hearing these screams, his parents would return to his bedroom, where they would remain until their child fell asleep. An extinction procedure was then implemented in which the parents would put the child to bed, leave the room, and not reenter despite the child's crying. By the tenth bedtime, the child's crying was extinguished.

In another study, Durand and Mindell (1990) reported on a graduated extinction procedure with a 14-month-old girl who remained awake until late at night and reawakened later in the night. This procedure consisted of the parents waiting for longer periods of time prior to going into the girl's room and checking on her only briefly when she awoke. The graduated extinction procedure was successful in eliminating the girl's bedtime problems and nighttime awakenings.

Classroom examples of extinction are also plentiful. Donald was a 9-year-old boy with limited speech skills. Whenever he had difficulty with a task he would shriek, and the teacher would provide him with assistance. As part of a behavior change plan, the teacher no longer responded to the shrieking, effectively placing it on extinction. Eventually, Donald's shrieking behavior underwent a significant decline in frequency.

Extinction in behavior modification is often used in a purposeful way to decrease the frequency of undesirable behaviors. However, appropriate behaviors are also subject to the laws of extinction, and what often happens is that desirable behaviors are inadvertently placed on extinction. Consider the case of Lori. Lori was a 16-year-old girl with a developmental disability, who worked a half day in a stock room pricing clothing. She had difficulty with her pricing gun and approached a supervisor for assistance. The supervisor was busy with another matter and did not respond to Lori's request. Lori tried several times throughout the day to obtain the supervisor's attention but did not succeed. Finally, she gave up and completed no more work for the remainder of the day. Her behavior of asking for assistance had undergone fairly rapid extinction, and a practical outcome of this process was that she was not able to proceed with her work for the day.

In another case, Jeffrey, a 10-year-old boy with communication deficits, took several minutes to answer a question. Jeffrey's responses to questions in school were often correct, but a listener had to be patient when waiting for Jeffrey to complete his answer. During the early part of the school year, Jeffrey often raised his hand in response to the teacher's questions, and the teacher often called on him. As time passed, however, Jeffrey's teacher became less patient with his language problems and called upon him less and less. Jeffrey then raised his hand less and less frequently. By mid-year, he no longer volunteered to answer questions in class. His behavior of volunteering responses was, in effect, placed on extinction.

Another case study illustrating extinction concerned Timmy, a 15-year-old boy with autism, who spoke often and cheerfully in school. His primary topic of conversation was trains. The school staff, however, soon lost interest in Timmy's persistent talk about trains, and no one responded to Timmy when he mentioned the topic. Gradually, he made fewer and fewer attempts to talk with his teachers, and one teacher remarked, during a conference, that Timmy had become quite withdrawn and hardly spoke. Timmy's conversational behavior, thus, had been placed on extinction. Over the course of the school year he had gone from a conversational extrovert to a quiet, withdrawn introvert.

Reduction Effects of Extinction

The primary effect of extinction is a reduction in the rate of behavior to operant levels. The behavior decreases in frequency to about the level at which it had occurred prior to its being reinforced. Figure 5.1 illustrates this effect.

Typically, the decline in frequency that occurs during extinction is gradual and may be erratic. There also may be an initial period of time that precedes any decrease in frequency. Three factors combine to determine what is referred to as *resistance to extinction*. These factors are the rate of decline in response frequency, the number of responses that occur before responding assumes its final level, and the final level of responding once extinction has had its full effect. There are several factors that affect the course of extinction and the resistance to extinction.

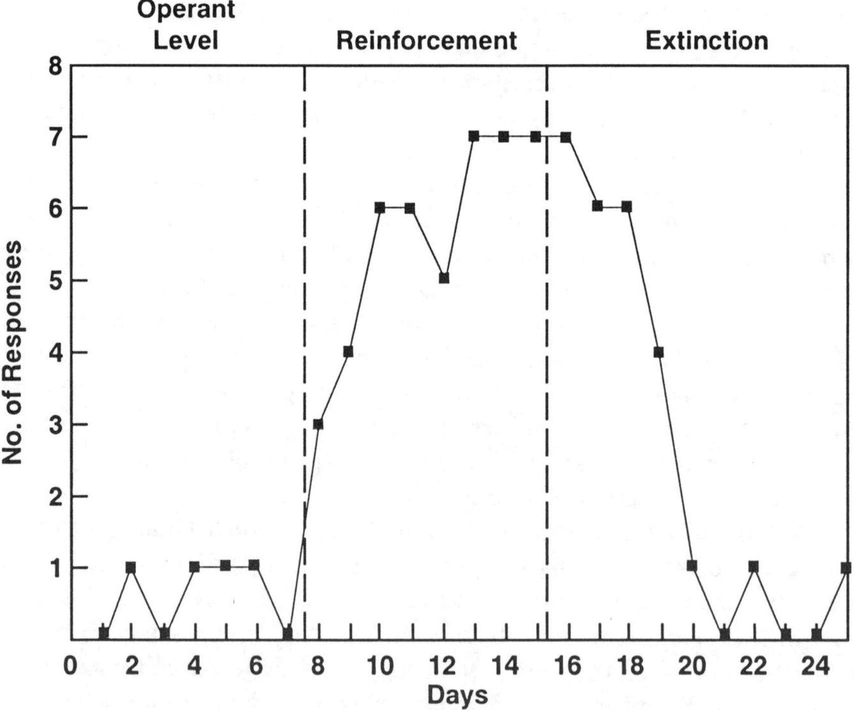

Figure 5.1 Frequency of behavior at its operant level, its reinforced level, and its decline under extinction.

Amount of Previous Reinforcers

The amount of previous reinforcers that have been delivered affects the rate of decline during extinction. A behavior that has a brief reinforcement history declines faster than one with a lengthy reinforcement history. For example, if Donald had used shrieking as a means of obtaining assistance for three years, one could expect that the rate of decline in the use of this reinforcer would be slower for Donald than for his classmate, who had received help after shrieking on only one or two occasions prior to the teacher placing the behavior on extinction.

In another example, if Clark has talked about feet for years, it likely will take weeks or months for the extinction process to take effect on his talk about feet. On the other hand, if his classmate Arnold has only recently begun to talk persistently about microwave ovens, it is likely that Arnold's conversational fixation with microwave ovens will decrease more quickly under extinction. Timmy, as previously discussed, had been talking about trains for years, and it took approximately three months for him to cease communicating about trains with his teachers.

Lynette and Bob, in yet another example, had been dating for six months when Lynette stopped answering Bob's telephone calls. He persisted in his calls for almost a month before his behavior declined under extinction. On the other hand, John, who had had ony two dates with Eve, stopped calling her after two rejections.

Magnitude of Prior Reinforcers

Another factor that affects resistance to extinction is the magnitude of prior reinforcers. Reinforcers of greater magnitude render a response more resistant to extinction than reinforcers of lesser magnitude. For example, if Lydia won $5,000 in a lottery, her behavior of buying lottery tickets will be more resistant to extinction than the behavior of Jill, whose largest lottery earning was $2. Lydia could conceivably continue to buy losing tickets for years, whereas Jill might give up after several months of buying losing tickets.

In another example, Martin and Sam are young men with developmental disabilities, who have part-time jobs as part of their high school programs. Martin's boss occasionally rewards high levels of productivity with $40 bonuses on payday. Sam's boss provides a $5 bonus for high productivity. Martin's high level of productivity, thus, might be more resistant to extinction than Sam's, since the reinforcers for Martin's high levels of productivity are of greater magnitude than those provided to Sam.

Prior Schedule of Reinforcement

A third factor affecting resistance to extinction is the previous reinforcement schedule. Generally, the denser the reinforcement schedule, the quicker the decline during extinction. Behaviors that have been reinforced on a continuous schedule of reinforcement tend to decline in frequency more rapidly than behaviors that have been reinforced on an intermittent schedule of reinforcement. The schedule of reinforcement can outweigh the effects of the amount and magnitude of previous reinforcers on the process of extinction.

For example, Leonard bought a soda from the soda machine each day on his lunch break, and on one day, after he put coins in the machine, no soda appeared, so Leonard's behavior underwent the immediate effects of extinction; i.e., he did not put more coins in the machine. His behavior had been reinforced under a continuous schedule of reinforcement; that is, each time he had put coins in the machine, his behavior had resulted in a soda. On the one afternoon when his behavior did not result in a reinforcer (i.e., a soda), the response of putting coins in the machine went into an immediate decline. On the other hand, if Leonard telephoned his friend every day at lunch and only on some days was the friend at home to answer his call, Leonard would continue to call his friend at lunchtime. Leonard's calling behavior would be on an intermittent schedule of reinforcement. Many days would have to pass without his friend's answering the telephone before Leonard's calling behavior would significantly decline.

In another example, Mary Jane, an 11-year-old girl with moderate mental retardation and some destructive behaviors, escaped from doing difficult schoolwork by being removed from the classroom as a consequence of destroying her papers. This removal unintentionally served as a negative reinforcer for her destroying papers. Mary Jane was on a continuous schedule of reinforcement for destroying her work. Each time she did it, she was allowed to escape from her schoolwork. However, when Mary Jane was provided with a new work paper and redirected to work when she destroyed her paper, her behavior of destroying her work underwent fairly rapid extinction, as it no longer was reinforced by escape from schoolwork. Within one week she stopped destroying her schoolwork.

The case of Sandy, a 4-year-old boy with a developmental disability and no speech ability, further illustrates how reinforcement schedules affect extinction. At nursery school, he occasionally bit other children and took their toys. For his misbehavior, he was occasionally reprimanded, and the teacher took the toys away from him. At other times, the incidents went unnoticed, and Sandy kept the toys. His biting and grabbing behavior was on an intermittent schedule of reinforcement, for it occasionally resulted in the reinforcer of obtaining a toy. When the teacher later prevented Sandy from grabbing toys from other children by intervening, Sandy's biting and grabbing behavior was put on extinction, for it was no longer reinforced with toys. However, since his behavior had been on an intermittent schedule of reinforcement, Sandy's grabbing and biting took almost a month to decline significantly in frequency.

In yet another example, Eileen, a 6-year-old girl with a learning disability, was frequently praised at the beginning of the school year for completing her tasks. Under these conditions of intermittent reinforcement, Eileen was a productive classroom worker. As time went on, however, the teacher gave her less and less praise and finally ceased providing any praise. Eileen's work behavior, previously reinforced by praise, was put on extinction, undergoing an erratic but persistent decline in frequency.

Effortfulness of Response

Another factor affecting the rate of decline under extinction is the effortfulness of the response. A response that requires a great deal of effort typically undergoes extinction more quickly than a reponse that requires a lesser effort. For example, the behavior of calling a friend who often does not answer his telephone will undergo extinction more slowly than the behavior of walking ten miles to visit a friend who often does not answer his door.

The case of Emma, a 15-year-old girl with diagnoses of mental retardation and autism, provides another example. She occasionally had episodes of severe head banging, screaming, and spitting. These episodes were often followed by people giving her back rubs, playing soft music, and providing her with favorite foods in order to encourage her to stop. Since these consequences served as positive reinforcers for her behavior, as part of a behavior modification plan, her behavior was put on extinction and no longer reinforced with back rubs, soft music, and food. Her severe head-banging behavior very quickly decreased to zero. Milder behavior problems, which took less of Emma's effort and included screaming and light taps to her head, were more resistant to extinction and persisted to some degree for several years.

Level of Satiation

Yet another factor that determines the resistance to extinction is the level of satiation. The food-seeking behavior of a man who has not eaten in several days, for example, will be more resistant to extinction than that of a man who just had a large meal. A person who is very thirsty and comes upon a soda machine will likely not stop trying to get a soda even though the first set of coins fail to work in the machine. He may even run out of coins before his behavior extinguishes.

The level of satiation is difficult to measure in a person, but more easily assessed is the amount of access an individual has to a reinforcer. For example, Gina has a problem with stealing food from her classmates. Although her teacher cannot directly measure her level of satiation, she can note the time and amount of her last meal. Gina's food-stealing behavior will be particularly hard to extinguish, as she often comes to school without having eaten breakfast. As the morning wears on, food becomes a powerful reinforcer for her. Carol, on the other hand, typically eats a full breakfast, so her food-stealing behavior should be relatively easy to extinguish.

Availability of the Reinforcer

Closely related to the issue of satiation is the issue of availablity of the reinforcer. A behavior is more resistant to extinction if the reinforcer is not otherwise available. Glenda's case provides a good example of availablity.

Glenda is a 4-year-old girl with moderate mental retardation. She receives a great deal of attention for her classroom temper tantrums, which include lying on the floor, crying, screaming, and kicking her feet. When she has tantrums, the teacher rushes over, hugs her, and talks to her soothingly. This attention, both verbal and physical, has served to reinforce Glenda's tantrums. If Glenda's teacher stops providing hugs and soothing talk following Glenda's tantrums, the girl's behavior will extinguish. Glenda's tantrums will extinguish more quickly if the teacher provides hugs and soothing talk under other conditions than if Glenda's only means of obtaining hugs and talks is through having tantrums.

In another example, Alan is a 6-year-old boy with an educational diagnosis of emotional impairment. He has a history of biting others and then grabbing their snacks. His behavior will extinguish much more readily if snacks are freely available to him than if his only means of obtaining desserts is through biting others and grabbing their snacks.

Previous Extinctions

Repeated extinctions have a slightly different course than do initial extinctions. Typically, behavior is more resistant to extinction during the first extinction period than during subsequent extinctions. So, for example, when Alan's biting and food-grabbing behavior are first put on extinction, it might take several weeks to decrease significantly the frequency of this behavior. If, after several months of extinction, Alan has several successful episodes of biting and grabbing and the extinction procedure is reintroduced, his behavior should decline more rapidly than it did during the initial extinction period.

The case of Alex, a 20-year-old man with autism and a history of spitting and throwing his shoes, provides another example. Initially, these behaviors were reinforced with staff attention, having Alex put on his shoes, and changes in task; and these events served as positive reinforcers. Alex's spitting and shoe-throwing behavior were then put on extinction. Spitting was not directly responded to at all, and if Alex threw his shoes, he was simply directed back to task with no mention of the misbehavior. After approximately two months, Alex's spitting and shoe-throwing behavior were eliminated. When new staff were hired after several months and began to pay attention to Alex's spitting and shoe throwing, his behavior increased in frequency. The new staff then put this behavior on extinction, and within two weeks Alex's spitting and shoe throwing were once again near zero in frequency. Over a period of years, the staff sometimes inadvertently provided reinforcers for Alex's behavior, but when extinction was reintroduced, the declines in frequency of his behavior were immediate and dramatic.

Other Effects of Extinction

Extinction has several effects and side effects, other than reduction, which can complicate the course of behavior management. Understanding these effects is the first step toward prevention in a behavior modification plan.

Temporary Increase in Frequency

Initially, behavior under extinction might increase to levels greater than the reinforced level. For example, a girl's crying might increase from several times a week to several times a day when her teacher first begins the extinction procedure. A young man might make several consecutive tries at making a date with a certain young woman in the face of her initial refusals. A student might increase, and persist with, his behavior of interrupting the teacher, in spite of the teacher's ignoring these interruptions.

The initial increase in frequency during extinction is temporary and followed by a decrease in frequency. This initial increase is not universal, however, and may not even occur. Factors that determine whether an initial increase in behavior will occur are the level of satiation, availability of reinforcers, prior schedule of reinforcement, previous extinction history, and magnitude of reinforcers.

Increase in Response Variability

The initial extinction process might result in initial response variability. The response thus might change in form as reinforcers are withheld for previously reinforced responses.

Ellen, for example, visited her friend Albert and rang the doorbell. Albert usually answered the door in response to the ring, but this time he did not. So, Ellen varied her response. Instead of simply ringing the doorbell, she knocked on the door and used the door knocker as well. (Conceivably, if the expected reinforcer [Albert] were of great enough magnitude, Ellen might have kicked the door next.) So, Ellen's response not only increased in frequency under extinction, but it also changed in form. Finally, as no reinforcer was forthcoming, Ellen walked away from the door. Her door ringing and knocking behavior was eliminated under extinction.

In another example, Lisa was a young girl with a language impairment, who tapped on her desk with her pencil in order to obtain assistance from the teacher. When the teacher no longer responded to the tapping, Lisa changed the form of her response. She tried rapping on the desk with her notebook, her hand, and finally her shoe. When these behaviors failed to get the teacher's attention, Lisa stopped all attempts.

When Timmy, the boy with autism who often spoke about trains, lost the attention of adults around him by talking about trains, he tried talking about trucks, automobiles, and other forms of transportation. He thus changed the form of his conversation as previous attempts were unreinforced. When all of his attempts at conversation went unreinforced, he finally stopped speaking. Craig, too, changed his behavior of head banging when this behavior, previously reinforced with verbal attention, was put on extinction. His form of self-injury changed to head slapping and self-kicking prior to a decline in frequency of self-injury.

Changes in the form of a behavior can have serious practical implications, especially if the new form is more problematic than the original form. Linden, for example, frequently raised his hand in class and was initially called upon frequently. The teacher then began to focus on encouraging other students to participate in class, and, in the process, put Linden's hand raising on extinction by no longer calling on him. The form of Linden's behavior then changed. Instead of raising his hand, he began calling out, and when that behavior was ignored, he began stomping his feet.

Increase in Intensity

Another initial, temporary effect of extinction is an increase in the intensity of the behavior. For example, Craig's head banging, when put on extinction, initially increased in intensity, with him hitting his head with more force when his lighter hits were ignored. Lisa's tapping on her desk increased in intensity to a banging on her desk when her teacher ignored the tapping. Ellen, when visiting her friend Albert, increased the intensity of her knocking on the door when he failed to answer her initial knocks.

Change in Structure

The process of extinction can also effect a change, most notably a deterioration, in the structure of the response during its decline in frequency. For example, Marla was an 8-year-old girl with profound mental retardation. Her teacher provided her with small treats for completing steps of a ten-piece puzzle correctly. At first, she began placing each piece in the puzzle correctly, but when her teacher stopped providing treats, Marla's puzzle-building behavior underwent extinction. Along with a decline in the rate of putting pieces in the puzzle correctly, the structure of her puzzle-building behavior changed. She began to put the pieces in the puzzle randomly, placing them incorrectly. This deterioration in the structure of her puzzle-building behavior occurred as her puzzle-building responses became extinguished.

In another example, Glenda had been receiving a great deal of praise and attention from her parents each night as she did her homework. When receiving such attention, she proceeded in an orderly fashion through her assignments. She completed each assignment correctly before proceeding on to the next assignment. About mid-year, however, her parents decided that Glenda no longer needed so much attention, and they ceased praising her for doing her homework. Glenda then would sit alone in her room with her books in front of her. Without praise, her homework behavior was, in effect, on extinction. A gradual deterioration in the structure of her homework behavior occurred, concurrent with a decline in productivity. She started and stopped assignments in a disorganized fashion, beginning one before completing the previous one. Thus, the organized structure of her homework behavior deteriorated as part of the extinction process.

Aggression

Aggression is a possible initial side effect of extinction. Individuals who have a history of receiving a reinforcer contingent on a certain response may respond aggressively if the reinforcer is no longer provided. Margie's parents, for example, had been holding her and giving in to her demands when she began crying and stomping her feet on the floor. Once they instituted an extinction procedure and no longer met her demands following such behavior, Margie reacted by hitting her parents. When Leonard put coins into a soda machine and received no soda, he varied the form and intensity of his response by pushing other buttons, pushing buttons harder, and jiggling the coin return.

When no coins were returned and no soda appeared, he reacted aggressively by kicking the machine.

Spontaneous Recovery

If an individual is returned to a situation in which extinction of a behavior had occurred, the previously extinguished behavior might increase to a higher level. This is termed *spontaneous recovery.* For example, John's whistling and hooting behavior during music class had been extinguished by his teacher's ignoring it during one class, but the next time John went to music class, the rate of the behavior increased, although by the end of the class it had diminished. This pattern continued over several weeks; that is, the rate of the behavior's occurrence was quite low by the end of class but would recover to a certain extent at the start of the next class.

Avoiding Undesirable Effects of Extinction

The primary effect of extinction—a reduction in the rate of occurrence of a behavior—can be a desirable outcome, particularly if the target behavior is a misbehavior. However, the many other temporary effects and side effects can be problematic. The undesirable side effects of extinction can be prevented or reduced by a variety of measures.

Teach Alternate Responses

A behavior will extinguish more rapidly if the reinforcer is available through another response. One method of hastening extinction and avoiding some of the undesirable side effects of extinction, such as increases in frequency, intensity, and variations of behavior, is to teach an individual another response that can result in the desired reinforcer.

Linda, for example, tapped her desk in order to obtain her teacher's attention. The teacher taught her to raise her hand when she needed something. Since Linda was able to obtain the teacher's attention by raising her hand, the extinction process for desk tapping was rapid and painless for all concerned. Linda was taught to meet her needs with an alternate response. Carr and Durand (1985) reduced problem behaviors in four children by placing the problem behaviors on extinction while teaching the children more acceptable behaviors for communicating and meeting their needs.

Reinforce a Less Effortful Response

High-effort behaviors extinguish more rapidly than low-effort behaviors. The extinction of behaviors can be hastened, and side effects minimized, if the alternate response taught to an individual is a relatively low-effort response. For example, Jean had no verbal skills and a long history of obtaining food by head banging. Whenever she banged her head, her mother offered snacks, and Jean would take the food and stop her head banging. She was then taught a less effortful response to obtain food: pointing at the refrigerator. This response quickly took the place of head banging, which extinguished rapidly.

Provide the Desired Reinforcer Contingent on Other Responses

Another method for hastening the extinction process and avoiding undesirable side effects is simply to provide the desired reinforcer contingent on other more acceptable behaviors. The case of Alex is a good example of this method.

Alex often screamed in class, and the apparent reinforcer of his screaming was teacher attention. Whenever he screamed, the teacher would rush to his side, calm him down, and stay with him several minutes. Concurrent with putting Alex's screaming behavior on extinction, the teacher provided extra attention contingent on a variety of acceptable behaviors, such as working on his task and waiting quietly between tasks. Since the teacher's attention became contingently available on Alex's behaving in other ways already in his repertoire, the extinction process for his screaming proceeded smoothly.

Provide the Desired Reinforcer Noncontingently

Another means of promoting the extinction process is to provide the desired reinforcer noncontingently in ample quantities. The desired reinforcer can be made either freely available or amply available on some timed schedule. For example, Albert, a young man with autism, had a severe biting problem. He bit many of his instructors, sending one of them to the hospital in need of plastic surgery; and he often bit others when he wanted food. In addition to having his aggressive behavior put on extinction, Albert was placed on a liberal snack schedule. Food was made plentifully available, so that Albert no longer needed to bite in order to obtain it. Extinction proceeded with no initial increase in the frequency or intensity of biting.

Promote Satiation

Promoting satiation is a useful method as an adjunct to extinction. If an individual is satiated on the desired reinforcer, the targeted behavior will extinguish more rapidly than if the individual is in a state of deprivation. Each of the previously mentioned strategies can serve the purpose of promoting satiation. An example of satiation involves Donnie, who often became aggressive at mid-morning and engaged in grabbing and hitting in order to steal food. When his teachers discovered that he was coming to school without breakfast, they made sure that Donnie ate an ample breakfast in the morning. Eating breakfast resulted in his achieving a state of satiation, and his grabbing and hitting at mid-morning underwent rapid extinction.

Provide Alternative Reinforcers

At times, the desired reinforcer is not feasible nor acceptable. In order to hasten the extinction process of such behaviors, it might not be possible to provide the actual desired reinforcer. In such cases, alternatives should be made available. For example, Billy is an 8-month-old baby who enjoys putting small toys in his mouth. Due to the risk of choking, Billy should be provided acceptable alternatives, such as larger, baby-safe teething rings.

The Use of Extinction in Behavior Change

The principle of extinction operates in behavior change situations involving both increasing desirable behaviors and decreasing undesirable behaviors. In both kinds of situations, it is necessary to examine the role of extinction as it operates in the baseline situation and then determine how to harness the effects of the principle in effecting desired behavior change.

Increasing Desirable Behaviors

Situations arise in which the problem addressed is the absence, or low frequency, of desirable behavior. For example, Linda would like her friend Lucy to call her more often. Cindy would like her aunt to resume sending her birthday gifts. Selma's teacher would like to have Selma answer questions in class as often as she did at the beginning of the school year. Robert's teacher would like to have Robert complete his homework more often.

All of these situations have one process in common: in each case, an individual's desirable behaviors have decreased as a result of extinction. Events that initially reinforced the desirable behaviors stopped occurring, and, as a result, the behaviors themselves gradually decreased in frequency. For example, Lucy may have stopped calling Linda because Linda started telling Lucy that she had no time to talk, that she had homework to do. So, Lucy's calling behavior underwent extinction, and eventually Lucy stopped calling Linda. Cindy's aunt may have stopped sending Cindy birthday gifts because Cindy stopped writing her aunt thank you notes for her birthday gifts. Selma, who initially volunteered often to answer questions in class, may have stopped volunteering because her teacher stopped calling on her in order to give other children a chance to speak. Robert may have stopped doing homework because his teacher stopped giving stars to students who turned in their homework.

In another case, the avoidance of desirable behavior was eliminated. Singer, Nofer, Benson-Szekely, and Brooks (1991) worked with four young children who had cystic fibrosis and often refused to eat. By using a combination of medical procedures to ease the eating process, positive reinforcement for eating, and extinction of avoidance behaviors, the researchers were able to increase the caloric intake of these children.

Often the absence of desirable behavior is due to a lack of learning or of competence. However, the possibility that a desirable behavior is at a low frequency due to the operation of extinction must always be investigated. If a behavior had occurred at a higher rate and had a prior history of being reinforced, it is possible that its lowered frequency is due to extinction—the reinforcer is no longer available.

Precision in Reinforcing

Extinction can play a role in the precise reinforcing of a target behavior. At times, it is desirable to reinforce a specific form of a behavior only. Reinforcement of the desired form of a target behavior, with extinction of any slight variation of the behavior, is known as *differential reinforcement.* For example, Bert was a child with a language delay. Initially, any verbal request he made was reinforced with a reponse from the teacher. Eventually, however, the teacher reinforced only those requests that included the word "please" and placed on extinction those requests not preceded by "please." Another example of extinction paired with positive reinforcement to strengthen a specific response is the instruction of an academic task. A teacher might, for example, initially reinforce any sentence a student writes. At some point, however, the teacher will reinforce only sentences with correct punctuation, placing sentences without correct punctuation on extinction.

Decreasing Undesirable Behaviors

The principle of extinction is critical in behavior change plans involving undesirable behavior. The existence of a behavior implies a history of reinforcement, and in order to decrease the frequency of that behavior, it is necessary to place it on extinction. In the context of a behavior change process, this involves identifying the reinforcers that are maintaining the undesirable behavior and severing their connection with the target behavior.

The functional assessment should identify the reinforcers that are maintaining the target behavior. The behavior change plan must then include an extinction component that specifically calls for nonreinforcement of the target behaviors. If, for example, a student's calling-out behavior was maintained by teacher attention, it would be necessary for the teacher to make sure that attention was no longer paid to the student when calling out. If the tantrum behavior of a child was reinforced by well-meaning parents who provided a great deal of comfort and cuddling immediately following each tantrum, it would be necessary for the parents to insure that the tantrums are no longer followed by comfort and cuddling.

In educational, home, and work settings, there are many more reinforcers operating than just the reinforcer of attention. The precise reinforcers must be identified and withheld contingent on the target behavior, in order to insure a valid extinction procedure. For example, Jimmy might have a tantrum in school to obtain the teacher's attention, and extinction of his behavior would involve withholding teacher attention following his tantrums. However, Jenny's tantrums might serve the function of allowing her to avoid a task, so extinction might involve continued instruction from the teacher, in order that she not be allowed to avoid instruction or tasks as a result of her tantrums.

In another example, Milly might cry at school because she enjoys the teacher's soothing words while she is crying. Placing Milly's crying on extinction would involve withholding teacher comfort following crying. If when Andy cries, his teacher calms him down by giving him milk, extinction might involve eliminating the milk during his crying episodes.

Iwata, Pace, Kalsher, Cowdery, and Cataldo (1990) did a study in which they systematically examined the functions of self-injury in seven children and adolescents. Where the function of the self-injury was identified as an escape response, treatment included an extinction procedure in which a child was prevented from escaping the demands of a task. The researchers reported a reduction in self-injury when *escape extinction* (prevention of escape from a task) was used for subjects whose functional analyses suggested that self-injury served an escape function. The researchers also discussed concerns about the use of extinction with self-injury, including the initial increase of self-injury that accompanied the onset of extinction for some of the participants.

Caution

When using extinction in behavior change, it is important to include measures that might prevent increases in intensity or form of behavior. Several such procedures have already been discussed and include satiation, the use of alternate means for obtaining reinforcers, and the use of more acceptable reinforcers. A behavior change plan might also require procedures to deal with any increases in intensity or variations in behavior that might initially occur. For example, Lenny is a 17-year-old boy with severe autism. He engages in self-injurious behavior, such as head banging. When his head banging is put on extinction, it will be necessary to include extra staff to insure that Lenny does not injure himself should there be an initial increase in intensity of his head-banging behavior.

Generally, extinction should not be used alone, especially in the case of young people who have severe behavior problems. Using extinction alone might eventually result in the elimination of the target behavior, but the process may be a painful one. Many instances of the behavior might occur prior to its final elimination, and increases in intensity or changes in the form of the behavior are also possibilities.

Lovaas and Simmons (1969) did an extinction study that involved an 11-year-old boy with severe mental retardation and a history of self-injury. Extinction sessions were carried out in which the child was placed in a room by himself and observed. It took ten 90-minute extinction sessions and 9,000 self-hits before the boy's self-injurious behavior extinguished. As this study illustrates, extinction can be a laborious, drawn-out, and even dangerous process if used as the sole behavior management strategy. However, extinction is an indispensable part of a multi-component intervention approach that includes replacing undesirable behavior with acceptable alternatives.

Applications

Case 1

Donnie was a 15-year-old boy with autism. He had severe aggressive behavior: he hit, kicked, and attempted to bite his teacher. A functional assessment revealed that during Donnie's aggressive episodes, the teacher tried to give him what he seemed to want, in order to terminate the aggressive episode. She provided him with favorite snacks, sang to him, and allowed him to do a favorite activity, thereby reinforcing his aggression.

Donnie's behavior change plan involved a dense schedule of positive reinforcement for acceptable behavior. Food, singing, and favorite tasks were no longer provided during or immediately following aggression but only for acceptable behaviors. The extinction component involved continuing to direct

Donnie to the task at hand despite his aggressive behavior. Within two weeks, Donnie's aggression was reduced from ten episodes an hour to one episode a day. Within six months, his aggression was eliminated.

Case 2

Sherry was a 15-year-old girl with a learning disability and deficits in social skills. She often greeted teachers by punching them in the shoulder and laughing. It appeared that the lectures she received as a result of her misbehavior were reinforcing the behavior. Her behavior change plan included a social skills component, in which she was taught how to greet others, and a reinforcement component, which called for social reinforcers for greeting others appropriately. The extinction component required that the person Sherry punched say nothing and walk away. When her misbehavior was ignored, Sherry quickly learned how to greet others acceptably.

Summary

Extinction is the process in which the connection between the target behavior and its reinforcer is severed, resulting in a decline in frequency of the behavior to operant levels or to zero. Although extinction has the primary effect of reducing the frequency of a target behavior, initial, temporary effects might also occur, such as increases in the intensity, or frequency, and variety of the behavior.

Several procedures can be included in a behavior change plan to offset the negative effects of extinction and to promote a more rapid reduction in the frequency of a targeted behavior. These procedures include teaching an alternate more acceptable behavior, providing other means for obtaining the desired reinforcer, and providing alternate more acceptable forms of the reinforcer. The use of extinction alone, especially in cases of severe behavior problems, is inadvisable. However, attempting to eliminate undesirable behaviors without including the use of extinction may well be impossible.

Study Questions

1. Define *extinction.*
2. What is the main effect of extinction?
3. What are other possible effects of extinction?
4. List at least four procedures that might offset the undesirable side effects of extinction.
5. Define *spontaneous recovery* and give an example.
6. List at least five factors that can affect the speed of the extinction process.
7. Why might it be a problem to use extinction alone?

Exercises

1. Angela is a 4-year-old girl who has episodes of severe tantrums, including throwing herself on the floor, banging her head, and screaming. When Angela has tantrums, her mother occasionally ignores her, occasionally spanks her, and occasionally comforts her and offers her special toys. How would Angela's tantrums be put on extinction? What other procedures might be included in the behavior change plan to speed up the extinction process?

2. Lennie and Judy were friends. Judy became very involved in a school play and did not have much time for Lennie. Lennie had enjoyed Judy's company but stopped calling Judy, and Judy wondered why. Explain how extinction might be at work here.

3. Billy often cried in school. The functional assessment revealed that his crying served the function of obtaining the teacher's help with difficult tasks. How would extinction be used as part of Billy's behavior plan? What other procedures might be included?

4. Draw graphs that demonstrate the course of Angela's tantrums and Billie's crying during the course of extinction with and without supplementary procedures.

SELF-MANAGEMENT PROJECT

1. If your targeted goal is the elimination of an undesirable behavior, what consequences are currently reinforcing the behavior? How might the behavior be placed on extinction?
2. If extinction would be a helpful procedure in your self-management project, describe how you would use it.
3. If your targeted goal is the increase in frequency of a desirable behavior, consider whether the behavior has ever undergone extinction. If so, describe the process as it applied to your behavior and identify past reinforcers of the behavior.

References

Carr, E. G., & Durand, V. M (1985). Reducing behavior problems through functional communication training. *Journal of Applied Behavior Analysis, 18*, 111–126.

Durand, M. V., & Mindell, J. A. (1990). Behavioral treatment of multiple childhood sleep disorders. *Behavior Modification, 14,* 37–49.

Iwata, B. A., Pace, G. M., Kalsher, M. J., Cowdery, G. E., & Cataldo, M. F. (1990). Experimental analysis and extinction of self-injurious escape behavior. *Journal of Applied Behavior Analysis, 23,* 11–27.

Lovaas, O. I., & Simmons, J. Z. (1969). Manipulation of self-destruction in three retarded children. *Journal of Applied Behavior Analysis, 2,* 143–157.

Singer, L. T., Nofer, J. A., Benson-Szekely, L. J., & Brooks, L. J. (1991). Behavioral assessment and management of food refusal in children with cystic fibrosis. *Developmental and Behavioral Pediatrics, 12,* 115–120.

Williams, C. D. (1959). The elimination of tantrum behavior by extinction procedures. *Journal of Abnormal and Social Psychology, 59,* 269.

6

Decreasing Behavior through Positive Reinforcement

Alex was a 10-year-old student who was severely disabled by autism. He spent much of his school day lying on the floor, banging his head, crying, and refusing to participate in tasks. Alex was often provided with promises of treats if he stopped and was given a great deal of physical attention by teachers who rubbed his back and spoke to him in soothing tones while he lay on the floor. Ms. Jones, Alex's teacher, decided that she needed to take strong measures to discourage Alex from banging his head and to encourage him to participate in his school work.

Noting that Alex's head banging resulted in physical attention, conversation, and promises of favorite treats, Ms. Jones rearranged the contingencies. She provided these reinforcers only when Alex was cooperative. So, when Alex sat at the table and participated in tasks, he was rewarded about every 15 minutes with favorite treats, handshakes, backrubs, and praise. Additionally, for every unit of work he completed, he was given a small amount of a favorite snack. These rewards made it worthwhile for Alex to get off the floor, keep his hands off his head, and participate in tasks. Within two months, Alex was a productive worker in the classroom, with very few incidents of lying on the floor or head banging.

The desirable behaviors of Alex's remaining in his work area, keeping his hands on his work (instead of on his head), and completing his assignments were strengthened through positive reinforcement. A secondary result of the process used to change Alex's behavior was that his misbehavior decreased in frequency. This chapter explores the process of reinforcement and its use in decreasing the frequency of undesirable behaviors.

Reduction through Reinforcement

Rationale

By definition, *reinforcement* is a process for strengthening behavior. However, this process for strengthening behavior can also be a powerful method for weakening behavior as well. Its use in behavior reduction is less direct and is fully understood only when viewed in terms of a functional assessment of the misbehavior.

The functional assessment reveals the functions that the misbehavior serves for an individual. An effective means of decreasing the frequency of a misbehavior is to insure that the functions served by the misbehavior are provided for in other ways. A new, more acceptable behavior must be strengthened by positive reinforcement, so that an undesirable behavior will become obsolete. Positive reinforcement, by strengthening a more acceptable behavior, plays an important role in decreasing the frequency of the misbehavior.

So, for example, if Alex's tantrums serve the function of obtaining the teacher's attention, one strategy for eliminating his tantrums is to provide other means for him to obtain teacher attention. A positive reinforcement schedule can be devised that provides teacher attention contingent on desirable behavior. This use of positive reinforcement will strengthen desirable behavior and at the same time help to reduce Alex's need for tantrums as a means of obtaining teacher attention.

In another example, Eileen shouted out in class in order to be called on by the teacher. For several weeks, the teacher responded to her shouts. Her shouting was therefore strengthened by positive reinforcement. When Eileen's teacher later decided that Eileen should learn to raise her hand to get attention, each time she did, the teacher called on her. Since Eileen could obtain the teacher's attention by raising her hand, the behavior of shouting out in class became obsolete; it was no longer needed. Shouting out in class then decreased in frequency while hand raising increased. The same schedule of positive reinforcement that had strengthened Eileen's desirable behavior helped to eliminate the need for her undesirable behavior.

Circumstances

There are several circumstances in which positive reinforcement is effective in reducing or eliminating behavior. One such circumstance is when an individual has a misbehavior and needs to learn an alternative, more desirable behavior. Positive reinforcement is used in the process of teaching and strengthening the more desirable response, so that misbehavior will no longer be needed.

Very young children provide examples of this process in their language development. Initially, babies cry to have their needs met, and their crying is reinforced: A baby cries and is fed. A baby cries and has a diaper changed. A baby cries and is held. A baby's crying is therefore reinforced by a variety of strong reinforcers. As a baby grows into a toddler and young child, speech replaces crying as a means of obtaining reinforcers. As more words are learned, these words obtain reinforcers that previously were obtained by crying. As the words are strengthened by positive reinforcement, the frequency of crying is decreased.

The teaching of more acceptable behaviors that then replace less desirable behaviors occurs naturally in classrooms. For example, Johnny, a kindergarten child, was initially praised for using blocks to solve simple addition problems. Later, he was taught to do these same problems with pencil and paper, and as this skill was learned and reinforced with praise, Johnny's use of blocks to solve problems became obsolete.

A second circumstance in which positive reinforcement plays a role in behavior reduction is in situations in which a more desirable behavior is in a person's repertoire, but the frequency of the behavior is low. The case of Eileen, a young woman with moderate mental retardation, provides a good example. Eileen had a job separating colored inserts from the newspapers at a recycling center. She had learned the task, but it occurred at a low rate of frequency, and she spent most of her time at work pacing and rocking.

A functional assessment revealed that pacing and rocking often resulted in Eileen's supervisor telling her what a good worker she could be, prompting her to work faster and even promising her treats if she worked faster. So, her off-task behaviors of pacing and rocking served the functions of obtaining attention and even snacks. Since Eileen knew how to sort newspapers, it was not necessary to teach her the task. It was necessary only to provide reinforcers for her on-task behavior. So, a reinforcement schedule was developed, and Eileen was provided with praise, attention, and snacks on a variable interval 15-minute schedule. As her work behaviors strengthened, her rocking and pacing behaviors decreased in frequency.

Reinforcement is also useful when a behavior occurs at too high a frequency and a lesser rate is desired. Bobby, for example, was a fifth-grade student who walked up to the teacher's desk approximately ten times an hour to talk to the teacher. The teacher wanted to decrease the frequency of Bobby's behavior but not eliminate it altogether. So, the teacher told Bobby that if he came up to the desk only once an hour, she would have time to talk with him. Positive reinforcement was therefore used to reduce, but not extinguish, the frequency of Bobby's behavior.

Schedules of Reinforcement

A variety of schedules of reinforcement are available to help decrease the frequency of certain behaviors while at the same time strengthening target behaviors. These procedures typically involve the reinforcement of some set of behaviors that are incompatible with, or different from, the targeted misbehaviors.

Differential Reinforcement of Other Behavior (DRO) Schedule

A *DRO schedule* reinforces any behavior other than the target behavior. For example, if John does a great deal of yelling, a DRO schedule would provide a reinforcer for any behavior other than yelling. DRO schedules are run as either *whole interval DRO*s or *momentary DRO*s. A whole interval DRO requires that the target behavior be absent for the length of a specified interval. So, if John's behavior is reinforced on a whole interval DRO of 30 minutes, in order to receive a reinforcer, John must display behaviors other than yelling for the entire interval of 30 minutes. If John's behavior is reinforced on a momentary DRO of 30 minutes, in order to receive a reinforcer, John must engage in behaviors other than yelling only at the end of the 30-minute interval, at the moment the reinforcer is available.

Since DRO schedules provide a reinforcer for any behavior other than the targeted misbehavior, they may be disadvantageous to use in classroom and work settings because the other behaviors reinforced may be undesirable as well. If John were on a 30-minute DRO to decrease his yelling in the classroom, he could sit on the floor and play during math class, for example, and, as long as he did not yell, be given a reinforcer.

Repp, Barton, and Brulle (1983) used whole interval DRO and momentary DRO schedules to reduce the disruptive classroom behaviors of three boys, aged 7 and 8 years, with mild mental retardation. The boys' behaviors included such off-task behaviors as looking away from work materials, getting out of their seats, and interrupting the teacher and other students. Candy and cereal were chosen as reinforcers for on-task behavior, and the whole-interval DRO was reported more effective in suppressing the boys' disruptive behavior than was the momentary DRO.

Differential Reinforcement of Incompatible Behavior (DRI) Schedule

A *DRI schedule* is a variant of the DRO. Behaviors other than the targeted misbehavior are reinforced, but the behaviors targeted for reinforcement are directly incompatible with the misbehavior. For example, if a

DRI schedule is used for yelling, a reinforcer might be delivered for talking quietly—a behavior directly incompatible with yelling. In another example, Mary is often out of her seat, a DRI schedule would provide reinforcers to keep Mary in her seat. The DRI schedule can have the same drawback as the DRO schedule though, which is that behaviors replacing undesirable behaviors may also be undesirable.

Azrin, Besalel, and Wisotzek (1982) achieved a significant reduction in the self-slapping behavior of a 35-year-old woman with mental retardation and a long history of institutionalization by using a DRI schedule. Behaviors incompatible with self-slapping, such as social interaction and self-care skills, were reinforced with a variety of reinforcers, including praise, stroking, and snacks. When used in combination with brief blocking (i.e., preventing her from slapping herself), the woman's self-injurious behavior was almost completely eliminated.

Smith (1987) achieved reductions in pica (eating inedible items) in a man with autism by using a DRI schedule. The man worked in the stock room of a department store and often left his work area to pick up pieces of metal and trash, which he then ate. Incompatible behaviors were reinforced, such as keeping his hands on his work, remaining in his work area, and maintaining a clear mouth. Approximately every 15 minutes, food, drink, and access to favorite activities were provided as reinforcers. In addition, the incompatible behaviors were reinforced with social attention (praise) every 10 minutes. If the man attempted to pick up metal and trash to eat, he was immediately redirected to his task. Pica was reduced within the first month, and a follow-up study completed one year later revealed that pica was at almost nonexistent levels.

Differential Reinforcement of Appropriate Behavior (DRA) Schedule

A *DRA schedule* requires that a behavior displayed during a designated period of time be appropriate. In a school setting, for example, behavior that is appropriate at recess may not be appropriate during math class. The DRA schedule can overcome the drawbacks inherent in the DRO and DRI schedules, which may require reinforcement of less than desirable behaviors, simply because they are other than or incompatible with targeted misbehaviors.

Differential Reinforcement of Low Rates of Behavior (DRL) Schedule

A *DRL schedule,* used to reduce the frequency of a behavior to designated, allowable levels, has several technical applications. When used in a laboratory setting, a DRL schedule typically requires minimum periods of no responding between responses. For example, a pigeon in a laboratory on a DRL schedule would be given a reinforcer only for pecking a key if minimum periods of time, such as 10 seconds, elapsed between key pecks. In applied settings, a DRL schedule usually specifies a maximum number of responses within a set period of time. For example, Janet, a 6-year-old child, may be allowed to talk out of turn no more than twice each hour in order to earn 10 minutes of free time at the end of each hour.

Handen, Apolito, and Seltzer (1984) successfully reduced the high frequency of repetitive speech in a 16-year-old adolescent boy with autism by using a DRL schedule. The schedule provided reinforcers for increasingly lower rates of verbal repetitions. During treatment, the DRL criterion level (maximum number of repetitions allowed for reinforcement) was changed over a series of nine phases. Initially, 4.4 repetitions were allowed each minute. By Phase 9, only 0.3 repetitions were allowed each minute. Reinforcers consisted of tokens that could be exchanged for items on a reinforcer menu.

Variable Interval (VI) Schedule

The VI schedule is helpful in reducing the frequency of undesirable behaviors also. It targets specific, acceptable behaviors and reinforces these behaviors according to the time parameters of the schedule. The opportunity to obtain reinforcers for specific, acceptable behaviors helps render the undesirable behaviors obsolete. The VI schedule also provides flexibilty in timing. In the classroom, for example, a teacher using a VI schedule is not obligated to make decisions based solely on the passage of a prespecified number of minutes.

Smith (1985) included a VI schedule of reinforcement in the treatment of a 22-year-old man with autism who had severe aggression, including hitting and kicking. A VI 15-minute schedule was used that provided food, drinks, favorite activities, and social attention for such adaptive behaviors as sitting cooperatively near housemates and staff, complying with tasks, and communicating by signs, pictures, or words. The reinforcers selected were based on a functional assessment that revealed the consequences that had reinforced the aggressive behavior. The use of a VI schedule in the treatment of this man resulted in his aggression being reduced to near-zero levels.

Ratio Schedules

Fixed ratio (FR), variable ratios (VR), and differential reinforcement schedules for high rates of behavior help reduce certain undesirable behaviors by strengthening more appropriate behaviors. These schedules typically aim at achieving specific rates of behavior. Ratio schedules are advantageous in situations in which specific task-related behaviors are directly incompatible with targeted misbehavior. By their strengthening another behavior, they effect a decrease in the frequency of the targeted misbehavior. So, a byproduct of the reinforcement process is the reduction of an unacceptable behavior.

The case of Liona, a young woman with mental retardation who worked at a manufacturing company, provides a good example of this result. Liona's rate of building computer cables was initially very low, for she engaged frequently in self-stimulatory behaviors that interfered with cable building, such as finger flicking and rocking. So, Liona's cable building behavior was put on a fixed ratio schedule of reinforcement. For each cable she completed, she was paid 5 cents. Liona enjoyed earning the money, and once her cable building was tied directly to it, she began working faster. A beneficial side effect of putting her on this schedule was that her finger-flicking and rocking behaviors decreased in frequency.

In another example, Ernie was a young man with moderate mental retardation who worked at a book bindery putting covers on books. Although he was capable of performing the task, he often stopped and stared into space. He also would leave his work area, walk around, and interfere with the work of other people. So, his book-covering behavior was placed on a DRH schedule, and he was reinforced for specific, high rates of book-covering behavior. If he completed a designated number of books within each half-hour period, he was given praise and a special, short activity to do with his job coach. Ernie's book-covering behavior increased in frequency, and, at the same time, his staring into space, wandering around, and interfering with the work of others were eliminated.

In yet another example, Margaret, a 16-year-old girl with moderate mental retardation, was learning to do an assembly task in her vocational class. She often darted from her work area to take the materials of other people. Her work behavior was then put on a VR 10 schedule, in which a reinforcer was provided, on the average, for every 10 units she assembled. Margaret's work rate escalated, and her behaviors of darting and taking the materials of others were reduced significantly in frequency.

Behavior Reduction and Young Children

The use of a schedule of positive reinforcement to reduce the frequency of a misbehavior assumes that there are desirable behaviors to strengthen. Older children and young adults often have the benefit of structured educational curricula or jobs. Incompatible, more acceptable behaviors to reinforce are also more readily available. However, with young children, especially children with developmental disabilities, there is often a dearth of desirable behaviors to strengthen.

Children with developmental disabilities may have short attention spans, high frequencies of self-stimulation, and be prone to tantrums when their demands are not met. In these cases, it often falls to the designer of the behavior plan to design an environment that provides the opportunity for acceptable behaviors that can then be reinforced. Once this environment is constructed, and positive reinforcement scheduled, behavior reduction can occur.

The case of Lily, 4-year-old girl with profound mental retardation, illustrates this point. Lily spent much of her day at home climbing on furniture, eating lint, destroying household furnishings, and crying. A schedule of positive reinforcement of more appropriate behavior would, theoretically, provide for a reduction in her undesirable behaviors. However, in her home situation there was very little opportunity to reinforce acceptable behavior, as there were few activities or situations to promote good behavior. Part of a behavior plan for Lily, then, required the scheduling of recreational and other activities that would interest her. Participation in these activities could then be reinforced with a schedule of positive reinforcement, such as VI or a DRA schedule. With either of these schedules, behavior reduction could be expected to occur.

Functional Assessment and Behavior Reduction

The functional assessment is critical in determining the events that are maintaining an undesirable behavior. The information obtained from the functional assessment determines whether it is useful to use a schedule of positive reinforcement to reduce the frequency of a misbehavior. As discussed in Chapter 4, the reinforcers that maintain an unacceptable behavior can be used to strengthen more acceptable behavior. In addition, the use of a schedule of positive reinforcement to strengthen more acceptable behavior will likely have misbehavior reduction as a byproduct if the events that reinforced the misbehavior are used in the schedule.

A good example of these occurrences is provided by a study performed by Durand and Crimmons (1987). They analyzed the functions of bizarre speech in a 9-year-old boy with autism. The child often repeated peculiar phrases, such as "fried eggs on your head." A functional analysis revealed that when task demands on the boy increased so did his bizarre speech. The experimental provision of a 10-second time-out following bizarre speech increased the rate of such speech, suggesting that its function was to provide an escape from difficult tasks. A more acceptable response was taught to replace the boy's bizarre speech and yet fulfill a similar function. When he said "help me," he was reinforced with assistance, and a significant reduction in the frequency of his bizarre speech was soon achieved.

Use with Other Strategies

The use of positive reinforcement alone may not suffice to reduce or eliminate targeted behaviors. Several other strategies may be critical to deal sufficiently with information provided by the functional assessment.

Extinction

The functional assessment should reveal the events that are maintaining a targeted behavior. If these events continue to consequate the misbehavior, a schedule of positive reinforcement for acceptable behavior may be relatively powerless. If, for example, Albert's tantrums are followed by cuddling and favorite treats, a schedule of positive reinforcement to strengthen more cooperative behavior may be relatively ineffective in eliminating his tantrums. In order for positive reinforcement to be used effectively in behavior reduction, it is necessary to put the misbehavior on extinction.

The case of Jerry, a 14-year-old boy with autism, provides a good example of the use of extinction. Jerry had frequent episodes of screaming, throwing his work materials on the floor, stripping off his clothes, and running from the classroom. A functional assessment revealed that this behavior often occurred during task presentation and was followed by a great deal of teacher attention. Teachers would talk to him, chase him, and try to persuade him to get dressed; they also would often remove the task.

Jerry was put on a reinforcement schedule that provided reinforcers about every half hour when he was dressed and on task. Small food treats, teacher attention, and back scratches were used as reinforcers. Extinction was used in conjunction with positive reinforcement. If Jerry threw his work materials or stripped off his clothes, he was simply redirected back to his assigned task with no mention of his misbehavior. The combination of extinction and positive reinforcement resulted in the elimination of Jerry's problem behaviors in two months.

Instructional Procedures

It may be necessary to provide in-depth instruction on the tasks that are to be reinforced. If, for example, Linda often cries during math class, simply providing reinforcers for her completion of math problems will probably not be effective if Linda's math skills are very low. Her behavior plan must include an instructional component that dictates how to teach Linda math. Good instructional procedures, coupled with positive reinforcers, will probably suffice to eliminate Linda's crying during math.

Instructional procedures that specifically target social skills may also be needed. When Jane, for example, saw a toy she wanted, she would sometimes grab it away from another child. So, she needed to be specifically taught sharing skills. Her sharing behavior could then be reinforced, and a decline in her grabbing behavior could then be expected. In another example, Willis and LaVigna (1988) treated a 17-year-old boy with severe self-injurious behavior by using positive reinforcement procedures in conjunction with systematic training on a variety of leisure, self-care, and domestic tasks and achieved a reduction in the boy's self-injury.

Scheduling Procedures

It may be necessary to deliberately arrange, or schedule, a certain sequence of activities or certain types of activities, especially in the use of behavior modification with young children. This sequence of activities can then provide opportunities for behavior that can be reinforced, with an effective reduction of a misbehavior following. Scheduling procedures are especially critical when the target behavior is self-stimulation.

The case of Judy illustrates this approach. Judy was a 6-year-old girl with mental retardation and no verbal language, who spent most of her time at home sitting and rocking. Her parents developed a structured schedule for her, which included opportunities for her to help with simple chores, recreational activities, and other activities. They used a positive reinforcement schedule to encourage her participation in the scheduled activities, and Judy's sitting and rocking behavior quickly declined.

Considerations

As previously mentioned, the use of positive reinforcement is an effective tool in the reduction of misbehaviors. To use this tool corrrectly to reduce or eliminate undesirable behavior, several considerations are necessary.

Choice of Behaviors to be Strengthened

The choice of target behaviors may affect whether or not there is a corresponding decrease in the frequency of the target misbehavior. The effortfulness of the desired response may affect the reduction of the misbehavior. For example, if a child's tantrums serve the function of obtaining adult attention and the reinforcement schedule reinforces behaviors that are complex and difficult for the child to perform, the child may continue the tantrums. If

10-year-old Ellen frequently cries and whines and these behaviors are typically followed by consoling remarks from the teacher, a reinforcement schedule providing teacher attention as a reinforcer for Ellen's completion of difficult math and spelling assignments will probably not be very effective. Her behaviors of crying and whining are more efficient means for Ellen to obtain teacher attention than working through difficult math and spelling assignments.

Choice of Reinforcers

The choice of reinforcers is critical to the success of a behavior modification procedure. Events that are randomly chosen or that reflect the taste of the planner rather than that of the child can be ineffective. Methods for choosing reinforcers are discussed in Chapter 4 and include the use of information obtained by the functional assessment, by observation, by interviews with people familiar with the person, and even by asking the person. If targeted behaviors are not strengthened and misbehaviors remain at baseline levels, it is likely that the reinforcers are not sufficiently potent.

A related problem is satiation. If an individual satiates on a reinforcer, adaptive behaviors will not strengthen and misbehavior may remain a problem. Varying reinforcers can help prevent satiation.

Scheduling of Reinforcers

If a desired behavior does not increase in frequency, it may be that the reinforcement schedule is too thin. A reinforcement schedule that is too thin fails to strengthen sufficiently the desired behavior. The misbehavior keeps achieving its function and does not decline. For example, Gerald was a young man with mild mental retardation who cursed at people and was occasionally aggressive. Since he was rewarded only about every two days for cooperative behavior, his misbehavior remained a problem. The schedule of reinforcement was too thin. When the schedule was changed to provide reinforcers daily, Gerald's cursing and aggression stopped.

It may be necessary to use two or more schedules of reinforcement in combination. For example, Haring, Breen, Pitts-Conway, and Gaylord-Ross (1986) used a DRO schedule to reduce self-stimulation in combination with a CRF schedule to increase the frequency of correct responses to tasks in a study of four adolescents with autism and high levels of stereotypy. Their stereotypic behaviors included repetitive speech and object slapping. The subjects worked in pairs, with one student giving reinforcers to each of the other students. The use of this combination of schedules resulted in a reduction of stereotypic behavior in two of the children and an increase in task performance in two of the children.

Incomplete Extinction

If a misbehavior is not effectively placed on extinction, the desired target behavior may be strengthened, but the misbehavior may remain as well. For example, Leonard was a 5-year-old boy who often had temper tantrums, in which he would scream and kick the floor. A functional assessment revealed that when Leonard behaved like this, his mother would often put him on her lap and explain to him, for 10 minutes or more, why he should not behave this way.

When a positive reinforcement schedule was used that provided his mother's attention for playing cooperatively with his toys, Leonard began spending more time in cooperative play. However, the frequency of his temper tantrums remained unchanged because his mother paid attention to him both when he was cooperative and uncooperative. Although she no longer took him on her lap following a tantrum, she continued to talk to him at length about his misbehavior. When Leonard's mother put his tantrums on extinction and used positive reinforcement for cooperative behavior only, his tantrums decreased.

Applications

Case 1

Bob was an 18-year-old student with severe autism and severe self-injury, including head banging and hair pulling. These behaviors occurred frequently, for hours on end. Bob often began his head banging when he saw desirable food items such as soda and candy, when given tasks to perform, and when asked to move from one area to another. His head banging often resulted in his being held, spoken to, or promised or given the desired items, or in his having the task or request withdrawn. A functional assessment revealed that self-injury served the functions of obtaining food, physical contact, and extended conversations with staff for Bob, as well as of having tasks withdrawn.

Initially, a whole interval, 5-minute DRO schedule was implemented that provided reinforcers for any of Bob's behaviors other than self-injury. A structured activity schedule and an extinction procedure were also put into effect. Reinforcers used were the items that were identified in the functional assessment: physical contact, verbal interactions, and a variety of food and drinks.

There was a rapid decrease in Bob's self-injury upon implementation of the DRO schedule in combination with extinction and the structured schedule. Later, the DRO 5-minute schedule was changed to a VI 15-minute schedule. With his cooperative behaviors reinforced about every 15 minutes, Bob's self-injurious behaviors declined to only one short incident per month.

Case 2

Alice was a 5-year-old girl with mental retardation and delayed speech. She hit and pinched other children and adults, often engaging in these behaviors when she was left alone for periods of time, was presented with tasks to perform, and had her demands not met. Her aggression appeared to serve the purposes of obtaining desired items and responses from adults and of escaping from or avoiding tasks.

A VI 30-minute schedule of reinforcement was implemented, which reinforced Alice's cooperative behavior with food and attention. She was physically prevented from hitting or pinching others, and her misbehavior no longer resulted in conversation, task withdrawal, or met demands. Alice's aggression toward other children and adults declined in frequency and was eliminated within two months.

Carr and Durand (1985) worked with four children, aged 7 through 14 years, with developmental disabilities and a variety of problem behaviors, including aggression and self-injury. Analyses were performed to determine the situations in which their problem behaviors were likely to occur, with the finding that low levels of adult attention and high levels of task difficulty were likely to produce their misbehavior. The children were then taught communication skills in order to request adult attention and to ask for help when having difficulty with a task. With these skills reinforced, the frequency of problem behaviors in all four children decreased.

Summary

Positive reinforcement procedures are effective tools in decreasing the frequency of undesired behaviors. These procedures include the use of differential reinforcement of other behavior (DRO), of incompatible behavior (DRI), of appropriate behavior (DRA), of low rates of behavior (DRL), and of high rates of behavior (DRH). They also include the use of variable interval (VI), fixed ratio (FR), and variable ratio (VR) schedules.

Positive reinforcement is effective in reducing undesirable behavior in several circumstances. For example, positive reinforcement is useful in shaping and maintaining a more acceptable alternative to a misbehavior. Positive reinforcement is useful in strengthening a more acceptable behavior that is in the person's repertoire but that is weak. Positive reinforcement is useful also when behavior occurs at a high rate and needs to be lowered but not eliminated.

Positive reinforcement usually needs to be accompanied by other strategies in order to reduce problem behavior effectively. These other strategies include instructional and scheduling procedures as well as extinction of the problem behavior, which is generally mandatory.

The effectiveness of positive reinforcement in behavior reduction depends on a variety of factors, such as the reinforcers chosen, the schedule used, the behaviors targeted for increase, the completeness of the extinction procedures, and the use of additional strategies. As with the use of positive reinforcement to strengthen desirable behaviors, its use to decrease undesirable behaviors is dictated by a functional assessment of the undesirable behavior.

Study Questions

1. What is the rationale for using positive reinforcement in behavior reduction?
2. Give an example of how tantrums can be reduced in a 4-year-old child by use of each of the following reinforcement schedules: *DRO, DRI, VI.*
3. Give an example of how a young adult with autism can have self-injury at his job reduced by use of each of the following reinforcement schedules: *DRA, VI, DRH.*
4. What role should the functional assessment play in designing a positive reinforcement plan to use in behavior reduction?
5. List and explain four considerations that might hamper the effectiveness of a behavior reduction plan that uses positive reinforcement.

Exercises

1. Ellen is a 10-year-old girl who frequently calls out answers during class. Explain how positive reinforcement might be used to reduce the frequency of this behavior.

2. Jimmy is a 7-year-old boy who is often out of his seat in class. Explain how positive reinforcement might be used to reduce the frequency of this behavior.

3. Sarah is a 9-year-old girl with profound mental retardation and a high frequency of self-stimulatory behavior, including rocking and finger flicking. Explain how positive reinforcement might be used to reduce the frequency of her self-stimulation. What other strategies might also be necessary?

4. Albert is a 15-year-old boy with mild mental retardation. He has problems with stealing and occasional aggression at his part-time job, which involves unpacking boxes at a local warehouse. Explain how positive reinforcement might be used to reduce his stealing and aggression. What other strategies might also be necessary?

5. Jane is an 8-year-old girl with a developmental disability. She has mild mental retardation and can speak in short phrases. Jane occasionally screams and hits other people while doing her class work. This behavior is most likely to occur when Jane is doing new tasks. Explain how positive reinforcement might be used to reduce her screaming and hitting. What other strategies might also be necessary?

SELF-MANAGEMENT PROJECT

1. If your target behavior is an undesirable behavior, consider whether positive reinforcement would be a useful procedure to decrease its frequency.
2. If you intend to use positive reinforcement to reduce the frequency of your targeted behavior, plan the following:
   - What is the targeted behavior or behaviors of the procedure?
   - What reinforcement schedule will you use?
   - What reinforcers will you use?
   - How will you avoid satiation?

References

Azrin, N. H., Besalel, V. A., & Wisotzek, I. E. (1982). Treatment of self-injury by a reinforcement plus interruption procedure. *Analysis and Intervention in Developmental Disabilities, 2,* 105–113.

Carr, E. G., & Durand, V. M. (1985). Reducing behavior problems through functional communication training. *Journal of Applied Behavior Analysis, 18,* 111–126.

Durand, V. M., & Crimmons, D. B. (1987). Assessment and treatment of psychotic speech in an autistic child. *Journal of Autism and Developmental Disorders, 17,* 17–27.

Handen, B. L, Apolito, P. M., & Seltzer, G. B. (1984). Use of differential reinforcement of low rates of behavior to decrease repetitive speech in an autistic adolescent. *Journal of Behavior Therapy and Experimental Psychiatry, 15,* 359–364.

Haring, T. G., Breen, C. G., Pitts-Conway, V., & Gaylord-Ross, R. (1986). Use of differential reinforcement of other behavior during dyadic instruction to reduce stereotyped behavior of autistic students. *American Journal of Mental Deficiency, 90,* 694–702.

Repp, A. C., Barton, L. E., & Brulle, A. R. (1983). A comparison of two procedures for programming the differential reinforcement of other behaviors. *Journal of Applied Behavior Analysis, 16,* 435–446.

Smith, M. (1985). Managing the aggressive and self-injurious behavior of adults disabled by autism. *Journal of the Association for Persons with Severe Handicaps, 15,* 228–232.

Smith, M. (1987). Treatment of pica in an adult disabled by autism by differential reinforcement of incompatible behavior. *Journal of Behavior Therapy and Experimental Psychiatry, 10,* 285–288.

Willis, T. J., & LaVigna, G. W. (1988). Non-aversive treatment of severe self-injury. Paper presented to the Annual Convention of the Association for Behavior Analysis, Philadelphia.

7

Stimulus Control

Mark F. O'Reilly and James W. Halle

Stimulus control is at work when a person goes to the door upon hearing the doorbell or picks up the receiver upon hearing the ring of a telephone. It also operates when someone hurries into the kitchen to get a cup of coffee when smelling coffee brewing or when someone steps up carefully when encountering a particular place where the slabs of cement in a familiar sidewalk do not meet evenly. Stimulus control is at work even when one reads the words in a book or newspaper. It operates for virtually every response people make throughout the day, whether they recognize it or not.

Much of this chapter is devoted to methods of establishing stimulus control to produce desired behavioral outcomes for learners with disabilities. (It is critically important, however, to understand that the operation of stimulus control applies to everyone, not only to people with disabilities.) This chapter also examines the role of prompting in the establishment and transfer of stimulus control. Finally, it discusses setting events as a special case of stimulus control that encompasses an expanded model of applied behavior analysis—a model with far greater complexity and sophistication.

Stimulus Control Defined

Like reinforcement, stimulus control is a principle of behavior (Skinner, 1953). It exists when there is a high probability that a particular response will occur in the presence of a particular stimulus.

A few assumptions are made when considering the implications of stimulus control for human behavior. One assumption is that behavior is not a random event; it is emitted under the control of some stimuli, regardless of one's ability to identify such control. Related to this assumption is an often overlooked aspect of the contingencies of reinforcement—one often speaks of

This chapter was written while J.W. Halle received support from a U.S. Department of Education Leadership Training Grant (No. H029D90107) awarded to the University of California at Santa Barbara. Partial support was provided also by a U.S. Department of Education Grant (No. H086P90024) awarded to the University of Illinois, Anne Smith, project officer. This material does not necessarily reflect the position or policies of the U.S. Department of Education, and no official endorsement should be inferred.

consequences reinforcing or strengthening behavior and neglects to consider that the unit reinforced is not behavior in isolation but, rather, behavior operating under a particular set of conditions. When the probability of a response increases due to reinforcement, the frequency of the response does not increase at random times throughout the day. Actually, the response occurs more frequently under a specific set of circumstances (i.e., the circumstances present when the response is reinforced). This relationship between a stimulus (environmental event) and a response is called a *stimulus-response relationship*.

Betty's response of running outside with money in her hand, for example, increases in frequency after the first visit of the ice cream truck to her neighborhood. However, she does not run outside randomly throughout the day with money in her hand. This response occurs only under a specific set of circumstances, i.e., when she hears the ice cream truck's bell. A stimulus-response relationship has been formed between the ice cream truck's bell and Betty's behavior of running outside with money in her hand.

Another assumption when considering the implications of stimulus control for human behavior is that the environment, both physical (e.g., place, temperature) and social (i.e., people), influences behavior. Physical and social aspects of the environment create situations in which certain kinds of behavior are more or less likely to occur. Rather than thinking of people as endowed with such traits as shyness, aggressiveness, or confidence that are *internally determined*, it is more accurate to describe people's behavior as *situationally determined*. For example, a student may be quite confident when discussing a homework assignment among her classmates and quite tentative when discussing the same assignment in the presence of the instructor. Similarly, a young man may be shy when meeting new people and assertive when interacting with his roommate.

A third assumption in regard to stimulus control pertains to the dynamic nature of stimulus control. At any moment in time, a stimulus-response relationship may be identifiable and measurable, but immediately upon the emission of the response, it may meet with a consequence that modifies the S-R relationship (e.g., weakens, strengthens, or changes the controlling variables of the relationship). Thus, stimulus control is ethereal and ever shifting—characteristics that defy simple identification and measurement.

Baer (1989) related a favorite example of his that captures the transitory nature of stimulus control and its complexity as it operates in the natural environment:

> If the problem is to buy a car, we discriminate manufacturer, price, year, body type, color, various performance characteristics, safety characteristics, room, convenience of operation, sensory appeal (looks good, smells good, handles well, doesn't shake, doesn't rattle), probable resale value, and even more than that, as all relevant to the response of buying one.
>
> If the problem is to cross the street safely, we discriminate *only* the distance from us, direction, and speed of the cars in the street as relevant

to the response of crossing; we need not and usually do not discriminate any of the above characteristics.

Thus, if we were car-shopping and were crossing the street just to enter an automobile agency's showroom, then in one moment we would change from discriminating only the three items in the second list to no longer discriminating them and instead discriminating all of the stimuli of the first list.

The point of the example is that, especially in the natural environment, stimuli do not have a stable, general salience; they are constantly being transformed from salient to irrelevant to salient again, as a function of ongoing changes in context; variability of context is very characteristic of the natural environment.

Stimulus control is a behavioral principle that has a multitude of everyday applications. A primary objective of this chapter is for readers to discover that much of their behavior is influenced by stimulus control. A convenient way to conceptualize how stimulus control is established is to divide examples of it into two distinct categories: those that are acquired naturally (as part of everyday living) and those that are acquired systematically (by application of a teaching program). The three anecdotes that follow demonstrate varying aspects of stimulus control. The first is an example of a systematic application; the latter two examples illustrate natural acquisition of stimulus control.

Tammy was a 13-year-old student at Alfonso Middle School, diagnosed as having Down Syndrome. As one of her learning objectives, Tammy learned how to purchase a snack at a fast-food restaurant. When the teacher gave the cue "It's time to buy your food," Tammy could order desired items and pay for them appropriately. When Tammy was with her mother at the same restaurant, however, she did not order a snack. Her mother said that Tammy seemed confused and forgot what items she wanted to order.

Stimulus condition: Teacher in restaurant Behavior: Ordering Reinforcer: Snack

Joe was on his way out of his house to go to work one morning. When he opened the outside door, he noticed that it was beginning to rain. He went back inside his house to get his umbrella.

Stimulus condition: Rain Behavior: Getting umbrella Reinforcer: Remaining dry

Pat drove down the street in her car. When she saw a stop sign at the end of the street, she reduced her speed. She brought her car to a halt at the stop sign.

Stimulus condition: Stop sign Behavior: Stopping car Reinforcer: Arriving safely

In these examples, the behavior of ordering a snack, taking an umbrella to work, and halting at a stop sign all occur in the presence of a certain set of conditions (i.e., the teacher, rain, a stop sign). The performance of these behaviors in the presence of these conditions leads to consequences that are reinforcing for Tammy, Joe, and Pat (e.g., getting a snack, staying dry, getting to a destination safely). Because the behaviors (e.g., getting an umbrella) are reinforced under a given set of conditions (e.g., wet weather), the probability of performing the behaviors under these conditions is increased. Joe, for example, is more likely to take an umbrella to work when it is raining. Under these circumstances, the presence of the teacher, wet weather, and a stop sign exert stimulus control over ordering a snack, getting an umbrella, and stopping the car.

It is important to realize that the relationship between the stimulus and the response in stimulus control differs from the relationship described in Chapter 4. In reinforcement, the stimulus occurs following an operant behavior and increases the future probability of the occurrence of that response. In stimulus control, the probability of a given response is increased in the presence of a particular stimulus once the behavior has a history of reinforcement in the presence of that stimulus.

Properties of Stimulus Control

Stimulus Discrimination

Consider for a moment what life would be like if people could not distinguish between cars traveling toward them at speeds of 20 miles per hour and 80 miles per hour or between sections of a swimming pool that are 3 feet deep and 10 feet deep. The consequences or repercussions of such discriminatory deficits could be devastating. *Stimulus discrimination* is a basic process of human (and nonhuman) behavior, without which the world would be a threatening and unpredictable place. People must be able to gain information from stimuli or cues in the environment to know how to behave differently in and adapt to varying situations.

Stimulus discrimination is accomplished when a response is consistently reinforced in the presence of one set of stimuli and not in the presence of other stimuli. Each set of stimuli signal the consequences that are likely to occur. The stimulus that is associated with the reinforced response is called a *discriminative stimulus* or an S^D. The presence of the S^D increases the probability of the response because the response has been reinforced in the past when it occurred in the presence of that stimulus. S^Ds signal that reinforcement is available for a particular response. While reinforced in the presence of one stimuli, the response may rarely be emitted in the presence of other stimuli. These other stimuli, called S–deltas or S^Δs, signal that reinforcement will not be forthcoming when the response is performed. When a student performs a behavior in the presence of certain stimuli (S^Ds) and not in the presence of other stimuli (S^Δs), a discrimination has been established.

For example, a bright sunny morning might be an S^Δ for Joe's bringing an umbrella to work because the umbrella is unnecessary for Joe to remain dry (reinforcer). The presence of the teacher at the fast-food restaurant may be a discriminative stimulus for Tammy's appropriate snack purchasing. The presence of Tammy's mother seems to be an S–delta for ordering and purchasing food (i.e., Tammy does not respond appropriately in the presence of her mother). Tammy's behavior is an example of the acquisition of a discriminative response that is inappropriate because Tammy should engage in appropriate food ordering and food purchasing at restaurants in the presence of both her mother and her teacher. Methods by which teachers can remediate such inappropriate stimulus control are addressed later in this chapter.

Perhaps one of the clearest examples of stimulus discrimination is the behavior people exhibit when encountering traffic lights while driving their cars. They are reinforced for proceeding through an intersection when the light is green. The green light is an S^D for proceeding; it is also an S^Δ for stopping (i.e., other drivers may yell or honk their horns at a person stopping at a green light, or they may accidentally bang into the person's car from behind, or police may issue the person a citation). By contrast, a red light is an S^D for stopping and an S^Δ for proceeding.

Stimulus Generalization

Another process of human behavior is *stimulus generalization*, which allows people to behave appropriately in new situations that are similar to ones they have encountered in the past. For example, with each advancing year in school, students enter new classrooms with new teachers and new classmates. In all these novel situations, they know how to behave in school. They have learned how to interact with teachers and peers, so they respond to new stimuli in a fashion similar to the successful ways they have behaved previously. If students were not able to see similarities with past experiences in these novel situations, they would have to be taught how to behave in every new situation. All of their waking hours would be spent in this endeavor.

Stimulus generalization is the process that describes the tendency of people to perform the same response in the presence of new stimuli that have similar physical properties to, or have been associated with, a past stimulus. Stimulus generalization is the opposite of stimulus discrimination, which involves responding differently to differing stimuli.

Stimulus generalization is at work if, for example, Joe takes his umbrella to work on mornings that are overcast. Overcast mornings are not identical to rainy mornings, but they share some of the salient stimulus dimensions of rainy mornings (e.g., cloudy, dull). Stimulus generalization is also at work for Pat when she stops her car each time she encounters a new stop sign. Stimulus generalization did not occur, however, for Tammy (i.e., she discriminated between the presence of her teacher and her mother when buying food at the restaurant).

It is important to note that common physical properties are not the only means that produce stimulus generalization. Stimuli can be associated through conditioning and thus responded to in a similar fashion. For example, if someone enjoys outdoor activities and has made many friends through a membership in the Sierra Club, he will likely greet new acquaintances who are members of the Sierra Club with more enthusiasm and interest than he will greet new acquaintances who are not club members. He thus will respond to these new acquaintances who are Sierra Club members in a manner similar to his original response to other Sierra Club members. Membership in the Sierra Club organization is the association that mediated the generalized response. Members of the Sierra Club have no necessary common physical properties.

Stimulus Characteristics

An essential feature of stimulus control is that people learn to discriminate between some stimuli and to generalize across others. They learn to perform similar behaviors in the presence of certain stimuli and different behaviors in the presence of other stimuli. What are the characteristics of a set of stimuli that exert control over a set of responses? For example, what are the similarities among mornings in which Joe takes his umbrella to work? Two types of stimulus characteristics help explain the relationship among stimuli that exert control over behavior.

First, there are *stimulus dimensions*, which are the generic properties of a stimulus, such as its size, shape, color, or weight. For example, the stimulus dimension for Joe's response of taking an umbrella may be the presence of rain, an overcast sky, and so on. Second, there are multiple *levels of the stimulus* within each dimension. For example, the levels within the dimension of weight range from very light to very heavy. The levels within the dimension of shape do not fall on a continuum but are a catalog of all possible shapes. Any given stimulus will possess only some of the possible dimensions, and each dimension will assume a single value for the level. The stimulus of a rainy morning that results in Joe's taking his umbrella to work, for example, may vary from being extremely wet and overcast, to wet and bright, to dry and overcast. Therefore, each stimulus can represent a cluster of stimulus characteristics that vary across dimensions and across levels within those dimensions.

Certain dimensions and levels of stimuli may be irrelevant, however, with their presence or absence having no relation to performance of an appropriate response. For example, the temperature in the morning has little influence over Joe's decision to take his umbrella to work. Temperature is an irrelevant characteristic in this instance. Tammy's food purchasing behavior, though, is an example of a response that has come under control of an irrelevant stimulus characteristic (i.e., the teacher), and it is on this basis that a discrimination was formed.

The Role of Prompting in Stimulus Control

Teachers often need to teach students to perform certain responses in the presence of specific *antecedent stimuli*. For example, John needs to learn that in the presence of having on one shoe (antecedent stimulus), he must then put on the second shoe (correct response). In many teaching situations the teacher uses supplementary stimuli, termed *prompts*, to insure the occurrence of correct behavior in the presence of the targeted antecedent stimuli. Prompts either are associated with the response to be performed (*response prompts*), or are supplemental stimuli that increase the salience of the targeted stimuli (*stimulus prompts*).

Response Prompts

Response prompts include verbal instructions (or cues), modeling, and physical guidance. These prompts are used to evoke correct performance of a behavior in the presence of the antecedent stimuli.

Verbal Prompts

Numerous forms of verbal prompts are used to evoke appropriate responses. Two forms are commonly used during instruction. In one, a teacher asks the student, in a general way, what behavior needs to be performed next: "Now that you have put on one shoe, what's the next thing you need to do?" Such an *indirect verbal prompt* cues the student to perform a behavior but does not specify the exact form the behavior should take. In the other, the teacher states specifically what behavior the student needs to perform: "Put on your other shoe." A *direct verbal prompt* includes a specific and precise statement of the response form expected. Both direct and indirect verbal prompts can effectively evoke the desired response once that response is established in the repertoire of the student. It is also important for the teacher to use words that are understood by the student being taught.

Modeling Prompts

When using a modeling prompt, a teacher actually demonstrates the behavior the student should imitate. The teacher also may pair the modeling prompt with a verbal prompt during instruction. Modeling is not restricted to behavior performed by another person; a model can be presented in picture form (i.e., in writing) for the student to imitate (i.e., to write the word).

Modeling is effective only with students who possess imitative skills and who attend visually to the model. The probability of successful imitation is also increased if a student possesses rudimentary component behaviors of the skills needed to perform a behavior prior to the modeling procedure (e.g., if a student can form letters to write, imitating a written word will not be very difficult).

Physical Guidance Prompts

Physical guidance is the most intrusive form of response prompt. It involves physically moving a student through the desired response. For example, a student with severe disabilities may need to be physically guided through the steps of toothbrushing. This procedure may entail the teacher's grasping of the student's hand in which the brush is held and guiding it through the desired movements.

Physical guidance is especially effective with students who have physical disabilities. These prompts may enable such students to participate partially in activities they could not engage in independently. Physical guidance is also effective for teaching the correct response when target behaviors are not easily amenable to verbal or modeling prompts. For example, physical guidance may be more effective than modeling for teaching toothbrushing motions inside the mouth because such motions are not entirely visible.

Stimulus Prompts

When natural conditions (or stimuli) do not produce desired responses, supplemental stimuli that do occasion such responses may be needed. Stimulus prompts are supplemental cues that are paired or associated with the targeted discriminative stimuli to increase the probability that the response will occur in its presence. Such prompts can be used along with response prompts during instruction.

A number of stimulus prompts have been identified. Redundancy cues, in which the salient stimulus dimension is highlighted, are one type of stimulus prompt. For example, a teacher may place an arrow at the target temperature on the oven dial to highlight the correct setting for the student. Movement cues are a second type of stimulus prompt. The target stimulus, for example, may be made more pronounced by the teacher pointing to it or moving it. A third type is position cues, in which the teacher might position the target stimulus so that it stands out from the other background stimuli.

Using Fading Procedures to Transfer Stimulus Control

Response and stimulus prompts are used to teach a student to perform a desired behavior in the presence of natural conditions. These prompts, however, are supplemental and need to be removed so that the targeted behavior will come to be controlled by natural stimuli. For example, Joe's mother would like Joe eventually to put on his second shoe without her verbal prompts. The cooking teacher would like the student eventually to set the oven dial without needing an arrow.

Typically, prompts are removed gradually during instruction. This procedure is termed *fading the prompt*. Fading techniques are used to transfer control gradually from the prompt to the targeted stimuli in the natural environment. The gradual removal of prompts minimizes the number of errors that a student will make in the presence of the targeted stimulus. For example, if a student needs an arrow to indicate oven temperature, abrupt removal of the arrow might result in the student setting the oven temperature incorrectly and burning food.

It is important to minimize the number of errors made because errors tend to be repeated. Since incorrect responding is not reinforced, there is an increasing probability that a student may engage in inappropriate behavior to access other reinforcers in the environment. If Joe makes multiple errors in dressing, for example, he will not receive reinforcers (e.g., praise or approval) for dressing. He may then engage in other, less desirable behaviors in order to receive attention. However, if he learns the tasks in a relatively error-free manner, his correct responses can be reinforced, minimizing the likelihood that Joe will attempt less desirable ways to access reinforcers.

Procedures for Fading Response Prompts

Four procedures for transferring response prompts to natural stimuli are described. These procedures can be used separately or in combination.

Most-to-Least Prompts

These prompt systems are often used when teaching students with severe disabilities. They can, however, be used with students of all ability levels. These systems frequently entail breaking a task down into its component steps, a process called *task analysis*. The prompting system is then applied to each step of the task analysis. Most-to-least prompt systems are particularly effective on task-analysis steps that are difficult to teach using less intrusive prompts (e.g., verbal prompts) because the target behavior may be difficult to describe verbally.

As a most-to-least prompt system implies, the teacher begins with the most intrusive level of prompt. Typically, this instructional procedure moves from physical guidance to modeling and finally to verbal prompts. The verbal prompts are subsequently removed to allow the natural stimuli to control the response. When possible, it is desirable to transfer control from physical guidance or modeling directly to the natural stimulus. The criteria for fading from one level of assistance to the next level depends on the student's mastery of that step of the task analysis under the level of prompt. For example, if the student made the correct change on three consecutive trials with a model prompt and if the criterion for fading was three consecutive correct trials, the teacher would use a verbal prompt on the next trial. If the student failed to respond on a predetermined number of trials for a given level of assistance, the teacher may reintroduce a more intrusive prompt for that step of the task analysis to reestablish control (i.e., to insure correct performance).

Least-to-Most Prompts

With this procedure, a student is given the opportunity to perform the target behavior independently (i.e., in the presence of the natural stimuli) on each trial before any prompts are introduced. The least intrusive level of prompts is introduced first. More intrusive assistance is introduced only as needed (i.e., when the student fails to respond correctly). The student is allowed to respond with the least amount of assistance on each trial. Least-to-most procedures typically consist of an indirect verbal prompt ("What do you need to do next?"), followed by a direct verbal prompt ("Put the cap on the toothpaste"), then a model, and finally physical guidance. A predetermined waiting period (e.g., 3 seconds) is provided between the presentation of each level of prompt to allow the student the opportunity to respond.

Error-correction procedures are often used by teachers in most-to-least, least-to-most, and time delay (discussed later) procedures. Because the student is given a predetermined period to respond, the opportunity to respond incorrectly exists; the student might perform an incorrect response following a prompt. As mentioned earlier, if students perform incorrect responses, they are likely to repeat them. Therefore, error-correction procedures may include interrupting the student prior to or during the performance of an incorrect response. The teacher may interrupt the student's performance and physically guide the student through that step of the task.

Graduated Guidance

Often defined as an instructional strategy in and of itself, *graduated guidance* is a strategy that requires the use of physical prompts only as needed. The physical prompt is faded when the student responds correctly. Two methods of graduated guidance have been identified in the literature (Foxx & Azrin, 1973). The first procedure, termed *shadowing*, involves the teacher's following of the student's movements with her hand near but not touching the student. This allows the teacher to intervene immediately with a physical prompt if the student responds incorrectly. Shadowing is often used by tennis or golf instructors.

The second procedure, termed *spatial fading*, involves changing the location of the physical prompt. For example, if the prompt is hand-over-hand, the teacher can fade her touch to the wrist, then to the elbow, and finally remove the prompt altogether. Spatial fading might be used when teaching a young child to write letters or numbers. The hand-over-hand prompts provide specific motor cues for producing correct responses. As these fine-motor responses are acquired, the wrist or elbow touch-prompts function more as cues to begin the response rather than as cues specifying particular movements.

Time Delay

This procedure transfers control to natural stimuli by systematically delaying the presentation of the prompt after the natural stimulus has been presented. While the other fading procedures described rely on changing the intensity and topography of the response prompts to transfer control from the prompt to natural stimuli, time delay involves the insertion of an interval of time between the presentation of the natural stimulus and the response prompt.

Two time delay procedures have been described in the literature (Snell & Gast, 1981). The first procedure, termed *progressive time delay*, begins with the simultaneous delivery of the natural stimulus and the prompt (0-second time delay). After a performance criterion is met (e.g., 3 consecutive correct trials at 0 seconds), the delay interval is increased by a preestablished amount (typically 1 or 2 seconds). When the criterion is met, the delay is again increased. This transfer procedure presumes that once students learn the response, they will anticipate or respond prior to the delivery of the prompt, thereby responding in the presence of the natural stimulus. For example, if the teacher's objective is to teach the label for an object (e.g., ball), the natural stimuli might be the presence of a ball and the question, "What is this?" The prompt might be a verbal model ("ball") provided by the instructor. At a 0-second delay, the question would be followed immediately by the model: "What is this? Ball." As the student's performance improves, the delay between the presentation of the object plus the question and the prompt ("ball") would increase. At some point, the student would begin to respond to the question prior to the model.

The second procedure, termed *constant time delay*, also begins with a 0-second time delay. After the performance criterion is met at the 0-second level, all subsequent trials include a fixed delay interval (e.g., 5 seconds) in which the prompt is delivered a certain amount of seconds after the natural stimulus. The procedure, again, depends on the student's anticipating the prompt by responding before its introduction. For example, Halle, Spradlin, and Baer (1979) implemented a constant time delay at mealtime with children who had severe mental retardation. Before the study began, the children, who resided in a residential facility, were called to a counter one at a time to receive their food trays. In the study, constant time delay was used to teach the children to say "tray, please." The children were called as before, but when they arrived at the counter, their trays were withheld and a 15-second delay was inserted. At the end of the delay, a model prompt ("tray, please") was provided. All six of the children learned to make the request prior to the presentation of the model, to access their food more rapidly.

Stimulus Fading and Shaping

Manipulations of stimulus prompts to accomplish the transfer of control from a prompt to natural stimuli include stimulus fading and stimulus shaping.

Stimulus Fading

During initial training, a dimension of the target antecedent stimulus may be made more salient than usual (with stimulus prompts such as redundancy cues) to increase the probability of a response. This exaggerated dimension can be gradually faded out during training in a procedure called *stimulus fading*. An example of stimulus fading is illustrated in the arithmetic example in Figure 7.1.

Another example of stimulus fading, illustrated in Figure 7.2, is used in teaching children to discriminate the letter *b* from the letter *d*. The stimulus dimension on which this discrimination is achieved is the right-left position of the vertical flag. By thickening, or exaggerating, the flag (a stimulus prompt), this critical dimension is made more salient. Once accurate responding is produced, the thickness of the flag is faded.

2 + 3 = 5 2 + 3 = 5 2 + 3 = 5 2 + 3 = _

Figure 7.1 Stimulus fading through the gradual elimination of the answer, 5.

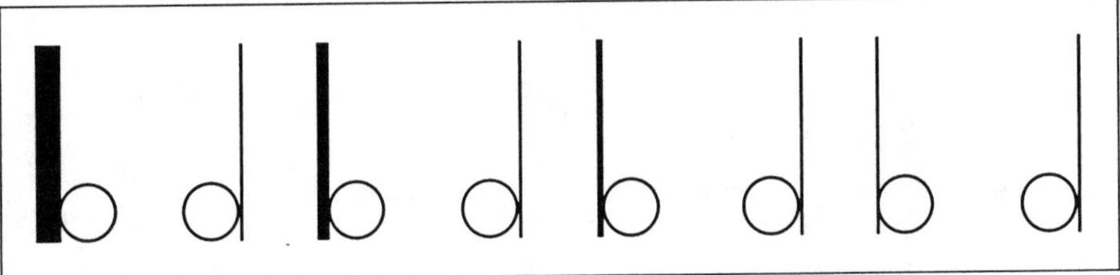

Figure 7.2 Stimulus fading through the gradual thinning of the exaggerated flags on the letter *b*.

Stimulus Shaping

Some instruction involves teaching a response to a target stimulus that initially might be difficult for a learner, such as the reading of the word CAT. Learning can be simplified by starting with a stimulus that already produces the desired response, then gradually changing the stimulus to resemble the word CAT.

Stimulus shaping is a procedure in which the dimensions of the stimulus are changed during instruction to capitalize on information already known by the learner. However, the terminal stimulus dimensions must evoke the correct response. So, the changes made to the overall stimulus configuration must be faded out completely. To do this, the dimensions of the shaped stimulus are gradually changed during instruction so that the terminal or appropriate stimulus exerts control over the desired response. Figure 7.3 gives an example of teaching word identification by using stimulus shaping.

Another example of stimulus shaping used for preschoolers who are learning numbers is shown in Figure 7.4.

Figure 7.3 Stimulus shaping to teach the word CAT.

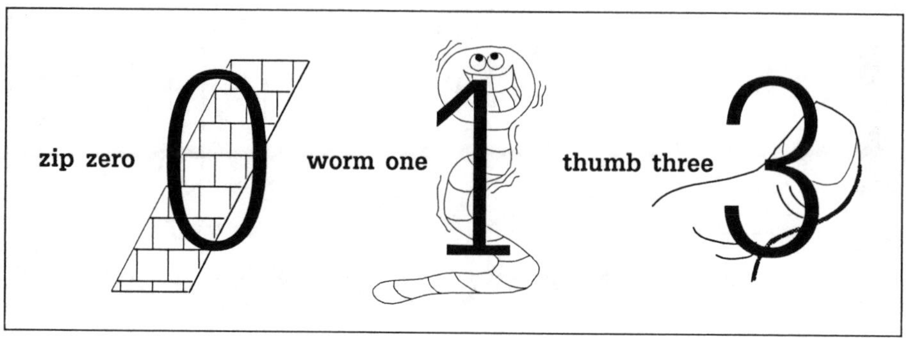

Figure 7.4 Stimulus shaping to teach *0, 1,* and *3.*

The Role of Setting Events as Controlling Stimuli

Up to this point, an approach to understanding human behavior that includes the influence of conditions present immediately preceding and subsequent to the behavior of interest has been advocated. In this approach, an analysis is made of the conditions that enter into a functional relationship with the behavior (i.e., the conditions that influence a behavior's probability of occurrence). By examining such behavioral antecedents and consequences, many of the determinants of human behavior are identified. However, it is naive to think that the only influences on behavior are those that occur immediately before, coincidental with, or immediately subsequent to the behavior of interest.

Behavior is not determined solely by the events or stimuli that immediately precede the behavior. Controlling events which have occurred some time prior to the behavior can influence the behavior also. Similarly, controlling stimuli are often more complex than a traffic light or an ice cream man's bell. Multiple events or complex sets of stimuli also can influence behavior.

Many examples are available demonstrating that more temporally distant and complex events may influence behavior. For example, Bijou and Baer (1961) employed a hypothetical case of an infant who had a routine of napping in his crib followed by lively play in his playpen. On a particular occasion, noises outside his room prevented his napping, and he remained active during his usual naptime. When his mother placed him in his playpen, he cried and protested. The outside noises and the sleeplessness they produced functioned as a setting event for the infant's crying when placed in the playpen.

This set of circumstances is different from a discriminative stimulus in two ways. The outside noises and sleeplessness are stimuli occurring earlier in time that together constitute an S–R relationship (i.e., the outside noises produced sleeplessness). They also are complex events occurring in combination, rather than as a simple discrete event (e.g., a green traffic light).

A good example of the influence of setting events involves those events operating in the determination of aggressive behavior. Gardner, Karan, and Cole (1984) identified six stimulus events (e.g., teasing by peers, correction for mistakes) that preceded occurrences of verbal aggression by John, a young adult diagnosed with moderate mental retardation. The researchers then gathered data on the frequency with which these stimulus events provoked aggression by John. Of the six events, teasing was found to be the most likely to produce aggression. Over a month's time, teasing occurred 55 times and provoked aggression on 18 of these occasions, or 32% of the time. None of the six events exerted powerful control over aggression; thus, other events or variables were thought to have been influencing John's aggression. By adding to the analysis such setting events as weekend family visits, difficulty arising in the morning, and the presence of a particular staff member, the predictability of John's aggression, given a particular setting event, was vastly improved.

Another example of the influence of setting events on behavior involves one of the authors of this chapter, who has three young children. The quality of his interaction with his children is adversely affected by lack of sleep, illness, or arguments with his spouse. These setting events may have occurred much earlier than the interaction with his children and defy description as discrete events.

In yet another example, suppose that a person is athletically inclined and arises every morning at 5:30 to run laps with a friend around a high school track. One Saturday morning when the alarm rings, the person has difficulty awakening. Why? The person had been talked into going to a party the night before and did not get to bed until 3:00 A.M. An analysis of this scenario follows.

Antecedents (i.e., discriminative stimuli):

- sounding of alarm
- early morning
- meeting with friend

Behavior:

- running of laps

Consequences:

- interaction with friend
- expenditure of calories (maintainance of weight)
- maintenance of health

Events other than the immediate antecedents and consequences are influential in this anecdote: lack of sleep and partying (too much eating and drinking) altered the reinforcing function of the consequences, which in turn modified the discriminative function of the antecedents. In other words, the person's sleeping for only 2½ hours strengthened sleep as a reinforcer and weakened the reinforcing properties of the typical consequences. Thus, the same antecedents that previously produced the person's arising and preparing to run now produce other behaviors that are associated with sleep, such as turning off the alarm, calling the jogging partner and giving an excuse to cancel the activity, and getting back into bed.

By including setting events in the analysis of behavior, professionals are not restricted to examining only simple events that occur in close temporal relationship to a behavior of interest. The inclusion of setting events permits an expanded analysis of conditions that may be influential in understanding human behavior.

In addition to the circumstances already mentioned in examples, other conditions serve as setting events. Gardner, Cole, Davidson, and Karan (1986) combined the suggestions of previous investigators (Bijou, 1976; Bijou & Baer, 1961; and Kantor, 1959, 1970) and generated three categories of setting events:

1. *Physiological Conditions.* Deprivation and satiation are influential conditions that determine behavior in some situations. Consider the behavior that occurs when someone has drunk large quantities of liquid and has not visited a bathroom for some time. At some point that person's bladder expands, and behavior will be directed at achieving one goal only. Another example of physiological conditions serving as setting events is that of sleep deprivation, as mentioned in the previous anecdote.

2. *Durational Events.* These events may be discrete or complex and occur concurrently with a behavior of interest. Examples include the presence or absence of people or events (e.g., attention from others), amount of space between or density of people, ratio of adults to children, availability of competing activities, time of day, and difficulty of task.

3. *Behavioral Histories.* These histories typically involve interactions that are separate in space and time (i.e., they may occur in another place at a much earlier time) from the current stimulus conditions and corresponding behavior. Examples of this category of setting events might include the effects that a weekend visit with family has on a person's aggressive behavior at work the following Monday or the effects of a prior argument between spouses on their interaction with their children.

For many years applied behavior analysts focused their efforts on consequence-based procedures. Much of the recent research in applied behavior analysis has concentrated on stimulus control and on the influence of events that occur prior to a behavior of interest. As this approach to human behavior matures, it is becoming increasingly complex to meet the difficult challenges that face it. By embracing the phenomena of setting events, a tremendous sphere of influence has become part of the approach and will be the subject of future investigation. The strength of applied behavior analysis lies in its flexibilty and in its accommodation of changes discovered through empirical investigation.

Summary

Stimulus control is acquired naturally or taught systematically. An examination of the properties and characteristics of stimulus control can permit its use in behavioral analysis and behavior change.

Discrimination is a key concept in stimulus control. As people learn to discriminate which events signal reinforcement and which do not, stimuli assume controlling influences. Stimulus discrimination occurs when characteristics of presenting stimuli come to signal the availability or nonavailability of reinforcement and when response probability changes accordingly. Stimulus generalization is the tendency to perform a response in the presence of stimuli that have some association with the original stimuli. Characteristics of stimuli, such as stimulus dimension and level of the stimulus, will affect the establishment of stimulus control.

Prompts can be used to establish stimulus control. For example, response prompts can be used to encourage the response in the presence of targeted stimuli. Examples of response prompts are verbal cues, modeling, and physical guidance. Stimulus prompts, such as redundancy cues, movement cues, or position cues, are used to enhance the salience of the targeted stimuli.

Instructional prompts may need to be faded during instruction, so that behavior can come under the control of natural stimuli. Systems of gradual withdrawal of prompts can be used, such as prompting systems, graduated guidance, and time delay procedures. Stimulus fading and shaping, which involve changing the level or configuration of the stimulus, are often used to transfer control from contrived or elaborated stimuli to targeted, terminal stimuli.

Setting events, as broader influences on behavior, affect the influence that antecedent stimuli have on behavior. Analysis of setting events permits a broader assessment of potentially influential events, making behavior management of even difficult and complex behaviors more successful.

Study Questions

1. What are three assumptions made about stimulus control and human behavior?
2. Define *stimulus control.*
3. Define *discriminative stimulus* (S^D). Give an example.
4. Define *S-Delta* (S^Δ). Give an example.
5. Define the terms *stimulus dimensions* and *levels of the stimulus.* How do these terms relate to stimulus control?
6. Give three examples of response prompts and three examples of stimulus prompts.
7. Describe three methods for fading response prompts.
8. Describe two methods for fading stimulus prompts.

Exercises

1. Melanie is a young girl with autism. She will readily order a hamburger and french fries from her usual waitress, Sandy, at Elton's Hamburger Shop. If Sandy is not there and another waitress tries to take her order, Melanie sits silently. How might her behavior be explained by the principles of stimulus control?

2. Johnny is a young boy who needs to learn how to brush his teeth. Design an instructional plan using response prompts.

3. Lena is learning to write. Design an instructional plan using stimulus prompts to teach her to write her name.

4. How could a constant time delay procedure be used to teach a child to answer the door when the doorbell rings?

5. Angela is a 6-year-old girl who has severe tantrums. Provide a hypothetical analysis of setting events and stimulus control that might affect her tantrums. Include in your hypothetical account any physiological conditions, durational events, and behavioral histories that might affect her tantrums. Explain, using stimulus control principles, why her tantrums are frequent when her mother is present and almost nonexistent when her father is home.

Self-Application

1. Consider a bad habit or undesirable behavior in which you occasionally engage. What stimuli control this habit? Under what conditions and with

which people is it likely to occur? Under what conditions and with which people is it less likely to occur? What setting events are likely to play a role? How?

2. Consider a productive behavior in which you engage, such as exercise, study, or volunteer work. What stimuli control this behavior? Under what conditions and with which people is it likely to occur? Under what conditions and with which people is it less likely to occur? What setting events are likely to play a role? How?

3. Your verbal behavior in a movie theater is likely quite different from your verbal behavior at the dinner table with friends. Explain the differences between your verbal behavior in these two settings (including volume and frequency). Explain how your verbal behavior comes under stimulus control in both settings.

4. Consider the behavior of speaking your mind. Under what conditions are you likely to engage in this behavior? Under what conditions are you not likely to engage in this behavior? Explain the influence of stimulus control over this behavior.

SELF-MANAGEMENT PROJECT

1. What influence does stimulus control hold over your targeted behavior?
2. Plan how you can apply the procedures based on the principles of stimulus control to your self-management project.

References

Baer, D. M. (1989). Personal communication.

Bijou, S. W. (1976). *Child development III: Basic stage of early childhood.* Englewood Cliffs, NJ: Prentice-Hall.

Bijou, S. W., & Baer, D. M. (1961). *Child development I: A systematic and empirical theory.* Englewood Cliffs, NJ: Prentice-Hall.

Foxx, R. M., & Azrin, N. H. (1973). *Toilet training the retarded: A rapid program for day and nighttime independent toileting.* Champaign, IL: Research Press.

Gardner, W. I., Cole, C. L., Davidson, D. P., & Karan, O. C. (1986). Reducing aggression in individuals with developmental disabilities: An expanded stimulus control, assessment, and intervention model. *Education and Training of the Mentally Retarded, 21,* 3–12.

Gardner, W. I., & Cole, C. L. (1984). Aggression and related conduct difficulties in the mentally retarded: A multicomponent behavioral model. In S. E. Bruening, J. L. Matson, & R. P. Barrett (Eds.), *Advances in mental retardation and developmental disabilities* (Vol. 2, pp. 41–84). Greenwich, CT: JAI Press, Inc.

Halle, J. W., Marshall, A. M., & Spradlin, J. E. (1979). Time delay: A technique to increase language use and facilitate generalization in retarded children. *Journal of Applied Behavior Analysis, 12,* 431–439.

Kantor, J. R. (1970). An analysis of the experimental analysis of behavior (TEAB), *Journal of the Experimental Analysis of Behavior, 13,* 101–108.

Kantor, J. R. (1959). *Interbehavioral psychology.* Granville, OH: Principia Press.

Skinner, B. F. (1953). *Science and human behavior.* New York: Macmillan.

Snell, M. E., & Gast, D. L. (1981). Applying the delay procedure to the instruction of the severely handicapped. *Journal of the Association of the Severely Handicapped, 5,* 3–14.

8

Behavior Change through Modeling

Gina is a 4-year-old child living in France. Her family is French, and she and all members of her family speak French. Jeanette is a 3-year-old child living in Germany. Her family is German, and she and all members of her family speak German. Peter is a 5-year-old child living in America. His family is American, and he and all of his family speak English. Juan is a 2-year-old child living in Spain. His family is Spanish, and he and all of his family speak Spanish.

These four children are from four different countries, and they speak four different languages. The children heard their parents speak their native languages, and each child in turn learned to speak the language that was spoken in the home. What these children have in common is the way in which they learned to speak their native languages. The learning of language by each child was heavily influenced by modeling.

Modeling Defined

Modeling is the process of learning or changing behavior as a result of observing someone else's behavior. Modeling is also referred to as imitation learning, observational learning, or copying. Modeling provides a shortcut to learning. The learner acquires or changes a behavior based on someone else's performance and in doing so may avoid a long process of trial and error. For example, Jimmy learns to play kickball by watching his buddies play it. Alice learns to play the piano by watching her teacher play it. Sara learns to cook by watching her mother cook. Two more examples of modeling follow.

At age 16, Johnny was old enough to drive. He took a course in driver's education, which taught driving through direct instruction, modeling by an instructor, and modeling by actors in driver's education films. Prior to taking this course, Johnny had observed many examples of driving and knew a number of driving rules, for he had been a passenger in cars throughout his childhood. In addition, he had seen many examples of the consequences of failure to follow driving rules before he saw these consequences in his driver's education class. By exposure to multiple demonstrations involving driving, Johnny learned to drive properly through modeling.

Jeanette was a 4-year-old girl who, with her family, moved to another town during her first year of nursery school. Her new nursery school functioned much differently from her former one, which was very unstructured, with children selecting their own toys and playing by themselves or with others. In Jeanette's new school there was circle time, group reading time, and art time. When Jeanette first entered her new classroom, she did not know how to behave. However, she noticed the other children sitting in groups, following instructions, and getting praise from the teacher, and through observation and imitation of their behavior, Jeanette quickly learned the new nursery school routine. She was able to adjust to her new school through modeling.

All examples of modeling have two factors in common. First, there is a person, or a symbol of a person, performing the behavior. Second, there is an observer who learns, or becomes more likely to perform, the behavior as a result of observation. The process of modeling occurs countless times throughout an individual's lifetime. Understanding and using this process in a planned way greatly enhances the process of behavior change.

Types of Models

Several types of models have been identified both in the theory and in the research literature of modeling. Models can be live or symbolic. Symbolic models take a variety of forms; these include video, audio, written, and pictorial models.

Live Models

A common type of model is the live model: people serving as models for other people. For example, children learn from observing the behavior of parents, teachers, siblings, and others. Adults learn from observing the behavior of other adults. People may learn from observing significant people in their lives or from observing strangers. Modeling may be planned, or it may occur inadvertently.

Planned learning takes place when an individual purposefully behaves in such a way as to provide a model for someone else. A teacher, for example, may deliberately talk in soft or moderate tones and avoid raising her voice so that her students will learn to speak quietly also. Parents may scrupulously avoid the use of profanity to avoid modeling the use of this type of language for their children. A job coach may work quickly and attentively at straightening shelves in order to provide a model for the student to follow.

Video Models

Models do not necessarily have to be live. People can learn a behavior from watching videos of other people performing the behavior. Behaviors are often learned through films or videos that people watch during leisure times. Inadvertent modeling often occurs when people watch movies and television, and then assume the attitudes, behaviors, and mannerisms of actors and actresses observed on the screen. Cartoons and children's programs have been accused of promoting violence by the violence that the shows' characters model.

People have also acquired skills through observations of filmed performances. For example, countless people have learned to exercise, cook, restore houses, garden, and perform a variety of other activities through watching videos and television. In addition, students of all ages have learned instructional tasks, social behaviors, and recreational behaviors by watching videos. The use of videos in education to model behaviors is widespread.

Charlop and Milstein (1989) used video modeling to teach conversation skills to children with autism. Three young boys with autism watched videotaped adult conversations about toys. The adults held a toy while talking about it. After watching the videotapes, all three boys were able to hold similar conversations. (However, one boy required 20 viewings of the videotape, while another boy required 3, and the third 6 in order to perform the modeled behavior.) Additionally, the modeled skills generalized to other topics of conversation.

Audio Models

Modeling occurs also through audio presentations. Foreign language tapes are good examples of audio modeling. Music is also a form of audio modeling, affecting many people.

Johnson, Gutkin, and Plake (1991) used audio models to teach children strategies of the game *Twenty Questions*. By listening to tape-recorded models of children playing the game using question-and-answer strategies, the children were able to learn specific types of these strategies.

Written or Pictorial Models

Symbolic models can be presented through pictures and books. Teachers and parents can effect behavior change in young children by reading to them about characters who demonstrate some desired behavior. Adults also have changed aspects of their own behaviors by imitating the behaviors of people about whom they have read.

Pictures have been used as models for people with mental retardation to teach them tasks and the sequencing of tasks. For example, people who cannot read have been taught to follow a daily schedule after being presented with pictures of themselves performing desired task-related behaviors. People have also been taught to do job-related tasks by viewing pictures of persons engaging in steps of the task.

Connis (1979) taught four adults with mental retardation to function more independently in a job setting by the use of photographs depicting their assigned tasks. The workers learned to look at each picture, complete the task, and mark an X after task completion. This procedure combined the use of symbolic models (the photographs) with self-recording (the Xs) to promote vocational independence.

Modeling Processes

The modeling process appears simple: an individual observes a model then imitates the behavior. Bandura (1977) has described four components of the modeling process: attentional processes, retentional processes, motor reproduction processes, and motivational processes. Consideration of each of these processes enhances the effectiveness of the use of modeling in behavior modification.

Attentional Processes

Bandura points out that attention to the model is a necessary condition for imitative learning. If a model is not present, imitative learning cannot take place. Absence of appropriate models or of sufficient models can be a factor in a child's failing to learn certain desirable behaviors. If modeling is a planned component of a behavior modification plan, it is necessary that the learner pay attention to the model in order to learn.

Attention can be gained by direct verbal instruction. An example of the use of such instruction is seen with Jimmy, a 6-year-old boy with attention deficit syndrome. His swimming instructor is trying to teach him to swim; but Jimmy, unlike many children his age, does not readily look at the instructor as he demonstrates floating. Rather, it is necessary to give Jimmy direct verbal instructions, such as, "Jimmy, watch me." It may also be necessary to reinforce attending behavior. Verbal praise or even tangible reinforcers may be needed to reinforce Jimmy's observation of the model.

Attending behavior is also encouraged by giving the model reinforcing characteristics. The use of cartoons to teach preschoolers is an example of using models with reinforcing characteristics. Television, movies, and music all present models in formats that are attractive to observers.

Retentional Processes

Imitation requires retention. A behavior that is forgotten cannot be copies. For example, Joan had watched her instructor demonstrate how to solve a certain calculus problem the day before it appeared on an exam. However, by exam time, she had forgotten what she had observed and could not imitate the problem-solving behavior. As a result, she did poorly on her exam.

When modeling is used in a behavior modification plan, it might be necessary to include strategies that will enhance retention. Repeated demonstration is such a strategy. The case of Alan provides a good example of this.

A young man with moderate mental retardation and social skills deficits, Alan needed to learn how to ask for new supplies at his part-time job; he did not readily learn by simple verbal instruction. Alan's supervisor used modeling, performed on a daily basis for several weeks, to teach him to ask for new supplies. Both the supervisor and co-workers performed the behavior in Alan's presence, to increase the likelihood that Alan would retain what he saw. Alan was also given daily opportunities to practice asking for new work materials, and these were instrumental also in helping him retain the behavior.

In addition, repeated presentations of a model promotes retention by providing the learner with the opportunity to focus on various aspects of the demonstration. During the first presentation, a person might learn most of the skill. However, it might take more presentations for the person to learn a more difficult but critical aspect of the performance.

Use of verbal explanations to accompany modeled behavior can aid in retention. Observers who verbalize or use labels or other codes to depict what they see are more likely to remember the modeled behavior. Agran, Salzberg, and Stowitschek (1987) successfully used modeling and self-instruction to teach social skills to five adults with mental retardation. The participants were instructed to observe a model demonstrate a behavior. The model provided verbal descriptions of the behavior while modeling it. The observers were told to repeat the instructions and copy the behavior.

Complex chains of behavior may need to be modeled in smaller steps. As the learner retains the information provided by one step of the behavior, the next step is modeled. Nancy, for example, is learning to sew. Although she could watch a model sew an entire dress, it is unlikely that Nancy would be able to imitate the behavior. However, if the teacher demonstrates the sewing process one step at a time, moving to another step when Nancy is ready, Nancy's retention would be enhanced.

Motor Reproduction

Bandura's third component of the modeling process, motor reproduction, refers to the actual act of performing the modeled response. Attention and retention alone do not constitute modeling. For example, Angie might see her brother brush his teeth. She might also remember how he did it. However, unless she herself brushes her teeth, modeling does not occur.

A copied behavior might be initially inaccurate. A student may, for example, observe an expert gymnast perform a feat on a trampoline and remember what the feat looked like, but the first several attempts at copying the behavior might bear little resemblance to the performance of the expert. Repeated practice, feedback, and even physical assistance may be necessary for the student to refine modeled responses.

Motivational Processes

Behavior is strengthened by its consequences, and this law of positive reinforcement includes modeled behavior. Behavior is more likely to be imitated and to remain in the student's repertoire if the behavior is reinforced. Modeled behavior that is not reinforced may, in effect, be on extinction. If the learner finds that the behavior serves no useful function, the behavior will cease to be performed. The following example illustrates this occurrence.

Betty was having trouble with her third-grade physical education class. She could not perform a forward roll. After watching her friend Maggie do a series of forward rolls, however, Betty was able to do one herself. Her physical education teacher immediately complimented her. Betty was pleased with the praise and attention and cooperated willingly in the gymnastics lesson.

Linda, in the class next door, also had trouble performing a forward roll. While her classmates participated in gymnastics, Linda sat and daydreamed. After several verbal prompts and demonstrations by the teacher, she, too, was able to do a forward roll. However, her efforts went unnoticed. Linda did her forward rolls alone on her corner of the mat; she was given no sign of recognition, attention, or praise from her teacher. Linda soon lost interest in participating in class and returned to daydreaming. Since Linda's modeled behavior was not reinforced, she ceased performing the behavior.

Students may be motivated to perform a behavior by observing that the model's behavior results in positive reinforcement. Likewise, an individual might be discouraged from performing a behavior by seeing that a model's behavior is punished. A man whose neighbor wins the lottery, for example might be encouraged to purchase lottery tickets himself. On the other hand, if the same fellow sees another motorist pulled over for speeding, he is likely to reduce his own speed. Thus, modeling is a powerful tool for achieving behavior change. Pairing positive reinforcement strategies with modeling strategies can be an effective combination, whereas using modeling without positive reinforcement for the new behavior can result in its becoming rapidly extinct.

Effects of Modeling

In addition to the learning of new behaviors, modeling can result in changes in the circumstances in which behaviors are performed or in changes in the frequency of previously learned behavior. Examples of how these changes occur follow.

Janet was a young woman with a learning disability and social withdrawal. She had been taught to greet others, but she usually did not. At a new job training site, she observed her supervisor greeting co-workers each morning. With prompting from her supervisor, Janet eventually began to greet co-workers. Through modeling, she learned to perform a previously learned response at appropriate times.

Albert worked very slowly at his job sorting books in the library. A new co-worker worked quite rapidly, getting praise from his supervisor and a raise for his good performance. After observing the co-worker's rapid work rate and the reinforcement of it, Albert's rate of sorting books increased.

The frequency of a behavior can also be decreased through modeling. For example, if Margaret has been passing notes to friends in class and sees a friend who also passes notes accused by the teacher of cheating and given a failing grade, Margaret's behavior of note passing will immediately cease.

Factors Affecting Modeling

Learning by example is a powerful method of learning. Almost everyone has relied on examples set by others to effect changes in their own behavior. However, people do not indiscriminately imitate every behavior or response they observe. Additionally, people vary in regard to their likelihood of imitating the behavior of others. Bandura (1977) discusses three factors that affect whether modeling will occur. These three factors are the characteristics of the model, the characteristics of the observers, and the contingencies for the modeled behavior.

Characteristics of the Model

The status, prestige, and competence of the model all affect whether the model's behavior will be imitated. A model with high levels of status, prestige, and competence, for example, is more likely to be imitated than a model with lesser amounts of these characteristics. Examples are seen in everyday life. For instance, children who are the most popular among their peers are the most likely to serve as models to other children. Television and movie stars are more likely to serve as models to others than are people cast in insignificant roles. Teenagers are more likely to imitate the fashions and mannerisms of teen idols than of wallflowers.

When individuals are faced with choices or dilemmas, they often follow the leads of influential people. Successful movie stars advertising credit cards on television are good examples of the deliberate use of high-status models to influence the behavior of consumers. Viewers admire the economic and professional success of these people and conclude that their choice of a certain credit card must be a wise decision, which should be imitated.

Classroom teachers often capitalize on the use of high-status models by putting their best students in more observable positions within the classroom. Good students might be asked to tutor other students, to help the teacher with handing out materials, and to display their work on the classroom or school bulletin board. Often in group work, good students are called on first, in order to model answers that the teacher finds acceptable. Physical education teachers and athletic coaches frequently use their best athletes to demonstrate athletic skills.

Characteristics of the Observer

Any observer is a potential imitator of modeled behavior. Ambitious, highly motivated people will intentionally seek out competent people to imitate. Less motivated people are also likely to seek models. However, people might model behavior more in line with their own goals. An aspiring track star, for example, will model the behavior of top runners. A disinterested physical-education student who is unsure of how to perform a skill might simply model the behavior of the student closest to him.

Teachers and parents often change the characteristics of the modeling situation in order to help children with disabilities that limit their ability to learn by observation. Mental retardation; autism; and hearing, visual, language and communication, and physical impairments all might limit a child's ability to imitate the behavior of a model. A good example of how modeling is promoted in situations such as these follows.

Betty, a child with autism, would not imitate the behavior of opening the door when she heard the doorbell ring. Rather, she would continue to pursue her own activity, with no response to a ringing doorbell. At age 15, when Betty was still not answering the door, her mother decided that Betty needed to be specifically taught to answer the door. She taught her by very obvious demonstrations because Betty needed cues to even attend to the model. She was provided with specific instructions to observe, and verbal instructions accompanied her mother's behavior, such as, "The door bell rang. I need to answer the door." After repeated demonstrations, accompanied by instructions to attend, verbal descriptions of the behavior, and multiple practice sessions, Betty learned to open the door when she heard the doorbell ring.

Vicarious Consequences

As previously mentioned, a person is more likely to imitate a model if the model's behavior is reinforced. This process of an observer's behavior being strengthened after the model's behavior is reinforced is referred to as *vicarious reinforcement.* In an example of this type of reinforcement, Eddie sees that Sam is praised and given a lollipop for raising his hand in class to answer a question. After Eddie observes the consequence of Sam's behavior, he immediately raises his own hand to answer a question.

In addition to the strengthening effects vicarious reinforcement can have on a behavior, it can also result in a person's behavior being weakened following observation of a model's behavior being punished. For example, if Margie sees her sister getting burned after touching a hot stove, she is less likely to touch the stove.

The use of vicarious reinforcement is especially important when the modeled behavior is not a highly preferred behavior. People are more likely to engage in less preferred behavior if they witness a model receiving a reinforcer for performing the behavior. For example, Audrey was a poor math student and preferred not to do math problems. However, when she observed her peers receiving a great deal of praise and attention and getting good grades for coming to class with their math homework completed, Audrey began to do her math homework. If Audrey had not seen her peers rewarded for bringing in their completed math homework, she would be less likely to imitate their behavior.

Arranging consequences for the model is an effective way of promoting modeling. The teacher who seeks to encourage students to adopt the outstanding academic behavior of a certain student in the class, for example, is well advised to arrange reinforcing consequences for this student. Likewise, the coach who would like the best athlete to serve as a model for the rest of the team might publicize the reinforcers provided for this athlete's behavior. Since schoolwork and athletics can be difficult, time-consuming ventures, providing reinforcers to the models for their efforts will make observers more likely to imitate modeled behaviors.

Vicarious reinforcement can be of critical importance when modeling is used with students with certain handicapping conditions, such as learning disabilities, autism, and mental retardation. Such desirable behaviors as performing schoolwork, job tasks, and social skills might be difficult for students with learning and language impairments to learn. The difficulty of the tasks renders them less likely to be performed. Shaping can be laborious because of the length of time involved and may jeopardize job placement for older students in work settings. So, providing positive reinforcers for the behavior of competent models can promote a student's more rapid adoption of desirable target behaviors.

Modeling and the Functional Assessment

A functional assessment might reveal obvious antecedents of a behavior and direct sources of reinforcement that are maintaining the behavior. Misbehavior is often immediately functional for the student, and this functionality can be discerned by a functional assessment. However, a functional assessment might not reveal obvious antecedents, consequences, or functions of maladaptive behaviors; that is, there may be factors that are not readily apparent in a functional assessment. So, considering the role that modeling might play in the maintenance of a behavior is useful.

As already mentioned, vicarious reinforcement can establish and maintain behavior. It can also be channeled into vicarious functionality. The case of Janet provides a good example of how this happens.

Janet was a 15-year-old girl who was fashion conscious. She noted that a glamorous rock star had begun to wear her hair and clothing in a certain style and had received a great deal of publicity for her fashion statement: she got her picture on the cover of several magazines, had an article written about her in the fashion section of a daily newspaper, and even appeared on television. After observing the rock star's fashions and the resulting reinforcers, Janet began to dress in a style similar to that of the rock star.

Although Janet did not receive the same reinforcers the rock star did, her behavior is influenced by vicarious reinforcement: reinforcement of the rock star's behavior has served to establish and maintain the behavior in Janet. A functional assessment will not reveal that Janet received publicity on television and in magazines for her fashion behavior. She might not have received more than a compliment from a friend for her behavior. However, the function of her behavior cannot be adequately described independently of the function that the behavior served for the rock star.

Another example of vicarious functionality involves Mr. Andrews, who has several highly competent math students. These students receive praise and high grades for their performance in math. Several less competent math students, striving to improve their performance, note these reinforcers for excellent math work. So, the less competent students model the math performance of the better students. The functions of the behaviors of the less competent math students are, therefore, in part related through vicarious reinforcement to the functions achieved by the better students.

People might begin to engage in maladaptive behaviors as a result of observing that those behaviors serve desirable functions in their peers. Smoking, drinking, and taking illicit drugs, for example, are all behaviors that often are initiated as a result of an individual's observing another person obtain reinforcers by engaging in the behaviors.

In another example, Leonard was a 14-year-old boy with a learning disability who recently started talking back to his math teacher. A functional assessment revealed that when a new student in Leonard's class talked back to the teacher, the student was sent from the room, thereby escaping math class. Talking back served an obvious function for Leonard's classmate, and so Leonard adopted the new behavior.

A completed functional assessment should consider such influences. In the course of doing this assessment, it might also be productive to see whether desirable target behaviors are being modeled and reinforced in the individual's environment. For example, Gloria is a young girl with mental retardation and a severe learning disability. She rarely speaks. An analysis of her environment reveals that she is in a self-contained classroom with six other students, most of whom have severe language deficits; so, Gloria has no model from whom she can learn. There are also no other children whom Gloria can observe speaking and obtaining reinforcers for their efforts. Gloria's language behavior might be more frequent and appropriate if she had models who were using language in functional ways with functional results.

A targeted desirable behavior might be occurring in low frequency also because an individual observed another person receiving punishment for that behavior. As previously mentioned, vicarious punishment can serve to decrease the frequency of a behavior as a result of the observer seeing the behavior punished in a model. For example, Johnny was a 7-year-old who did not like to leave his house and spent most of his time playing alone at home. A functional assessment revealed that a child in Johnny's neighborhood was beaten badly by a neighborhood bully. Johnny's behavior of playing outside was reduced as a result of a punisher (the beating) that was delivered to a model (the neighbor child). Therefore, when a functional assessment is performed to determine why a desirable target behavior might be low in frequency, it is useful to consider how this behavior is reinforced or punished in models.

Information from a functional assessment can be used to determine whether modeling should be used as a strategy for behavior change. For example, a functional assessment might reveal that a maladaptive behavior serves a function that could be effectively served by a more acceptable behavior. When a functional assessment reveals the need to teach a new behavior, modeling might be the strategy of choice or a strategy to be used in combination with other behavior change procedures.

A functional assessment might suggest that the maladaptive behavior was originated or maintained by modeling or vicarious reinforcement. This information provides insight into how an individual learns and how susceptible the individual is to modeling influences. If the maladaptive behavior was learned or maintained through modeling, it might be effective to use modeling to influence the adoption of a more acceptable behavior.

Strategies Using Modeling

There are a variety of behavior change strategies that rely on the principles of modeling. Some strategies are obvious, direct applications of modeling principles. Other strategies have modeling principles embedded within them. Several of these strategies are reviewed, as they have practical value in work with children and youth of all ability levels.

Teacher/Instructor Behavior

"Do as I say and not as I do" is a dictum that does not work well in the classroom. This adage is especially unsuited to students with learning problems or other handicapping conditions. Students with behavioral, cognitive, or communication deficits might not learn effectively from verbal instructions. Instead, these students might attend to a variety of other cues to learn how to behave. Teacher behavior is such a cue. A student observes how a teacher or an instructor behaves and adopts that behavior.

The behavior of a teacher or an instructor is important for effecting behavior change in students. A teacher who wants to promote cheerful, cooperative behavior among her students, for example, does well to model such behavior when interacting with students as well as with other adults within observational range of the students.

In yet another example, parents are often surprised when overhearing their children use foul language. Inspection of their own vocabularies frequently targets the culprit, i.e., the parents themselves. If parents want to promote the use of tempered language in their children, the first step is to eliminate offensive language from their own vocabularies.

Another example where the behavior of an instructor is important is in cases involving individuals with language and communication disorders who speak very loudly or engage in loud echolalia (repeating what is heard). The instructor who speaks softly when speaking with these individuals can be an effective model of the use of a low voice for communication.

Thus, people who seek to change other people's behaviors are well advised to evaluate their own behavior to insure that desirable behavior is being modeled or that undesirable behavior is not being inadvertently modeled.

Demonstration

One of the most common forms of instruction by parents, teachers, or instructors of any skill or behavior is simple demonstration. Showing a student how to perform a skill can save hours of trial and error. If an individual is having a difficult time performing a skill or behavior, it might be that sufficient demonstration has not been provided. Judicious use of demonstration can also help students with handicapping conditions overcome the obstacle presented by the handicap. For example, a child who has a problem with auditory processing might learn much more effectively by being shown than by being verbally instructed.

Systems of Prompts

The use of modeling, or demonstration, is also found within other instructional strategies, such as those that involve systems of prompting. These instructional procedures systematically use prompts to encourage learning of a skill and then independence in using the skill. One such system initially provides a person with a great deal of assistance, such as hand-over-hand assistance, then fades to demonstration (modeling), then to verbal instruction, and finally to independence. Another system provides a lesser prompt, such as a nonspecific verbal cue, then a specific verbal cue, then demonstration (modeling), and then physical guidance.

Role Plays

Direct teaching of social or other skills can be an effective way of decreasing maladaptive behaviors. As an individual learns more acceptable and effective ways of achieving desired functions, these desirable behaviors replace maladaptive ones. Social skills training, as well as training of other skills, is frequently accomplished in packages of strategies. Often embedded in these training packages are strategies based on modeling.

A typical package for teaching social skills, for example, has the following components: instruction (the student is told what behavior to perform), modeling (the instructor or a peer models the desired behavior), and rehearsal (the student practices the behavior). A reinforcement component might include reinforcers either for participating in the social skills–training session or for displaying the desired behavior in actual situations, or for both. A critical element of this type of instructional package is the modeling component.

This type of package optimizes the effectiveness of the modeling procedure. The initial instruction not only conveys information about the desired behavior but also provides information on what behaviors of the model need attention. The desired behavior is then modeled, saving the learner a trial-and-error process. Finally, the adoption of the behavior might be reinforced, increasing the likelihood that the new behavior will occur in the future.

The use of modeling within social skills training can facilitate acquisition of new social skills. For example, a child might not have the behavior of waiting for a turn to speak, and social skills training can be useful to teach this skill. Modeling can also be used to encourage a more appropriate and well-timed use of a skill already in an individual's repertoire. The case of Jimmy, a 19-year-old boy with mild mental retardation, provides a good example. Jimmy works in the stock room of a department store pricing clothes and hanging them on racks. He says "hello" each time a co-worker passes by his work area. The problem with this behavior is that some co-workers pass by him up to 12 times an hour, and Jimmy greets them every time. A more acceptable social interaction would be for him to greet them only the first time they pass by. Social skills training can be used to teach Jimmy to do this and to continue working when co-workers make repeated trips by his work area.

Modeling with social skills–training packages can be used to teach a variety of specific social skills. Such skills include sharing; saying "please," "thank you," and "excuse me"; accepting criticism; asking for help; waiting for a turn to speak; and revealing problems.

Vicarious Reinforcement

As previously discussed, a person's behavior can be strengthened by observing someone else receiving reinforcers for the behavior. Although this principle operates inadvertently in many situations, a behavior modification plan can make deliberate use of this strategy for changing behavior. In many situations with children and youth, praise alone can function as a reinforcer in vicarious reinforcement situations: when a student observes a classmate receive praise for a certain behavior, that student is more likely to emit the behavior. Some cases, however, require the use of more tangible reinforcers. For example, a young man with profound mental retardation who is working at his first job might need to see a co-worker receive a tangible reinforcer (e.g., coffee) as well as receive it himself in order to strengthen acceptable work behaviors.

Instructors and teachers must also be alert for situations in which peers are receiving positive reinforcers for undesirable behaviors. These reinforcement situations may need to be eliminated if behavior change in observers is to occur. Arlene's case provides an example of this situation.

Arlene's classmate often brought her homework in late. The teacher typically accepted the homework and gave Arlene's classmate high marks on it. When Arlene observed her classmate's homework behavior reinforced, she began to turn in her work late. The first step in modifying Arlene's new homework behavior would be to insure that her classmate was no longer reinforced for turning in her homework late.

Pictorial Models

The deliberate use of pictorial models is an effective way of changing behavior. Pictures in books or by themselves that illustrate correct or desirable behaviors are used as behavior change strategies.

An example in which pictures are particularly effective in changing behavior is with individuals with mental retardation, learning disabilities, or developmental delays who have significant problems with completing assigned tasks and have trouble reading or are nonverbal. Posting pictures of an individual engaged in the desired tasks in the sequence in which these tasks should be completed can be a good way to teach desirable on-task behavior to such individuals. The use of still photograph models can also be an effective component of a behavior modification plan to promote on-task behavior.

The use of pictures within books can be an effective means of teaching new skills. For example, parents use books that depict young children using the toilet when they are toilet training their children. In another example, Alvord and O'Leary (1985) examined the effects of symbolic models on the sharing behavior of nursery school children. An illustrated story about sharing was read to the children, and they were shown the pictures. Children who were exposed to the books about sharing engaged in more sharing than a control group that consisted of children who were exposed to stories unrelated to sharing. Additionally, these children had more knowledge about sharing than did the control group.

Positive Reinforcement for Modeling

The use of positive reinforcement for the learner's adoption of modeled behavior is a useful strategy that promotes behavior change. If a teacher wants the behavior of a conscientious student modeled, it might be necessary to provide reinforcers—in the form of attention, grades, or other events—for the adoption of those desired behaviors. Archie's teacher, for example, encouraged him to observe and adopt the study habits of his peer. Once Archie began to work quietly, as his peer did, the teacher provided him with praise and special privileges as reinforcers to strengthen this behavior.

Provision of Peer Models

The use of peer models has been demonstrated as an effective means of promoting positive behavior change in children and youth. At times, the use of peer models might be structured and deliberate, as in the case of social skills training.

The use of peer models is also important in natural settings. Students who are having problems with their behaviors need strong role models to observe. A disadvantage of segregating students by their disabilities is that the opportunity for modeling is severely restricted. For example, a young child with a language deficit who is placed in a class with eight other children who also have language deficits will not have the benefit of having well-spoken peers as models. A child with autism who is placed in a class with five other children with autism will be deprived of the opportunity to observe children with good social skills and to adopt those behaviors. Therapy or social skills groups that include only children with handicaps fail to provide what these children need most—competent peers to demonstrate the desirable skills.

Some situations dictate the purposeful development of some children as models. A teacher or an instructor might observe, for instance, that many of the children in the class lack such social amenities as manners. One method of encouraging manners in all class members is to develop these skills in one or two popular students and promote them as models for the rest of the class.

Egel and Koegel (1981) reported on the use of normal peer models to improve the task performance of four schoolchildren with autism who were having problems responding to discrimination tasks, such as choosing items of certain colors or shapes. All three children showed dramatic improvement in task performance after observing normal peer models.

The structuring of antecedent events, setting events, and contingencies are all effective means of changing behavior. However, the presence of good models of appropriate behavior is an important, if not overriding, influence on a desirable behavior change.

Application

Stokes and Kennedy (1980) used peer modeling to eliminate disruptive, and promote cooperative, behavior in eight children during visits to the dentist. The children exhibited such behaviors as head moving, crying, and complaining. In an effort to eliminate these disruptive behaviors, the children were urged to come early to their appointments to observe other children undergoing dental treatment. The children themselves were observed by the other children also. Small trinkets and the opportunity to raise and lower the dental chair were used as reinforcers for low levels of uncooperative behavior, and feedback was given if reinforcers were not earned. The researchers reported that the use of peer models and reinforcement was effective in reducing the frequency of the children's uncooperative behavior at the dentist.

Summary

Much of human behavior is learned by modeling. An individual observes another person perform a behavior, and the observer then adopts the behavior. Modeling is performed by live demonstrations, by video or audiotaped demonstrations, or by other forms of symbolic modeling, such as pictures in books.

Modeling can play a role in an individual's learning a new behavior, learning when to use a previously acquired behavior, or ceasing to perform a behavior. Bandura (1977) has described four components of the modeling process: attention, retention, motor reproduction, and motivation. Teachers can facilitate modeling as a behavior change strategy by maximizing each of these four components.

A number of factors influence whether or not modeling takes place, such as the status of the model and the characteristics of the observer. Additionally, reinforcement contingencies that are in effect for either the model or the learner can affect the modeling process.

Modeling can play a significant role in behavior change. A variety of strategies incorporate modeling principles, including social skills–training packages, systematic prompting instructional strategies, and use of symbolic models.

Study Questions

1. Define *modeling*.
2. Describe Bandura's four components of the modeling process.
3. Give one example of how each component of the modeling process can be maximized.
4. Describe four behavior change strategies that incorporate modeling principles. For each strategy, give an example of a behavior that can be changed by that strategy.
5. Describe three types of models.
6. Describe three effects that modeling can have on behavior.

Exercises

1. In Mrs. Elliot's class of first graders, there is a great deal of talking out of turn. How might Mrs. Elliot use modeling to bring social order to the class and encourage children to work quietly and wait for their turn to speak?

2. Andy is a 5-year-old boy with mental retardation who has trouble dressing himself. How might modeling be used to teach Andy how to dress himself?

3. Jane is a 16-year-old girl with autism who has a part-time job in an office. She works very slowly, yelling out the names of foods while she works. How might modeling be used to increase her productivity and lower her voice volume?

4. Donnie is a 10-year-old boy with a learning disability who has poor social skills. He attempts to make friends, but the majority of his attempts are actually annoying to the other boys. He goes up to the boys, grabs their belongings, calls them names, laughs, and runs away. How might modeling be used to teach Donnie more acceptable ways of establishing interactions with other boys?

Self-Application

1. Describe a behavior that you learned from modeling. From whom did you learn this behavior? What reinforcers were delivered to the model as a result of this behavior? What reinforcers have been delivered to you contingent on this behavior?

2. Describe a behavior that you learned to use more selectively as a result of modeling.

3. Describe a behavior that you have not engaged in as a result of observing or learning of the behavior punished in someone else. What was the punishment?

4. Who or what type of model would you look for to learn each of the following behaviors: diving, computer operations, fashionable dressing, public speaking?

SELF-MANAGEMENT PROJECT

1. If your targeted behavior is an undesirable behavior, consider how it was acquired or influenced by modeling. Who or what kinds of people served as models of this behavior for you? Did vicarious reinforcement operate? If so, how?
2. If your targeted behavior is a desirable behavior, who or what kinds of people can serve as models of this behavior for you?
3. Consider and plan how you might use the principles of modeling in your self-management project.

References

Agran, M., Salzberg, C. L., & Stowitschek, J. J. (1987). An analysis of the effects of a social skills training program using self-instructions on the acquisition and generalization of two social behaviors in a work setting. *The Journal of the Association for Persons with Severe Handicaps, 12,* 131–139.

Alvord, M. K., & O'Leary, K. D. (1985). Teaching children to share through stories. *Psychology in the Schools, 22,* 323–330.

Bandura, A. (1977). *Social Learning Theory.* New Jersey: Prentice-Hall, Inc.

Charlop, M. H., & Milstein, J. P. (1989). Teaching autistic children conversational speech using video modeling. *The Journal of Applied Behavior Analysis, 22,* 275–285.

Connis, R. T. (1979). The effects of sequential pictorial cues, self-recording, and praise on the job task sequencing of retarded adults. *The Journal of Applied Behavior Analysis, 12,* 355–361.

Egel, A. L., Richman, G. S., & Koegel, R. L. (1981). Normal peer models and autistic children's learning. *The Journal of Applied Behavior Analysis, 14,* 3–12.

Johnson, K. M., Gutkin, T. B., & Plake, B. S. (1991). Use of modeling to enhance children's interrogative strategies. *Journal of School Psychology, 29,* 81–88.

Stokes, T. F., & Kennedy, S. H. (1980). Reducing child uncooperative behavior during dental treatment through modeling and reinforcement. *The Journal of Applied Behavior Analysis, 13,* 41–50.

9 Punishment

Mindy was a 16-year-old girl with autism. She lived at a residential school for children with developmental disabilities. Mindy had no verbal language skills and several problem behaviors, including screaming, head banging, and striking out at other people. Her teachers attempted to manage her behavior with a combination of positive reinforcement and punishment. She was put on a DRO 5-minute schedule, which called for teacher praise if she did not scream, hit herself or hit others. If she did engage in these behaviors, she was punished. The following description of an incident provides a detailed accounting of how punishment was administered.

Mindy was up late at night screaming. In response to her behavior, the staff at the school administered the first punisher: they said to her, "Stop that!" When Mindy continued to scream and also began to bang her head, the staff administered the second punisher: they put ammonia capsules under her nose. When Mindy still continued to scream and hit herself, the staff administered the third punisher, an electric shock. Because at this point Mindy was wildly flailing, she was also placed in mechanical restraints in a room by herself for the remainder of the night.

When Mindy first came to school, she was very active and very vocal. Although she had some screaming and hitting behaviors, the episodes of these were often the result of unexpected changes in her routines or repeated demands on her. She made frequent attempts to interact in a positive manner with her teachers. After the punishment procedure was instituted, Mindy became withdrawn. Her screaming, self-injury, and aggression decreased in frequency. Her attempts at social interactions with staff also decreased.

This chapter explores the process of punishment, its effects on behavior, and the ramifications of its use with children and youth.

Punishment Defined

Punishment is a process in which behavior is weakened by its consequences. It can involve the presentation of an aversive stimulus contingent on a specific behavior. It can also involve the removal of a positive reinforcer contingent on a specific behavior. In both circumstances, the likelihood of the behavior occurring again is reduced by its punishing consequences.

The first type of punishment is illustrated when Janie takes a hot pot off the stove without a pot holder and burns her hand. Her behavior of removing a pot bare-handed is followed by an aversive consequence (a burning sensation). The consequence of being burned reduces the likelihood that Janie will remove a pot again with her bare hands.

The second type of punishment is illustrated when Allen drives his car at 45 miles per hour in a 25 mile-per-hour zone and is stopped by a police officer and fined $80. The removal of a positive reinforcer (money) follows his behavior of speeding. This consequence makes Allen less likely to speed in the future.

Punishment does not occur simply because an aversive stimulus is presented after a target behavior. Rather, it is a process in which a behavior is weakened as a result of a consequence. Punishment is said to occur only if the probability that the behavior will occur in the future is reduced as the result of the contingent application of an aversive stimulus or the contingent removal of a positive reinforcer.

A teacher, parent, or trainer, for instance, can attempt to arrange a punishing situation, but whether the situation is termed punishing depends entirely on the effects of the consequences on the frequency of the target behavior. If the consequences decrease the likelihood that the behavior it followed will occur again, punishment has occurred.

The situation of Doug, who had problems with talking out of turn, provides an interesting example. Doug's teacher decided to punish Doug's behavior by reprimanding him each time he talked out of turn and explaining to him why he should not do this. However, the frequency of Doug's behavior increased rather than decreased. Apparently, the teacher's reprimands and explanations served as positive reinforcers rather than as punishers for Doug's behavior. Although the teacher intended the consequences to be punishing, they were actually reinforcing.

Types of Punishers

Punishers are stimuli or events that reduce the likelihood of a behavior occurring again. These events are normally considered to be undesirable, such as aversive stimuli or unpleasant activities. These events can involve the presentation of negative reinforcers or the removal of positive reinforcers. A variety of aversive stimuli and aversive activities have been used as punishers, in addition to situations which involve removal of positive reinforcers.

Aversive Stimuli

Aversive stimuli to punish human behavior have been widely explored. Such stimuli have included those involving taste, smell, sound, and touch. Aversive taste stimuli have included the squirting of liquids with unpleasant tastes into the person's mouth, such as lemon juice, tabasco sauce, vinegar, shaving cream, and pepper sauce. Such aversive tastes have been used with babies with eating disorders and with young children, youth, and adults with developmental disabilities in attempts to manage their behavior problems.

The use of an aversive taste stimulus to punish behavior was reported by Altmeyer, Williams, and Sams (1985). They treated the biting behavior of a 16-year-old girl with severe mental retardation and blindness, who had been institutionalized since 4 years of age. Tabasco sauce was squirted into her mouth up to 5 times a day contingent on her biting. Time-out followed the use of the tabasco sauce. If she continued to bite, she was placed in padded leather ankle and wrist restraints. The researchers reported a significant reduction in the girl's biting and concluded that tabasco sauce is effective in the treatment of biting.

Aversive smells and sounds have been used in punishment procedures with young children, youth, and adults in attempts to manage their undesirable behaviors. Probably the most common aversive smell used is ammonia. Crushed ammonia capsules are placed under a person's nose following an undesirable behavior. Aversive sounds used have included white noise at high decibel levels and horn blasts.

In addition, aversive tactile stimuli have been used in punishment procedures with people of all ages, particularly children and youth with mental retardation, autism, and emotional disturbances. These stimuli have included electric shock, slaps, tickling, hair tugs, cold baths, water squirted at one's face, and ice pressed against one's skin.

Rojahn, McGonigle, Curcio, and Dixon (1987) reported on the use of aromatic ammonia and water mist to suppress pica in a 16-year-old girl with mild cerebral palsy and autism. If the girl tried to eat a nonfood item during the aromatic ammonia condition, a crushed capsule containing ammonia was placed directly under her nose and held there for 3 seconds; during the water-mist condition, water mist was sprayed at her face. The researchers concluded that water mist was more effective than ammonia capsules in controlling pica, and was an effective means of control. The girl began to show aggressive behavior, which may have been related to spraying water mist in her face.

In another study, Tate and Baroff (1966) treated a 9-year-old blind boy diagnosed with psychosis who had chronic self-injury. The child was a resident of a psychiatric facility and had been transferred to a state institution for the mentally retarded for treatment on a research basis. The boy received the punisher of withdrawal of human contact contingent on self-injury in one phase of the study and electric shock delivered to his lower right leg during the second phase. The researchers concluded that both punishment procedures effectively reduced the boy's self-injury.

Absence of sensory stimuli has also been tried in punishment procedures. *Visual screening* is an example. This procedure involves placing a screen over an individual's eyes to block vision temporarily, as a consequence for some target behavior. Sensory deprivation has also been used. For example, a child is placed in a small booth with no stimuli except white noise.

Activities that a person finds aversive have also been used in punishment procedures. Forced exercise and forced body movements, for example, have been used in behavior management. Luce, Delquadri, and Hall (1980) reported on the use of forced exercise with two children in a class for children with severe emotional disturbances. The children were required to engage in exercise following either aggressive behavior or aggressive remarks. The exercise consisted of standing up and then sitting on the floor 10 times. A reduction in the children's problem behaviors occurred, and the researchers concluded that contingent exercise, with medical consultation, might be an acceptable and effective procedure for the management of deviant behavior.

Overcorrection has been studied and used extensively. It requires an individual either to make a certain set of movements following a target behavior or to perform certain restorative activities. Foxx and Martin (1975) reported on the use of overcorrection to manage the scavenging behavior (pica and ingestion of feces) of a woman with profound mental retardation, who had been institutionalized for 20 years. The overcorrection procedure for eating feces included her brushing her teeth and gums for 10 minutes, washing her hands and fingernails for 10 minutes, mopping the area in which she was seen eating the feces, and flushing all the toilets on the ward (if the feces she ate had come from a toilet). This procedure, which lasted about 30 minutes, was required each time the woman was found eating feces. The researchers reported that it was effective in eliminating her scavenging behavior.

Time-out has also been widely studied and used as a punishment procedure. It refers to time out from positive reinforcement. A time-out procedure involves removing an individual from the opportunity to earn reinforcers for a designated length of time following the target behavior.

Time-out has been accomplished in a variety of ways. For example, a child can be removed from the room in which reinforcers are available or be allowed to remain in the room but be required to face a corner or sit behind a screen while reinforcers remain available to others. A child may also be allowed to remain in the room but be required to observe other people given the opportunity to earn reinforcers.

Response cost is a punishment procedure that involves taking reinforcers contingent on performance of target behavior. A fine for speeding is an example of response cost. Response cost has been used to reduce the frequency of misbehavior in children and adults with disabilities. Luiselli (1984), for example, reported on the successful treatment of aggression and property destruction in two boys with hearing and visual impairments by methods that included a response cost procedure.

Effects of Punishment

It is necessary to do a close examination of the effects and side effects of punishment because its use in behavior management has the potential for causing greater harm than good. The primary effect of punishment, by definition, is suppression of the target behavior. This suppression of responding is often immediate. For example, a child talks out of turn in the classroom, the teacher raps the child's knuckles with a ruler, and the child immediately stops talking. A young man with autism bangs his head, he is given an electric shock, and he stops his head banging.

Although the primary effect of punishment is suppression of the target behavior, this suppression is only temporary. In fact, punishment may be seen as postponing a behavior, not necessarily eliminating it. For example, the child whose knuckles are rapped stops talking out of turn for the moment but shortly resumes the behavior. The young man with autism ceases his head banging for the moment but may soon begin again.

The degree of suppressive effects depends on several variables. The strength and the duration of the aversive stimulus are two of these variables. A hot stove, for example, is an intense, powerful aversive stimulus and may suppress behavior permanently. A child will likely touch a hot stove only once. Most punishers that are used in classrooms and homes are considerably milder than a hot stove, so their suppressive effects are often temporary. Mild and moderate punishers may have little effect, with suppressed behaviors eventually resuming.

The history of the punishment procedure is a third variable that determines the degree of suppressive effects. In the initial phases of the procedure, suppression is greatest. As the procedure continues, the intensity of the stimulus determines the degree of suppression. An example of this effect involves Patricia, who was often out of her seat in her first-grade classroom. When her teacher first reprimanded her for her behavior, Patricia returned to her seat and remained there for most of the morning. When Patricia ventured out again and was again reprimanded, her return to her seat was more temporary. By the end of the first week of school, Patricia was out of her seat almost as much as she was prior to the beginning of her teacher's use of reprimands.

Unless the stimuli are extremely strong, the effects of punishment are typically temporary; punishment must be repeated to remain effective. Some research suggests that when punishment is discontinued, the frequency of a behavior increases beyond prepunishment levels. So, in Patricia's case, if her teacher withholds reprimands, Patricia may not only resume her former rate of out-of-seat behavior but even exceed it.

The effects of punishment are strongly tied to the conditions under which the punishment occurs. If a target behavior is punished under one set of conditions, the behavior will be suppressed under that set of conditions but may actually increase in frequency under other conditions. The suppressive effects of punishment, then, do not generalize to other conditions.

Billy, for example, has autism and severe self-injurious behavior. Electric shock is used in the classroom as a punishing consequence following his self-injury. When Billy sees the shock rod, his rate of self-injury is low. If the shock rod is not in sight, Billy's self-injury occurs at rates higher than baseline. In another example, Margaret's use of foul language has been punished by her mother. When she is at home with her mother, she avoids the use of offensive language. When she is out of her home, she freely resumes her use of foul language.

Side Effects of Punishment

Basic research on punishment reveals limitations on its ability to suppress behavior. As previously mentioned, the effects of punishment are often temporary, limited to the conditions under which it is applied; and increases in target behavior can result under nonpunished conditions. Additionally, unless the punishing stimulus is of high intensity, punishment must be used repeatedly to maintain behavior suppression. There are also side effects of punishment, which further limit its usefulness.

Escape and Avoidance

Punishment can result in attempts by the individual to escape from or avoid the situation. These efforts can present dilemmas in applied situations. If an individual can successfully escape from a punishing situation, the punishment procedure would obviously not be effective. This possibility, then, places limits on the effectiveness of the procedure. In order to avoid this outcome, the punishing conditions must be escape-proof.

A more serious concern involves the avoidance responses that can be generated to aspects of the punishing conditions. Elmer, a 5-year-old boy who has developed an avoidance response to school, is a case in point. Elmer's teacher loudly reprimands Elmer for his out-of-seat behavior. As a result of her yelling, Elmer cries and complains of a stomachache each morning when it is time to go to school. He has learned to avoid the punishing situation.

Individuals with developmental disabilities have to be taught a great deal by their teachers, instructors, and parents. In order to learn, they must be available for learning. Behavior management procedures that result in avoidance or escape responses interfere with the critical learning of adaptive behaviors. If an individual attempts to escape from or avoid an instructor, the likelihood of learning taking place is seriously diminished.

Emotional Effects

Punishment can result in emotional responses from the person being punished. Crying, screaming, and whining often occur following the application of aversive stimuli. These behaviors suggest the presence of emotional effects, such as fear, anger, agitation, hatred, and general distress.

In certain settings, emotional responses to punishers create problems greater than the target behavior. The case of Alex illustrates this effect. A 15-year-old boy with autism, Alex had such maladaptive behaviors as talking loudly to himself, rapidly flicking his fingers in front of his face, and occasionally slapping his face. While walking through a department store with his teacher, Alex began to slap his face. His teacher administered a punishment procedure, i.e., sprayed water mist in Alex's face. Alex then began to scream, cry, and run from the teacher. His emotional responses and escape response created larger problems in the store than his face-slapping behavior created.

The emotional side effects of punishment can be ignored or managed within the privacy of a home or the seclusion of an institutional setting. In the past, many people with developmental disabilities were confined to these settings. However, as these people now have more opportunities to attend school and to work in the community alongside nonhandicapped peers, the use of procedures that result in an emotional response, such as crying, or an escape response, such as running, becomes problematic.

Aggression

Punishment can result in aggressive behavior as an immediate response to the aversive stimuli. Behaviors such as striking back at a punisher, striking out at nearby property, or even self-striking can be evoked by punishment. For example, staff and other people have been hit, been kicked, had their hair pulled, and been bitten by individuals after the application of aversive stimuli. In some cases, the aggression is aimed at bystanders and staff not directly involved in the application of the aversive stimuli. Several examples of how punishment effects aggressive behavior follow.

Ellie was a young woman with profound mental retardation who occasionally spit at others. Ellie's spitting behavior was punished with the application of ammonia capsules under her nose following incidents of her spitting. The use of ammonia capsules, however, resulted in Ellie's striking out at her instructor as he attempted to place the ammonia capsule under her nose.

Gerald was a 14-year-old boy who was labelled emotionally impaired by his school psychologist. When Gerald cursed at or threatened his teacher, he was placed in a time-out room. By the end of the first week of school, Gerald had greatly damaged the time-out room: he had punched holes in its walls and kicked holes in its door. Gerald's cursing and verbal threats had thus escalated to property destruction when he was placed in time-out.

John was a 9-year-old boy with autism who had problems with self-injury and aggression. The consequences of his hitting other people were a reprimand and a slap by his instructor. When John was slapped, he responded by screaming and then by banging his head. Punishment procedures, therefore, provoked incidents of self-injury.

Bert, a young child with a developmental disability, often laughed without apparent reason. When he laughed, he was given an electric shock. After one such incident, Bert ran over to a staff member who was passing by and bit her, leaving a permanent scar.

Modeling

Imitation of aggression is another possible side effect of punishment. Individuals who themselves are punished may turn to punishment as a means of controlling others. For example, people who receive slaps, pinches, hair tugs, and other forceful stimuli following certain behaviors are likely to use these same stimuli on other people whose behaviors they wish to eliminate. To illustrate, Marjorie, a 6-year-old girl who is often spanked by her mother for misbehavior, in turn often slaps her 3-year-old sister during the course of their interactions.

Tissue Damage

Aversive stimuli that cause discomfort can have the side effect of actually causing tissue damage. Ammonia capsules can, for example, injure a person's nasal passages or skin (if the ammonia makes contact with the skin). Loud noises present a risk to an individual's hearing. Aversive tastes, such as pepper sauce, can cause damage to one's tongue or lips. Electric shock can leave burns on the skin, and cases of children having multiple burn marks on their bodies from the shocks have been reported.

Suppression of Other Behaviors

Punishment does not always have specific, precise effects. It is possible that the punishment procedure will suppress not only a target behavior but also other behaviors. In some cases, these other behaviors may be desirable and adaptive ones.

The behavior of Jill, a 10-year-old girl with a learning disability, illustrates these effects. A very shy, withdrawn child, Jill rarely participated in class. When she finally did raise her hand to answer a question, the answer she gave was incorrect. The teacher startled Jill by reprimanding her for her response. This punishing behavior by the teacher not only suppressed Jill's incorrect answering but also eliminated Jill's volunteering any answer.

In another example, Martin was a young man with mental retardation who started working part-time pricing items in the stock room of a local department store. During his second day on the job, he made an error in pricing, and his job coach sharply criticized him. As a result of the criticism Martin made no more errors; he also did no more pricing. He never even returned to work. Punishment, therefore, not only suppressed Martin's inaccurate pricing, but also all of Martin's pricing behavior.

Often with children and with individuals with developmental disabilities or learning problems, desirable, adaptive behaviors may occur with low frequency. Suppressing such adaptive behaviors can be an unfortunate side effect of the punishment process.

Negative Reinforcement

As mentioned previously, punishment has the immediate effect of suppressing a behavior. This cessation negatively reinforces the punishing behavior of the punisher, making it more likely that the punisher will use punishment again in the future to stop the behavior. The strengthening of the punisher's behavior may cause an individual to continue to use punishment to suppress the behavior, despite the fact that, over time, the procedure may be ineffective. The following case illustrates this situation.

Johnny was an 8-year-old boy with mental retardation who occasionally banged his head. His parent decided to use electric shock to control the head banging. When Johnny began head banging, the parent administered a shock, and Johnny immediately stopped head banging. This immediate suppressive effect reinforced the parent's behavior of applying shock. Since the shock terminated the head banging, the parent used shock again to suppress Johnny's head banging: each time Johnny banged his head, his parent administered a shock, and Johnny stopped his behavior. The problem with this process was that, over time, Johnny continued to bang his head. The parent also continued to use shock because its immediate suppressive effects reinforced the use of shock.

Functional Assessment and Punishment

There are two ways to consider the functional assessment and punishment. These ways will be addressed in the following cases.

Case 1: Reducing the Frequency of a Target Behavior

If an individual has a behavior that is maladaptive, a functional assessment must be done to determine the function of the behavior. The functional assessment will then dictate which intervention strategies will be effective. Depending on the functions of the target behavior, it may be desirable to provide other means of achieving those functions by teaching more acceptable behavior, providing the reinforcers noncontingently, and introducing extinction of the misbehavior. It also might be necessary to enrich the environment, change the controlling stimuli, change the difficulty of the task, and otherwise manipulate antecedent events or setting events.

The functional assessment does suggest many interventions that can increase the likelihood of more acceptable behaviors occurring. It also suggests how to implement extinction effectively. One strategy that is not suggested by the information provided by a functional assessment is punishment. A functional assessment suggests reasons for maladaptive behaviors and even remedies, but the punishment process does not logically follow as a strategy from any information provided.

Many clinicians are capable of formulating behavior intervention plans from the information provided by an examination of the environment and by a functional assessment. When the all of the functions are addressed in some manner by the intervention plan, successful behavior change can be expected. As for punishment's role in this plan, it can be seen as an uninvited, troublesome dinner guest at an otherwise carefully planned and orchestrated dinner party.

Case 2: Increasing the Frequency of a Desirable Behavior

Knowledge of the punishment process is useful in determining why more acceptable behaviors are not occurring. A functional assessment may reveal that certain desired target behaviors are inadvertently being punished. The following case provides a good example of the inadvertent operation of punishment.

Carly was a 9-year-old girl who had a condition that has been called school phobia: she refused to go to school. Each morning upon awaking, she would cry, complain of a stomachache, and try other means of avoiding going to school. Unknown to her parents, Carly was being threatened and slapped at school by a larger child who would take her lunch money from her. Carly's desired behavior—school attendance—was being punished by this bully. By staying home from school, she was seeking to avoid this bully. This avoidance behavior, as discussed earlier, is a byproduct of punishment.

In another example, Johnny was a young man with a severe learning disability who had started a part-time job. After several days at work, he became reluctant to go. A functional assessment revealed that Johnny's co-workers had been teasing him and telling him that he was stupid. His reluctance to go to work was an avoidance response to a punishment procedure: by not going to work, he avoided being teased and called names.

To help Carly achieve good school attendance, an understanding that her attendance was being punished was necessary. Strategies aimed at teaching her to deal with the schoolyard bully or at preventing this child from terrorizing her could help her achieve cooperative school attendance. Johnny's intervention plan needed to either eliminate the teasing from his work environment or provide him with ways of dealing with the punishing situation.

It is possible, then, that the reluctance of an individual to engage in a certain desirable behavior is an avoidance response to a punisher. Attending school, participating in sports, and participating in class are examples of desirable behaviors that may be low in frequency due to past punishment histories. Strengthening these behaviors may involve pinpointing the operation of a punishment procedure and then eliminating it.

Strategies for strengthening desired behavior might involve teaching a child adaptive avoidance responses to those situations in which the punishment operation cannot be eliminated. Margaret, for example, was reluctant to go outside during rainstorms. Being pelted with water was a punisher that reduced the likelihood of going to playmates' houses during rainstorms. Teaching Margaret to use an umbrella is an example of teaching her an adaptive way of avoiding the punishing effects of the rainstorm.

Use of Punishment in Behavior Change

Mild stimuli that serve as punishers—reprimands, sharp glances, redoing homework—are often natural and appropriate consequences in classroom and home settings. The use of more aversive stimuli is more controversial. Several advocacy groups for people with disabilities have issued formal statements opposing the use of stimuli that are painful or harmful or that cause discomfort. In addition, the use of punishment with children and youth who have special needs has a number of disadvantages, leading some parents, professionals, and interested groups to oppose its use. Some of these disadvantages are technical while others are philosophical.

Side Effects

Several side effects of punishment can cause a worsening of a problem and an escalation of problem behaviors upon application of an aversive stimulus. As previously discussed, when confronted with aversive stimuli, individuals can emit strong emotional responses, aggressive behavior, and dramatic escape attempts. Any of these outcomes can make a difficult situation untenable in community settings. In job settings, an escalation of undesirable behaviors can cost an individual a job; in school settings, dismissal from school. In any setting, escalation of such behaviors can result in injury to the individual or to other people. The larger the individual, the more difficult the side effects can be to manage. Thus, the possibility of these side effects can be considered unacceptable risks of the punishment procedure.

Natta, Holmbeck, Kupst, and Pines (1990) studied sequences of child-staff interactions on a psychiatric inpatient unit. They found that if staff behaved in punishing ways toward the children, the children were more likely to have subsequent increases in negative, or undesirable, behaviors and significant decreases in positive, or desirable, behaviors. This study, therefore, demonstrates the occurrence of two side effects of punishment, i.e., an increase in negative behaviors and a suppression of desirable behaviors.

More long-range side effects, such as imitation of aggressive behaviors, can be unacceptable also, especially when dealing with an individual who has aggression in the repertoire or may be prone to becoming aggressive. Additionally, the acquisition of aggression to an already challenging repertoire of behaviors can be an unacceptable risk.

Long-range avoidance responses or long-term suppressive effects of non-targeted behaviors can be unacceptable, too. Problems presented by avoidance responses can be mild in some cases but devastating in cases dealing with such disabilities as autism. An individual with autism, who already has difficulty relating to other people, may become so withdrawn as a result of punishment procedures that engagement in new learning situations can be extremely difficult. For individuals who have a small repertoire of adaptive responses, using a procedure that can restrict this repertoire even further is unacceptable.

Acceptability

In the past, children and youth with disabilities were often educated in segregated school situations and not seen out in the community. With school integration of children with handicaps, these children now are frequently seen outside the classroom or home. As a child with disabilities grows older, the child may obtain jobs working alongside nonhandicapped people with the support of teachers or job coaches. With increasing integration comes the issue of acceptability of the intervention.

Interventions that were readily accepted in segregated institutional settings are often not acceptable to neighbors, to co-workers, or to advocates for people with developmental disabilities who witness them in the community. For example, the use of aversive stimuli, such as shock, water mist to the face, ammonia capsules under the nose, slaps, and other noxious stimuli can be offensive to onlookers. Using procedures with low acceptability can create situations in which an individual with a handicap and attendant staff are not welcome.

The case of George, a young man with autism, provides a good example of such a situation. In a grocery store with his classroom teacher, George starts to jump, flap his arms, and scream. His teacher then applies electric shock to George's leg. In response to the shock, George begins to scream, run, and hit his head. The use of electric shock by the teacher and its effects on George are offensive to the store's customers, and George's instructor is asked not to return to the store.

Although this situation is fictitious, it is not beyond the realm of possibility. Even if over time electric shock were to reduce the frequency of George's problem behavior, its offensiveness to staff and onlookers might outweigh its possible benefits.

In a second scenario, George is in the grocery store and displays the problem behaviors just mentioned. His instructor directs him to keep his hands on the cart and walk quietly through the store. If this does not work, he escorts George out of the store. In either case, there is no risk of offending onlookers with the use of an unacceptable intervention.

Legal Issues

The use of certain aversive or restrictive procedures is illegal in some states and jurisdictions; that is, some states allow corporal punishment and others forbid it. Likewise, the use of aversive or noxious stimuli in behavior modification plans is banned in some jurisdictions and states and allowed in others. So, clinicians, educators, and professionals must consider not only the effectiveness of a procedure, but also its legality in the jurisdiction where it is to be used.

Philosophical Issues

The use of aversive or noxious stimuli to control behavior has been a point of philosophical debate. Choosing an intervention based on its purported effectiveness cannot be done in isolation of a value system. Some people believe that the ends justify the means and have even argued for the right of an individual to receive any treatment deemed appropriate by the treating clinician. Other people have made a philosophical commitment to preserving the dignity of the individual, declaring the use of painful and noxious stimuli inhumane and undignified. Before making a choice of an intervention procedure, one must examine one's values as to how an individual should be treated as well as the effectiveness of the intervention.

Effectiveness

The justification for choosing punishment in a behavior modification plan is often based on the argument that research supports the effectiveness of punishment. Within this context, a clinician may then try a positive reinforcement procedure, fail with it, and fall back on punishment. Many opponents of the use of punishment procedures have argued that the research on punishment is fraught with methodological difficulties and that its effectiveness is overrated. Similarly, there are clinicians who have been successful in managing even severe destructive behaviors without the use of punishment.

A concern exists that clinicians who are not adept at using positive procedures are quick to go to punishment procedures, which are, themselves, of questionable effectiveness. Given the temporary nature of the suppressive effects of punishment, long-term use may be necessary. So, a short-term try at positive reinforcement is followed by a long-term course of punishment. Questions of the effectiveness of punishment procedures converge with questions about the competent application of nonaversive procedures. The result is concern about the use of punishment, its effectiveness, and its necessity.

Effective Alternatives

Much of the research literature focuses on single strategies, used without benefit of other strategies and chosen without a functional assessment. This research has had less than optimal results, causing researchers and clinicians to feel the need to resort to punishment.

Competent use of a functional assessment, followed by good choices of interventions and faithful program implementation, has been effective in eliminating or significantly decreasing even the most challenging behaviors, such as self-injury, property destruction, and aggression. Behavior modification, when done well, creates positive behavior change and allows individuals with even severe autism to be successful at home, school, and work. This availability of effective alternatives allows for behavior change without the use of noxious stimuli and without the undesirable side effects of punishment.

Summary

Punishment is the process of weakening behavior by its consequences. Punishment can involve either presentation of an aversive stimulus following a target behavior or removal of a positive reinforcer following a target behavior.

Punishers can be aversive stimuli, such as noxious tastes or smells, electric shock, and slaps. They can be forced activity, such as forced exercise or forced movement. They can also be removal of stimuli, such as visual screening. Time-out can be a punisher. Overcorrection, which can involve forced movement or forced activity, can also function as a punisher.

The immediate effect of punishment is the suppression of behavior. This suppression is typically temporary, except in the use of very intense stimuli as punishers. Behaviors that have been suppressed with mild or moderate stimuli typically reemerge, and the use of punishment may then need to be ongoing and long term.

The use of punishment can be problematic. Mild punishment, such as traffic fines for speeding, poor grades for poor schoolwork, and reprimands for disobedience is often a fact of life in today's society. The use of stronger stimuli to punish behavior has been called into question, especially the use of punishment for older individuals with developmental disabilities and similar disorders.

Many parents, professionals, advocates for people with developmental disabilities, and professional organizations have made formal statements against the use of painful or noxious stimuli in behavior change procedures. Other problems with the use of punishment in these procedures include undesirable side effects, moral qualms, and questions about its effectiveness. The competent application of more positive strategies, when based on a functional assessment, can make the need for punishment obsolete.

Study Questions

1. Define *punishment.*
2. What are the effects of punishment?

3. What are the side effects of punishment?
4. What types of stimuli have been used as punishers?
5. Give an example of punishment.
6. What is the role of the functional assessment in the use of punishment?
7. List four common objections to the use of punishment.
8. Explain how negative reinforcement plays a role in the continued use of punishment.

Exercises

1. Ellen is a 14-year-old girl with profound mental retardation. She often engages in self-stimulation instead of participating in chores at home. Her parents are advised to spray her in the face with water mist when she begins self-stimulation. What are some possible effects and side effects of this procedure?

2. Allen is a 19-year-old boy with severe autism who occasionally bangs his head. He has a part-time job at a department store under the supervision of a job coach. He works in the stock room putting prices on items. A consultant has recommended that the job coach take a cattle prod to work and give Allen an electric shock every time he bangs his head. What are some possible effects and side effects of using this procedure?

3. Janie lives in a group home for children with severe mental retardation. Each morning a bus comes to take her to school. When the bus arrives, she cries, screams, and tries to hide in her closet. What might a functional assessment reveal regarding this behavior?

References

Altmeyer, B. D., Williams, D. E., & Sams, V. (1985). Treatment of severe self-injurious and aggressive biting. *Journal of Behavior Therapy and Experimental Psychiatry, 16,* 159–167.

Foxx, R. M., & Martin, E. D. (1975). *Behavior Research and Therapy, 13,* 153–162.

Luce, S. C., Delquadri, J., & Hall, R. V. (1980). Contingent exercise: A mild but powerful procedure for suppressing inappropriate verbal and aggressive behavior. *Journal of Applied Behavior Analysis, 13,* 583–594.

Luiselli, J. K. (1984). Treatment of an assaultive, sensory-impaired adolescent through a multicomponent behavioral program. *Journal of Behavior Therapy and Experimental Psychiatry, 15,* 71–78.

Natta, M. B., Holmbeck, G. N., Kupst, M. J., & Pines, R. J. (1990). Sequences of staff-child interactions on a psychiatric inpatient unit. *Journal of Abnormal Child Psychology, 18,* 1–14.

Rojahn, J., McGonigle, J. J., Curcio, C., & Dixon, M. J. (1987). Suppression of pica by water mist and aromatic ammonia. *Behavior Modification, 11,* 65–74.

Tate, B. G., & Baroff, G. S. (1966). Aversive control of self-injurious behavior in a psychotic boy. *Behavior Research and Therapy , 4,* 281–287.

10

Self-Management

Bobby was an 18-year-old boy with moderate mental retardation. He attended high school in the morning and went to work in the afternoon at a local drugstore, where he stocked shelves with candy. Bobby had two problems at work that interfered with his performance. One problem was that Bobby often talked to himself while he worked, and this behavior annoyed his co-workers and alarmed the store's customers. The second problem was that, in addition to stocking the shelves with candy, he also stocked himself, eating several candy bars over the course of each afternoon. This behavior not only was a poor work habit but also contributed to a weight problem for Bobby.

Bobby had a job coach during his first week on the job. However, since Bobby learned the job quickly, his job coach stopped by only once or twice a week to check on his progress. So, the job coach was not available to implement a behavior modification plan with Bobby on a daily basis.

Since Bobby was eager to succeed at work, he agreed to work out his own self-management plan, with the help of his job coach. In the plan, Bobby was responsible for recording his own data and delivering his own positive reinforcer. He gave himself a check each hour he worked without self-talking. If he earned a check for each of the three hours he worked, he rewarded himself with a candy bar. His self-management plan was successful, for Bobby ceased his self-talking and limited his candy to one bar a day.

This chapter explores the use of self-management and its role in behavior change.

Self-Management Defined

Self-management is the process of applying the principles of behavior to modify one's own behavior. This process is also called *self-modification*. The process of changing one's own behavior is very similar to that of changing someone else's behavior. The exception, of course, is that the target behaviors are one's own, rather than someone else's.

Because self-management involves the systematic application of the principles of behavior to change one's own behavior, it is different from simple, sporadic attempts at stopping or starting a target behavior. The difference between the two is illustrated in the following examples.

Ellen decided to start an exercise program. She purchased workout clothes, workout shoes, and bought a book on exercising. She also announced to her friends that she would be exercising regularly. However, she exercised for only one day. Her workout clothes then collected dust, and her book went unread. Although Ellen set a goal for her behavior, she did not systematically apply the principles of behavior to achieving this goal, and so she does not provide an example of self-management.

Debbie also decided to start an exercise program and used self-management to change her exercise habits. She set a goal of working out three days each week for 30 minutes a session. She set a specific time to exercise that was convenient for her schedule: Monday, Wednesday, and Friday at 8:00 a.m., before she got ready for work. The night before a workout morning, she laid out her clothes, put her exercise tape into the VCR, and put a sign on her door that read "exercise." Precisely at 8:00 a.m. the next day, she put on her exercise tape and began her routine. After completing the exercise routine, Debbie put a large check on her calendar, to record that she had exercised. She then spent 15 minutes reading the newspaper, an activity she enjoyed but often did not take the time to do. If she exercised during all three scheduled sessions for the week, she purchased a croissant at a nearby bakery for breakfast on her way to work.

Debbie used stimulus control by providing stimuli that signalled the onset of exercise, i.e. her exercise clothes, her tape, and her sign. She also used modeling principles by playing a video exercise tape that showed a person exercising whom she could imitate. She made use of self-recording, too, by checking her calendar when she completed her exercise routine. For self-reinforcement, she read the newspaper after each exercise session (Fixed Ratio 1 schedule of reinforcement) and bought a croissant each week.

As already mentioned, self-management is a process that consists of procedures that are parallel to those used in behavior modification for another person's target behaviors. An interesting feature of self-management is that often one or more steps of the process become treatments that effect a change in behavior. So, it is frequently not necessary to proceed through the entire process to realize behavior change.

The steps of self-management apply not only when applying behavior modification to one's own behavior but also when assisting another person design a self-management plan. It is not necessary to design a plan totally by oneself in order for it to qualify as self-management. For example, a teacher can assist a student, a parent can assist a child, or a job coach can assist a worker in designing a behavior management plan. For maximum effectiveness, though, the designer should be competent in assisting in the design of the plan, and the individual who will be applying the plan should be part of the design process.

Goal Setting

The first step of the self-management process is to set the goal of the plan. The goal should be specific, detailing what the plan will accomplish in terms of behavior change. The goal should be behavioral; that is, it should refer to an observable behavior and provide a quantitative goal in relation to that behavior. Debbie's goal, for example, was to complete a specific set of exercises three times a week. Bobby's goal was to work without talking to himself for the daily three hours he worked. In other examples, Linda began a self-management plan to cut down on her caloric intake, and her goal was to eat no more than 1800 calories a day. Betty wanted to quit nail biting, and her goal was to have no incidents of nail biting. Susie began a self-management plan to get her homework done; her goal was to complete four half-hour assignments each night.

In yet another example, Mrs. Jones assisted some of her students in her eighth-grade class in developing goals for self-management plans. Lenny, a 13-year-old boy who often started fights on the playground by name calling, set for his goal the elimination of his name-calling behavior on the playground. A concurrent goal of Lenny's was to initiate one pleasant interaction each day with another child. Cindy, who was very shy and reluctant to ask for help in math and, consequently, failed several math quizzes, set for her goal asking the teacher for assistance each time she had difficulty with a math problem.

Goals must be realistic. They must be achievable and practical. Debby, for instance, thought that exercising three days a week was achievable for her. She knew that if she had a goal of exercising seven days a week, she would fail to meet it, become discouraged, and quit exercising altogether. Bobby thought that it might be difficult to stop talking to himself completely, but he knew that if he did not, he might lose his job. He also knew that he could not completely stop eating candy, but eating one candy bar a day seemed to him achievable.

Mrs. Jones assisted her students in developing realistic goals also. Since Cindy was having trouble in math, a goal of earning an A in math was unrealistic. However, a goal of asking for assistance each time she had difficulty with a math problem was probably achievable.

Occasionally, simply setting a goal can effect change or have an instructional effect. For example, once Cindy's teacher helped her set the goal of asking for assistance, she became much more likely to do so. The goal setting itself was instructional for her. Previously, it had not occurred to her to ask for help. Lenny had a similar experience following setting a goal for name calling. Once the matter had been discussed with him in terms of a self-management goal, Lenny's name-calling behavior virtually ceased.

Data Collection: Self-Recording, Self-Monitoring

After a goal is set, the next step involves collecting data. In self-management plans, this procedure often takes the form of self-recording: the individual records his or her own data. Data collection can provide a quantitative baseline level; it can also provide information necessary for a functional assessment.

Self-recording can make use of the same type of data-collection procedures used in conventional behavior modification plans. Individuals can do tallies of their behavior. To illustrate, when Betty decided to eliminate her nail-biting behavior, she made a check on a sheet each time she bit her nails. A time block can also be used in self-recording. Bobby, for instance, used a simple data sheet at work, divided into hour intervals. Each hour, he marked a check if he worked without talking to himself and a zero if he talked to himself.

Data collection can also involve procedures for determining antecedents and consequences of a target behavior, so that a functional assessment can be done. In self-management plans, this data might take the form of either a diary or a structured diary. Lisa, a 12-year-old girl with mild mental retardation who often cried in school, provides a good example. When asked, Lisa could not really describe why she was crying and would simply say that she was sad. Her teacher assisted her in setting up a simple structured diary. After each incident of crying, she recorded what happened prior to her crying and what happened afterwards. This data allowed Lisa to do a functional assessment to determine the functions of her crying.

Data collection can also involve self-monitoring, in which an individual performs some type of behavior monitoring. In some cases, self-monitoring alone can result in behavior change; in other cases, it is part of a self-management package of strategies.

Dunlap and Dunlap (1989) investigated the effects of self-monitoring to increase the accuracy of math skills of three fifth- and sixth-grade students with learning disabilities. The students were taught to self-monitor their math performance on subtraction and regrouping problems by checking off items on a checklist that were related to their math–problem solving. Increases in math accuracy were found as a result of the self-monitoring checklist. Additionally, these high levels of accuracy were maintained after the checklists were removed.

In another study, Ackerman and Shapiro (1984) used self-monitoring to increase the vocational productivity of five adults with mental retardation. Their work productivity was initially improved by verbal praise and encouragement given contingently for improved productivity. The participants were then taught to self-monitor by recording on a daily production chart first the number of units of work completed and then the work rate. Self-monitoring was successful in maintaining higher work rates during the phase when verbal praise was no longer provided.

Functional Assessment

A functional assessment can be done in self-management plans, and it can be as important as when done in conventional behavioral problem solving. The individual examines the data, setting events, antecedents, and consequences of the target behavior to determine the functions the behavior serves. Some people may be aware of the functions of their behaviors, while many others are less analytical. Children and adolescents, particularly, are not well aware of the functions of their behaviors. The case of Billy provides such an example.

Billy was a 12-year-old boy who had a problem with talking back to the teacher. He was often in trouble for this behavior and agreed to participate in a self-management plan, in which he was taught to take simple Antecedent-Behavior-Consequence data on incidents of talking back. He found that he often talked back after being corrected for his incomplete or inaccurate work. The consequence was typically that the teacher became exasperated and walked away. The function of Billy's behavior appeared to be the termination of teacher corrections.

The functional assessment allowed Billy to see his role in the problem. Rather than seeing the teacher as a nag, he began to see that the whole chain of events began with his incomplete or inaccurate work. His original self-management goal had been to decrease the frequency of talking back to the teacher. After doing the functional assessment, a new goal was added: to complete work fully and accurately.

It is possible that some children and youth with problems stemming from a neurological disorder affecting abstract thinking or from a marked degree of mental retardation may not be able to do or comprehend a functional assessment. However, this inability does not rule out a self-management plan. In these cases, it may be feasible for the teacher, instructor, parent, or counselor to do the functional assessment and then assist with the design of a self-management plan. The person with the disability cannot assess the functions of the behavior but may be able to use self-management strategies to effect behavior change.

To illustrate, Melinda was a young woman with autism who had mild retardation and severe deficits in her abstract-thinking abilities. She had several behavior problems, such as scratching herself and hitting others, and was not able to participate in a functional assessment of her behavior because of her problems with abstract thinking and communication. A functional assessment revealed that Melinda often scratched herself or was aggressive toward others when she had a disappointment or had a change in her schedule. As a result of her behavior, she often obtained extra staff assistance with her problem or disappointment.

A self-management plan was developed that addressed the functions served by Melinda's problem behavior. By the use of a combination of self-instruction, self-rating, and self-reinforcement, Melinda was able to achieve a significant decrease in self-scratching and aggression. Although she could not perform a functional assessment, she was able to use self-management strategies to change her own behavior.

Behavior Change Strategies

There are a variety of strategies that can be used in self-management plans to modify behavior. A functional assessment can suggest which of these strategies might be most useful. Several of these strategies are reviewed.

Shaping/Smaller Goals

Self-management can be effectively realized by the use of shaping. Children and adults often set such high goals for themselves that these goals cannot be attained, and they stop trying. Starting with small goals and changing a goal gradually can be effective means of self-management. Examples of shaping follow.

Dr. K. was a psychologist who should have known better. She exercised daily for about 20 minutes. When she decided to increase her exercise program, she hired a trainer to help with the design of it. He developed an elaborate workout schedule for Dr. K., and when she saw it, she was overwhelmed and gave up exercising altogether. Dr. K. moved from a reasonable self-management exercise program to one whose goals were too large. The result was total abandonment of an exercise program.

Jinny wanted to improve her fitness and decided to take up running. The first day out she ran for 20 minutes. She returned home exhausted, and her muscles were sore for the next several days. Thus, her running career was over very shortly after it had begun. By contrast, Gail's self-management plan for becoming a runner was much more effective, as it centered around the principles of shaping. She began with short walks and gradually increased to longer walks. Over time, she changed from walking to walk/running. It took her three months to build up to a 20-minute run, but when she did, she completed a run feeling good, without the exhaustion and muscle soreness that Jinny had experienced.

Johnny, a sixth-grade student, used a series of small goals to improve his grade in spelling. Each Friday, he was tested on 25 new spelling words; and each Thursday night, he attempted to memorize the spelling of all 25 words. Since he usually earned a grade no higher than a B on his tests, he decided to start studying five days before the test and learn 5 words each night. In doing so, he broke the task down into manageable steps and began getting A's on his spelling tests.

Stimulus Control

It can be useful to create stimuli purposefully to serve as cues, signals, or reminders for affecting a behavior. Stimulus-control procedures can be effective alone or when used with other procedures. Stimulus control can make use of visual or auditory stimuli. Other stimuli might also serve to affect behavior, including olfactory, tactile and taste stimuli. Visual stimuli can take many forms when used in self-management plans. An individual might use objects or written signs or reminders to engage in or refrain from a target behavior.

For example, Betty used stimulus control in the form of a visual cue as part of her self-management plan to eliminate nail biting. She kept her nails covered with a favorite color of polish as a visual reminder for her to refrain from nail biting. In another example, Debbie used several forms of stimulus control in her self-management exercise plan. Each evening before an exercise day, she laid out her clothes, her exercise tape, and a sign with the word exercise on it. These were visual cues to exercise. Her clothes, laid out by the side of her bed, also provided tactile cues, since she would either have to wear them or move them in order to exit from her bed. The exercise tape provided auditory cues, as she came to associate the music on the tape with her exercise routine.

Auditory cues can take other forms in self-management plans. Tape recordings can be useful in providing cues as to task instructions or to social skills. Bobby, for example, can study the French language prior to going to France with the use of instructional audiotapes. Linda, who is shy in social situations and wants to initiate more social interactions, can listen to a motivational tape on social interactions prior to engaging in social activities.

Written instructions can also be powerful forms of stimulus control. To illustrate, Arnold was a 15-year-old boy with mild mental retardation, who had a part-time job at which he worked very slowly. He wanted to increase his speed, so that he could raise his income. His work/study supervisor helped him discover that he worked so slowly because he was unsure of the steps of the task. She wrote the steps out in words that he could understand and posted them in his work area. By using the instructions, Arnold was able to complete his tasks with greater speed.

In another example, Marie was a high school student whose grades were falling because she often forgot parts of her homework assignments. Her self-management plan consisted of purchasing a homework notebook and writing down in it each assignment as it was announced. Each evening, she would cross an assignment off the list as she completed it. This common way of using written instructions was effective in controlling Marie's behavior.

Agran, Fodor-Davis, Moore, and Deer (1989) used a self-management package to increase vocational instruction-following behaviors of five students with intellectual disabilities. Their package included several strategies that used prompts such as self-generated verbal prompts and picture cues. Students were taught to give themselves verbal prompts; that is, they told themselves what to do and where to do it. The researchers reported effective and rapid improvement in instruction-following skills of all participants.

Self-instruction can be a useful means of providing stimulus control over a target behavior. For example, Ernie was a 10-year-old boy who was interested in improving his swimming technique. His swimming coach explained to him that he needed to lengthen his reach on his arm pull to maximize the power of his crawl stroke. Ernie found that he could remember to do this by saying "Reach, reach" to himself as he swam. His self-talk provided the reminder of how to execute the stroke.

Other forms of self-talk, and even self-thought, have been used effectively in behavior change. People with fears, for instance, have been taught to pair thoughts of feared objects with thoughts of pleasant circumstances. People dealing with difficult tasks or circumstances have been taught to visualize being finished with them.

Pictures can be helpful forms of stimulus control as well. People with profound mental retardation can be taught to follow picture schedules that depict either the steps of an individual task or a series of tasks they are expected to perform. These people, who may have no verbal skills, might be willing to follow their own pictorial cues in order to complete assigned job, school, or home tasks.

Self-Reinforcement

Although people often have trouble denying themselves reinforcers or delaying reinforcers, self-reinforcement can be a valuable component of a self-management plan. Individuals can be taught to deliver reinforcers to themselves contingent on the presence or absence of specified target behaviors. Inherent in self-reinforcement strategies is self-evaluation. An individual has to determine whether or not the target behavior has met the criterion necessary for reinforcement. Self-evaluation and self-reinforcement can be learned through direct instruction or through copying the reinforcement patterns of others. Reinforcers can be food items, events, or activities that the person enjoys. Reinforcement schedules can be any of those previously mentioned, such as fixed ratio, variable ratio, differential reinforcement of other behavior, and variable interval schedules. Examples of the effective use of these schedules follow.

Marla was on a self-management plan to increase her study time. In her plan, she included a component that consisted of making a telephone call to a friend after every half hour of study. Jeannie, whose self-management plan was aimed at completing math problems, took a reinforcer after completion of sets of five math problems. Ernie, who had trouble keeping his room clean, began a self-reinforcement plan with a Fixed Ratio 10 schedule. After picking up sets of ten items from his floor, he would take a break and read a page of his comic book. Saul, a 16-year-old boy with severe mental retardation and also nonverbal, had a job sorting candy into trays for a vending-machine company. He was taught to reward himself with a small piece of candy each time he completed three trays.

Self-Extinction

Self-extinction involves an individual making sure that certain target behaviors are no longer reinforced and are effectively on extinction. Denying oneself a reinforcer for certain undesirable target behaviors can be difficult but not impossible. To illustrate, Mandy had a problem with overeating. She often went to the refrigerator, opened the door, looked at the food inside, and took something to eat. She decided to put this behavior on extinction by not taking food after opening the refrigerator door. She would open the door, look into the refrigerator, and then walk away. She helped make this extinction procedure effective by no longer stocking her favorite food items in the refrigerator.

In another example, Linda had a problem with overspending. She often went to the mall and directly into a record or clothing store to shop. She decided to put mall shopping on extinction by eliminating her trips to a record or clothing store. By avoiding these stores, Linda, in effect, put mall shopping on extinction, and she was more effective at budgeting her money.

Combining Strategies

As with other behavior modification plans, combining several procedures might be necessary for success. In a self-management plan, it might be necessary to use stimulus control as well as self-reinforcement or self-extinction. Debbie's exercise plan, for example, combined several elements. She used stimulus control procedures, self-recording, and self-reinforcement to increase the likelihood that she would exercise.

In another example, Buddy, a 7-year-old boy, began a self-management plan for brushing his teeth each morning because he often forgot to brush his teeth and was dependent on his mother's reminders. His self-management plan had an element of stimulus control, consisting of a picture of a smiling mouth with large teeth placed on his door. He put up the picture each night directly after brushing his teeth and before going to bed. His plan also included self-reinforcement. He picked out a good-flavored toothpaste at the grocery store, which made toothbrushing itself reinforcing.

Cole, Gardner, and Karan (1985) used a combination of self-management procedures to reduce behavior problems of six adults with mild and moderate mental retardation. The participants were taught to self-monitor, self-evaluate, self-reward, and self-instruct. The authors reported immediate reductions in problem behaviors and also durability of effects across time.

Gardner, Clees, and Cole (1983) used a combination of self-management procedures to decrease the frequency of loud, nonspeech sounds of a young man with moderate retardation. His caretakers believed that these noises were self-stimulatory and that the young man was unaware of how disruptive they were to other people. The young man was taught to self-monitor and self-evaluate his verbal behaviors; he was also taught to self-consequate. The program was successful in eliminating his talking to himself.

Evaluating Effectiveness

With any behavior modification procedure, it is necessary to evaluate the effectiveness of the self-management plan. This evaluation can be done by comparing data taking during baseline with data taken while the strategies are being implemented. If the data reflects behavior change in the desired direction, the plan is considered effective; if not, changes are necessary in either the goals or the strategies of the plan.

Figure 10.1 displays the data on the number of times Debbie exercised each month. Prior to beginning her self-management exercise plan, she did not exercise at all, and these data are reflected as zero on the graph. Following implementation of her self-management plan, she began exercising about 13 times per month (consistent with her goal of three times per week), and these data are also reflected on the graph.

Fading

With any behavior modification plan, it may be possible to fade the strategies. However, fading these strategies might mean the abolishment of gains made during plan implementation. Jinnie's self-management plan for eliminating nail biting illustrates successful fading. Jinnie's nails grew long, and she received many compliments on their appearance. After several months, she was able to drop the elements of her self-management plan without resuming

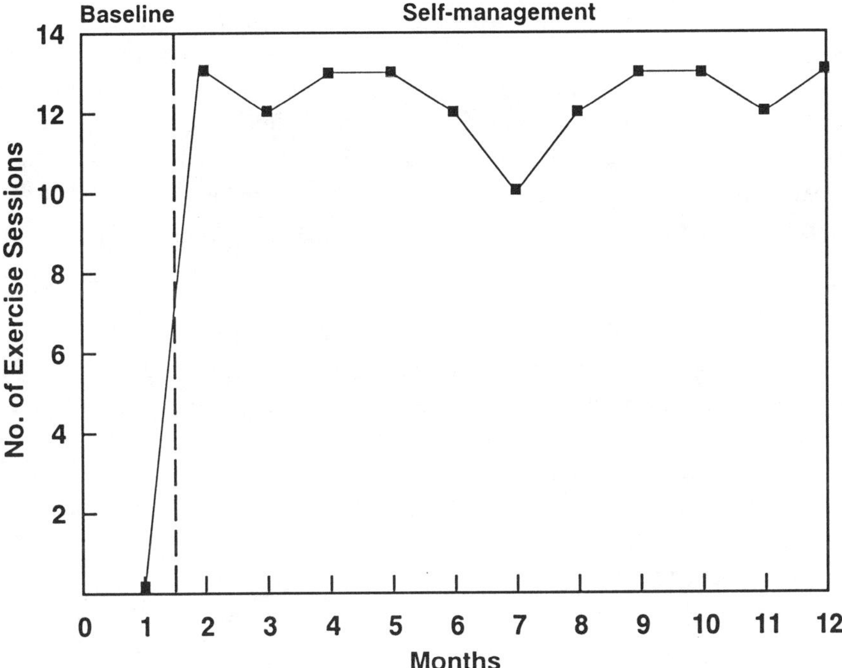

Figure 10.1 The number of exercise sessions per month during baseline and during self-management programming.

nail biting. On the other hand, Debbie was able to fade some aspects of her exercise plan but not others. She no longer needed the exercise sign nor the self-reinforcement component. However, she continued to lay her clothes out each evening and have her exercise tape ready, as these cues seemed critical to her continued success.

Applications

Case 1

Sandy was a 14-year-old girl who often fought with her friends. With the help of her teacher, she worked out a self-management plan. She began by keeping a diary in which she recorded each argument, the circumstances preceding it, and the events following it. She found that the fights often began when a friend teased her. She would respond with rude comments to the teasing, and the argument would escalate, ending with Sandy and a friend not speaking to each other. The arguments often ended with Sandy's friend making an apology.

Sandy realized that the teasing became a cue for her to begin arguing. So, when teasing occurred, rather than argue, she planned to respond with a simple remark, such as "yeah, sure." Using self-instruction, she would say to herself "yeah sure" when one of her friends made a teasing remark and then would say this to her friend. Sandy also planned a self-reinforcement schedule. Each Saturday, she would have a donut for breakfast if she had not argued with her friends during the preceding school week. By her applications of self-recording, self-talk, and self-reinforcement, Sandy was able to reduce the number of arguments she had with her friends.

Case 2

Jimmy was an 11-year-old boy who often did not complete his homework; many evenings, he never even began his homework. His self-management plan used a combination of stimulus control, shaping, and self-reinforcement. After each class, he wrote his homework for that class on a homework sheet. Each evening, he worked for small units of time (about 10 minutes) and then took short breaks as reinforcers. Each week, he increased the length of work time by 5 minutes, so that by the end of the first month, he was working for about 25 minutes before taking a break.

Case 3

Alan was a 15-year-old boy with mental retardation. He worked afternoons in a stock room hanging pants. His self-management plan emphasized self-reinforcement. After hanging each box of pants, Alan rewarded himself with a small reinforcer, usually a small food treat. Alan took the reward, ate it, and then returned to his task. Although Alan had a severe handicap and was under the supervision of a job coach, he was able to use self-reinforcement at his job.

Case 4

Dennis was a young man with moderate mental retardation and severe autism. He went to school each morning and had a job sorting books in the library each afternoon. Dennis had several problem behaviors, which included talking loudly while working, leaving his work area without permission, and neglecting his work for long periods of time. Dennis's teacher put him on an hourly checklist for specific behaviors. Each hour he was rated on whether or not he remained in his assigned location, worked steadily, and worked quietly. As his behavior improved, his teacher changed the plan from a traditional behavior modification plan, implemented by the teacher, to a self-management plan run by Dennis. Dennis took over the responsibility for his own self-rating. Each hour, he would take out his report card and rate himself on each of the target behaviors. He then would return this card to his briefcase and continue with his work. Dennis maintained his gains in his work adjustment, even as his plan became one of self-management, using self-recording as the only component.

Summary

Self-management is the application of the principles of behavior to one's own behavior. Children and youth can often participate in their own self-management plans, although the plans might be designed by or with someone else. Even individuals with severe disabilities, such as developmental disabilities, can benefit from self-management procedures.

Self-management follows the same course as behavior modification. Typically, the process involves targeting the behavior; self-recording; a possible functional assessment; and then the application of such principles as positive reinforcement, shaping, stimulus control, or self-extinction. Self-management, when used alone or in combination with other behavioral procedures, can be an effective way of achieving behavior change.

Study Questions

1. Define *self-management.*
2. What are the steps in developing a self-management plan?
3. How is data typically collected in a self-management plan?

4. Give two examples of the use of stimulus control in self-management.
5. Give one example of each of the following strategies as applied to self-management: *self-reinforcement, self-extinction, shaping, self-recording.*

Exercises

1. List several behaviors of your own that you would like to change with a self-management plan.

2. Compile a list of events, objects, and items in your environment that could function as reinforcers in a self-management plan.

3. Choose one activity or behavior that you do regularly and do not particularly enjoy. List the stimuli in the environment that control this behavior. List the reinforcers that might be maintaining it.

4. Bessie is a 13-year-old girl who belongs to a swim team. She likes the exercise that being on the swim team provides but often skips practice. Design a self-management plan for Bessie to increase her swim-team participation.

5. Saundra is an 18-year-old girl with mild mental retardation. She often speaks rudely to other people and curses. She realizes that this behavior is unacceptable and would like to stop it. Design a self-management plan for Saundra to help her speak more considerately to others.

6. Ernie is a 14-year-old boy whose mother is ill. He would like to become more helpful around the house; however, he does not know where to begin. Design a self-management plan for Ernie that uses shaping to help him become more helpful at home.

SELF-MANAGEMENT PROJECT

1. Select strategies for use in your self-management project.
2. Begin to implement your chosen strategies.
3. Continue to take data, as you did during the baseline period.
4. Graph your data daily.

References

Ackerman, A. M., & Shapiro, E. S. (1984). Self-monitoring and work productivity with mentally retarded adults. *Journal of Applied Behavior Analysis, 17,* 403–407.

Agran, M., Fodor-Davis, J., Moore, S., & Deer, M. (1989). The application of a self-management program on instruction-following skills. *Journal of the Association for Persons with Severe Handicaps, 14,* 147–154.

Cole, C. L., Gardner, W. I., & Karan, O. C. (1985). Self-management training of mentally retarded adults presenting severe conduct difficulties. *Applied Research in Mental Retardation, 6,* 337–347.

Dunlap, L. K., & Dunlap, G. (1989). A self-monitoring package for teaching subtraction with regrouping to students with learning disabilities. *Journal of Applied Behavior Analysis, 22,* 309–314.

Gardner, W. I., Clees, T. J., & Cole, C. L. (1983). Self-management of disruptive verbal ruminations by a mentally retarded adult. *Applied Research in Mental Retardation, 4,* 41–58.

11

Generalization and Maintenance

Jolenea Ferro and Glen Dunlap

As Valerie prepared to graduate, her teachers were excited about the prospect of her leading a productive and independent life. In the classroom she had demonstrated that she could care for her personal needs, make a bed, dust, keep personal belongings in order, and fix simple meals. She worked independently when given vocational tasks in school and participated in a work program at a local grocery store. Valerie's job at the grocery store was to take produce out of its packing case and stack it in grocery bins. She was able to work at this task for 20 minutes with occasional feedback and praise from the vocational instructor who worked with her at the grocery store.

However, six months after graduation Valerie spent most of her time at home watching television and waiting for placement in a sheltered workshop. Her mother complained that Valerie did not know how to clean up after herself, make her bed, or keep her room tidy. Valerie had been laid off from her job at a cleaning plant because she was easily distracted by other workers standing near her. Her supervisor was unable to leave her alone because she required repeated instruction to complete a task. When she was assessed by the staff in her new training program, Valerie was unable to perform most of the tasks that were given to her. Even when she could do a task, she was unable to stick with it for more than a minute. The skills she had learned to perform for her teachers had failed to maintain and generalize.

Valerie's teachers had attempted to provide Valerie with the skills needed to function as independently as possible in society—the most important goal of classroom instruction. They identified and taught her self-care and domestic

Preparation of this manuscript was supported by Cooperative Agreement No. GOO87CO434 from the National Institute on Disability and Rehabilitation Research. However, the opinions are those of the authors, and no official endorsement should be inferred.

and vocational skills. Valerie learned those skills and exhibited them during training sessions in the classroom and in the grocery store. However, her instruction failed in two important ways: her responses did not continue when training stopped, and they did not transfer to a new setting and a new supervisor. These failures left her dependent and unproductive. One could say that Valerie's school experience had no meaningful impact on her life.

As Valerie's case demonstrates, the desirable responses that students with disabilities learn seldom maintain and generalize without specific instruction. Reductions of problem behavior may also fail to maintain or generalize to new settings and people. This chapter defines generalization and maintenance, identifies the strategies that have been most effectively used to increase the likelihood that responses will maintain and generalize, and discusses the limitations of these strategies.

Maintenance and Generalization Defined

Teachers and parents often teach skills and behaviors in training environments, such as the classroom or the home. However, the ultimate goal of most instruction is to teach skills that will generalize to other settings, other people, and other circumstances. *Generalization* includes three processes: maintenance, stimulus generalization, and response generalization.

Maintenance

Maintenance refers to the durability of responding, or generalization across time. To say that a response has maintained means that a student performs a skill appropriately without teacher assistance and frequent reinforcement in the setting in which it was learned. Another way of stating this is to say that the student is able to perform the skill independently. In Valerie's case, maintenance would have been demonstrated for the produce-stacking task if she were able to stack produce without receiving feedback and reinforcement from her instructor. The type of reinforcement schedules used during training can affect whether maintenance will occur. The likelihood that a response will maintain can also be increased by teaching functional activities in the natural environment.

Stimulus Generalization

Generalization actually refers to two processes, stimulus generalization and response generalization. *Stimulus generalization* occurs when the desired behaviors are exhibited in the presence of stimuli that are different from those present during training; e.g., when target skills are exhibited in different settings, with different people, or with different materials and instructions. For example, Phil, a 12-year-old student with moderate disabilities, has successfully learned to make peanut butter and jelly sandwiches with his teacher at school. Sandwich making is considered to have generalized if he makes sandwiches at home (another setting) or if he makes them with his mother (another person). If Phil also makes ham and cheese sandwiches, the skill has generalized to different materials.

Stimulus generalization is often a factor with problem behaviors. For example, Larry learned that if he poked John on the shoulder, John talked to him. Later, he poked Sally and Tim, and they also talked to him. Larry soon began all of his social interactions by poking someone on the shoulder.

Strategies used to achieve stimulus generalization emphasize the manipulation of antecedent stimuli. Several examples of strategies using antecedent stimuli were described in Chapter 7, including response prompts and stimulus prompts. Generalization can be promoted by using strategies based on both the principles of stimulus control and the principles of reinforcement.

Skills learned in training situations often do not generalize to other settings. Such failures can often be understood in terms of the principles of stimulus control. For example, during a typical training session, the target response is repeatedly reinforced in the presence of antecedent stimuli and is not reinforced in the absence of those stimuli. Over time, the response comes under the control of the antecedent stimuli designed to assist the learner. These stimuli may include aspects of the setting, the person delivering the instruction, the instructional prompts, and the instructional materials. Reinforcing stimuli may include teacher feedback, attention, and artificial reinforcers such as tokens. Often, these antecedent and reinforcing stimuli are not present in settings other than the training setting. When these stimuli are absent or different in other nontraining settings, generalization and maintenance failures occur.

Response Generalization

Response Generalization occurs when changes in one class of responses influence or change another class of responses. In other words, one response is changed directly through a specific teaching strategy and other responses are affected indirectly. These indirect effects are often referred to as *response covariation, collateral effects*, or *side effects*.

Response generalization refers to the target behaviors themselves rather than to antecedent stimuli or reinforcers. For example, George was a 6-year-old student who threw or tore up materials when he was asked to complete a task. A functional analysis of his behavior identified it as an escape response: George destroyed material when he did not know how to complete the task.

After George's teacher taught him to ask for help, his asking for help was directly affected by the procedure. George began to ask for help more often, and he stopped destroying task material. George's teacher also noticed that George spent more time working on tasks and that he smiled more often during instruction. Response generalization was demonstrated by the increase in on-task and smiling behaviors and by the reduction of destroying task material. None of these three responses were directly addressed in the teaching program.

Strategies to Promote Skill Maintenance

Say a student demonstrates a behavior correctly at one point in time, but the behavior change is not lasting. As time passes, he fails to continue to use the new skill. Such a situation might involve a skill deficit that is actually a maintenance problem: the learned behavior has failed to maintain. If a skill deficit has been identified as a maintenance problem, systematic changes in schedules of reinforcement must be undertaken to achieve maintenance. Procedures designed to encourage maintenance are illustrated in Table 11.1. They include exploiting current functional contingencies, manipulating schedules of reinforcement, and increasing naturally available reinforcement. These strategies may be most effective when used in combination and as part of a multi-component approach.

Exploiting Current Functional Contingencies

Teaching Functional Skills

Maintenance can often be enhanced by using reinforcers that occur naturally in the settings in which students live. One way of exploiting these naturally occurring reinforcers is to teach skills that are useful, or functional. Useful skills often provide frequent opportunities for reinforcement in the natural environment, so that maintenance is more likely to occur. A student who learns to prepare simple meals, for example, is likely to maintain that behavior because it provides access naturally to a variety of reinforcers. One obvious reinforcer would be eating the finished product. Additionally, food preparation might also increase social reinforcers, such as praise and social interaction with those who may share the meal.

Use Natural Reinforcers

Another strategy that exploits current functional contingencies and facilitates maintenance is to use reinforcers during training that are likely to be available in the natural environment. This means avoiding the use of such artificial reinforcers as candy or unusual tokens. It also includes identi-

Table 11.1 Strategic Categories to Promote Skill Maintenance

Strategies	*Procedure*	*Description*
Exploit current functional contingencies.	Teach functional skills.	Teach behaviors that are useful and provide frequent natural opportunities for reinforcement.
	Use natural reinforcers.	Include such natural reinforces as increased attention and social interaction with peers, co-workers, etc.
	Use a time-based schedule.	Reinforce after a certain number of minutes rather than after responses.
Manipulate schedules of reinforcement.	Use intermittent contingencies.	Increase gradually the number of responses required before the student is reinforced.
	Use indiscriminable contingencies.	Decrease predictability by changing to a variable schedule.
Augment normally available reinforcement.	Teach students to solicit reinforcement.	Teach students to ask for feedback from supervisors.
	Teach self-reinforcement.	Teach students to deliver a predetermined reinforcer to themselves.

fying those tangible reinforcers that are naturally available for performance of the skill as well as identifying those persons who might typically deliver the reinforcer. Naturally available reinforcers may be *extrinsic* to the skill or activity; that is, they are not part of the skill itself. Examples of extrinsic reinforcers are attention and increased social interactions with peers, co-workers, parents, or others. In preparing a meal, a naturally available extrinsic reinforcer is the social interaction that can occur while the meal is being prepared and when it is eaten.

Reinforcers may also be *intrinsic*, meaning that there is something enjoyable or preferable about doing the task. For example, some people enjoy cooking even if they do not eat what they have cooked. Other natural reinforcers are directly related to the outcome of the task. A natural reinforcer that is an outcome of preparing a meal, for example, is to eat it. The natural reinforcer for writing a letter (handwriting practice) may be to send it to a friend. Increasing access to natural reinforcers promotes maintenance. Such practice activities as copying material that is discarded or opening empty cans subvert the natural outcome of an activity and should be avoided. An example follows.

Helen, a 16-year-old student, was required to copy four sentences from the blackboard every day. She could write, but she required repeated prompts and reinforcers from her teacher to complete this task. When the task was changed to copying a letter that Helen could send to a friend, both prompts and extrinsic reinforcers were faded within one week.

Reinforcement should also be transferred from trainers, such as teachers or aides, to people who would typically be available in the natural environment. These people include parents, peers, co-workers, supervisors, and others who are frequently with the student. For example, Robert was being taught to buy his lunch in the school cafeteria. He had progressed very well but only if he was with his teacher. If she did not walk through the line with Robert, he would not put items on his tray. To promote maintenance, the people serving food at the cafeteria were enlisted as assistants. At each station, the server praised Robert for putting food on his tray. Eventually, the teacher successfully faded her presence. This strategy not only achieved maintenance but also resulted in social interaction between Robert and the food servers.

Praise, attention, and feedback delivered by a trainer are not intrinsically part of the natural environment. These reinforcers, typically scheduled during training, may overshadow other more naturally occurring sources of reinforcement. The student then becomes dependent upon the reinforcers provided during training, and maintenance is impeded.

Important strategies for enhancing maintenance are redesigning curricula to include activities that are functional (with useful and meaningful outcomes) and identifying natural reinforcers that include peers, co-workers, and others in the environment. However, some students may be unresponsive to stimuli that are available in the natural environment. In these cases, it is necessary to establish the naturally occurring events as reinforcers by pairing them with a reinforcer that has been found to be effective (e.g., tangibles, teacher praise). If artificial reinforcers are required, the shift to reinforcers available in the natural environment should occur as soon as possible without decreasing response accuracy.

Manipulating Schedules of Reinforcement

Use Intermittent Schedules of Reinforcement

During the initial stages of a program, reinforcement is usually scheduled after every response or attempt to respond. This dense schedule is necessary when building responses because it increases the probability that a student will perform accurately. An error often made at the end of a training program is the abrupt withdrawal of the reinforcement schedule. This abrupt reduction of reinforcers resembles an extinction condition and results in decreased responding.

Chapter 5 on extinction describes many instances of this phenomenon, but consider one more illustration. Margaret frequently interrupted her teacher during group instruction. She asked or answered questions in a loud voice without waiting for the teacher to call on her. Margaret's teacher designed a program to teach Margaret to raise her hand and wait until she was called on before she spoke. Initially, Margaret's teacher acknowledged Margaret every time she raised her hand. So, the program was successful, and after two weeks, Margaret consistently raised her hand before speaking. However, Margaret was dominating the group instructional sessions giving the teacher little time to present new material and making it impossible for any other student to participate. During the next week, Margaret continued to raise her hand, but her teacher decided she would only acknowledge her as often as she acknowledged the other students, about two times during an instructional session. For a while, Margaret continued to raise her hand; but as the week progressed, her hand raising decreased, and she returned to calling out to the teacher in a loud voice—a behavior always acknowledged in some way.

The natural environment cannot usually support behavior that is maintained on a continuous and predictable reinforcement schedule. For example, Margaret's teacher could not continue to acknowledge Margaret every time her hand was raised. If she had, no other student would have had the opportunity to respond during group instructional sessions. The problem was not that the teacher stopped acknowledging Margaret every time but that she did it so abruptly.

Maintenance can be facilitated by systematically and gradually changing from a continuous to an *intermittent schedule of reinforcement* during training. These schedules more closely resemble naturally occurring reinforcement schedules, which are normally thin. Intermittent schedules increase the probability that a behavior will maintain and not extinguish.

Although the process of changing from a continuous to an intermittent schedule of reinforcement seems simple, the example of Margaret raising her hand illustrates that it is not. It requires more planning than simply reinforcing a response less often. A specific program should be designed that schedules a systematic and gradual increase in the number of responses required before a reinforcer is delivered. Data collection on student performance can allow the teacher to monitor the success of the change. Student performance indicates whether a change has been too large or too small or whether the student has met the goal. Examples of systematic and gradual changing of reinforcement schedules follow.

Maria was a 5-year-old student who had just learned to eat with a fork. During the learning phase of her program, she was praised every time she took a bite of food using her fork to bring it to her mouth. Her teacher, Mr. Foley, began the maintenance phase of her program by requiring Maria to take 2 bites of food to obtain a reinforcer. When the data indicated that Maria was maintaining correct responding on this new schedule, reinforcers were given after 5 bites of food. This, too, was successful. Next, Mr. Foley provided reinforcers after 10 bites of food. At this point, Maria began holding her fork for several seconds before she put the food in her mouth, and she occasionally tried to pick up food with her hands instead of with the fork. Mr. Foley could tell from her performance that the schedule change was too big for Maria. So, he returned to the schedule in which reinforcers were provided after every 5 bites and made future schedule changes more gradual.

John's performance resulted in a different schedule of reinforcement reduction. John also learned to eat with a fork and was praised after every bite. Mr. Foley began the maintenance phase of John's program in the same way that he had begun Maria's. First, he required John to take 2 and then 5 bites of food before he praised him. Both changes were successful: John continued to use his fork. Then, Mr. Foley required John to take 10 bites before he praised him. John continued correct responding, and Mr. Foley was able to discontinue all reinforcers until the end of the meal.

Because each student is different, there is no so-called canned program providing a sequence for changing reinforcement schedules that works across all students or even across all behaviors within the same student. As the previously mentioned examples illustrate, student performance must be evaluated each time.

Use Indiscriminable Contingencies

The more unpredictable the schedule of reinforcement, the more likely maintenance will occur. So, in addition to the shifting of a schedule from a continuous to an intermittent schedule of reinforcement, the predictability of a schedule can be manipulated also to enhance maintenance responding. Using *indiscriminable contingencies* refers to the practice of providing reinforcement on a schedule that a student cannot predict. Decreased predictability resembles naturally occurring contingencies and sets up a condition in which responses are more resistent to extinction. The predictability of both time- and response-based reinforcement may be decreased by changing from a fixed to a variable schedule of delivery (as described in Chapter 4). This schedule change should also be based on student responding as described in the previous section on intermittent reinforcement.

Use Time-Based Schedules

Naturally occurring reinforcers are often delivered after the passage of a time interval rather than after specific responses. For example, many employees must learn to wait a week or two for their paychecks to be issued. Once a paycheck is issued, a person may have to wait to cash it and to wait again before spending the money. Praise for a job well done may come at the end of the day or even the next day. It is, therefore, important that students have experience with *time-based schedules* and that they are taught to wait for the delivery of reinforcers.

Waiting can be taught by a delayed reinforcement procedure. Delaying reinforcement refers to increasing the time between a correct response and the delivery of a reinforcer. For example, Jeff was taught to fold towels in the laundry room of a local motel. Initially, Jeff was praised for folding each towel correctly. Eventually, his reinforcement schedule was thinned so that he would have to fold 50 towels before he was praised. However, the reinforcer for the other employees in the laundry room was that they could go on break after they had worked for an hour and a half. So, Jeff's job coach changed Jeff's schedule to a time-based schedule of reinforcement, teaching Jeff to wait in order to access the naturally occurring break as a reinforcer.

First, Jeff's coach calculated the average time Jeff took to fold 50 towels as 1 hour, and he began providing Jeff a reinforcer every hour. Next, he set a timer so Jeff would have a visual cue that a reinforcer would be delivered. Then, he gradually began to increase the time between reinforcers until reaching 1-1/2 hours. At that time, he began taking Jeff to the employee's lounge as a reinforcer to encourage his interaction with other employees. Finally, he taught Jeff to take a break on his own.

Augmenting Normally Available Reinforcement

Naturally occurring reinforcers are often delayed. Strategies that augment normally available reinforcement can then be effective. Reinforcers can be augmented by teaching students to seek additional reinforcers or to deliver reinforcers to themselves as part of a self-management strategy. For example, Sylvia takes a break to listen to music on a Walkman after she completes an activity. Charlie uses the computer after he has completed his tasks. Both students have been taught to reinforce their own behavior as part of a self-management strategy.

As an alternative, students may be taught to request feedback from others. For example, Cleo, like Jeff, also worked in a motel laundry room. However, she had difficulty washing linens correctly because she could not wait for a break before receiving a reinforcer. Her job coach had to teach her to ask a co-worker whether or not she was doing her job correctly.

Strategies to Promote Stimulus Generalization

Maintenance failures result from problems with the reinforcement contingencies. Some cases identified as maintenance failures may actually be generalization failures. This means that both reinforcement contingencies and antecedent stimuli are different from those that were available in the training environment. To correct generalization failures, either the environment is modified to resemble more closely the training environment or the deficit is addressed with generalization strategies.

To say that a behavior has generalized usually refers to stimulus generalization. This means that the student performs the target behavior without additional training, in different settings, with different people, and with different materials than those used during training. Sometimes generalization happens naturally. However, it is often necessary to use specific strategies to promote generalization.

Tactics designed to encourage stimulus generalization are illustrated in Table 11.2. They include exploiting current functional contingencies, training diversely, incorporating functional mediators, and using general case programming.

Exploit Current Functional Contingencies

Teach Functional Skills

It is important to create training conditions and use stimuli that are routinely available in the generalization setting. This situation is made more likely if functional skills are taught and if consequences are provided that parallel those ordinarily found in target settings. Target settings are settings to which a skill must be transferred.

Use Common Stimuli

Generalization can be improved by analyzing the target setting. Antecedent stimuli that occur in the target setting can then be included in the training environment. Generalization will be more likely if the stimuli are similar. For example, Andrew was learning to wash dishes at school. His

Table 11.2 Strategies to Promote Stimulus Generalization

Strategies	*Procedure*	*Description*
Exploit current functional contingencies.	Teach functional skills.	Teach behaviors that are useful and provide frequent, natural opportunities for reinforcement.
	Use common stimuli.	Analyze the generalization setting and include in training those antecedent stimuli that direct the student's responses in that setting.
	Train in the natural environment.	Use real materials and train in the setting at the time of day when the skill would normally be used.
Train diversely.	Train sufficient exemplars.	Expose the student systematically to planned variations of the situation in which the skill will be applied.
Incorporate functional mediators.	Use self-management.	Teach students to use a device such as a wrist counter to prompt responding. Teach students to verbalize the directions for performing a task or to label salient characteristics of the task.
	Use picture prompting.	Teach students to use pictures that illustrate each step in a chain of responses.
Use general case programming.	Use general case programming.	Define the instructional universe and the range of relevant stimulus conditions. Select and sequence examples for training. Use multiple positive samples and include negative samples.

teacher's goal was for Andrew to become a more independent adult. She knew that he would never wash dishes in a classroom as an adult but that he would be washing dishes at home. In order to facilitate transfer of this skill to his home, Andrew's teacher obtained a description of Andrew's kitchen from his parents, as well as a list of items and materials found in his home. His teacher discovered that at Andrew's home, soap was kept in a cabinet under the sink and leftover food from dishes was scraped into a trash receptacle before the dishes were washed. After Andrew's teacher obtained materials resembling those used in his home, she trained Andrew in the steps she knew would be necessary for him to wash dishes at home. As a result, Andrew's dishwashing skills transferred to his home with minimal prompting.

Train in the Natural Environment

Another method of implementing this strategy is to provide instruction in the actual target setting, with real materials and at the time of day when the skill would normally be used. Students, for example, should be taught vocational skills in a work environment. Shopping skills can be taught in grocery and drug stores.

However, a natural environment may not be enough to produce generalization. Rather, a specific plan might be needed in which generalization probes are performed at each training step. The skill should be tested in other similar settings with different people providing feedback and reinforcement. For example, Mrs. Daniels taught grocery-shopping skills to her class at the local supermarket. Three times a week, she and her students walked to the store and practiced shopping for groceries. All of her students became very adept at shopping in the store, but Mrs. Daniels was not satisfied. So, once a month, she took her students to a different store that was farther away. At first, her students were confused because the items in the second store were in a different place. However, they soon were able to perform as well here as in the first store. When Mrs. Daniels took her students to a third store to test their grocery-shopping skills, all of them performed correctly.

Train Diversely

Training environments often use narrow, unchanging stimulus conditions. The more restricted the conditions are during training, the less likely generalization will occur in other settings. Generalization is enhanced if the stimulus conditions in training vary enough to resemble the conditions in other nontraining environments. Establishing this variety is referred to as *training diversely*.

One tactic in training diversely is to train in a variety of sample situations with a variety of relevant stimuli. The student is systematically exposed to a variety of situations in which the skills can be applied. Antecedents, target responses, settings, and trainers may be varied. For example, Mrs. Fraser is very conscientious about training diversely. When she taught Steven to wash clothes, she provided three different training settings—a classroom and two laundromats. Sometimes she and Steven would wash clothes in the classroom and sometimes they would go to one of the laundromats. Steven learned quickly in all settings. In a very short time, his behavior had generalized to his home. In another example, Mrs. Fraser used several trainers when she taught Anna to request materials and information. Anna first learned to make requests of Mrs. Fraser; then, of one classroom aide; and then, of another aide. When Anna took the initiative in requesting information from the librarian, Mrs. Fraser knew the behavior had generalized.

Such subtle environmental factors as distracting noises and the presence or absence of people should also be used in training. In this way, students are exposed to variations that may be encountered in typical environments. This exposure increases the probability that correct responses will occur in subsequent generalization environments. Tony, for example, was easily distracted by the presence of other people in the training environment. Mrs. Fraser began training him to buy items at the local drug store during times when she knew no other people would be there. As Tony became more proficient, she changed the timing of their trips to when more and more people would be in the store. Eventually, Tony was able to buy items even when the store was very crowded.

Incorporate Functional Mediators

A *functional mediator* is a stimulus that is used to help transfer learning from the training situation to the target setting. A functional mediator is established as a discriminative stimulus during training and is then introduced into the generalization environment. For example, Johnny was taught at school to follow a diagram to assemble a bicycle. When he went to work at the bike shop, he used the diagram to assemble bicycles. The diagram served as a functional mediator.

Functional mediators are often used in self-management strategies. A physical device, such as a wrist-counter, tally sheet, or checklist, is used to promote the desired behavior and to keep track of the frequency. The device itself becomes an S^D for correct behavior, and stimulus control is demonstrated. Lester, for example, learned to assemble computer cables at his school in preparation for a job with a computer firm. His program included a self-monitoring component that consisted of a checklist. Each step of the task was on the checklist. When he finished each step, he would place a checkmark next to the item. When all items were checked, he took the checklist to the instructor so his work could be evaluated. When Lester began work at a computer firm, the checklist was modified slightly and sent with him. Using the checklist, Lester was able to complete his duties at work with very little instruction.

Self-management training may also include self-verbalization procedures that can function as discriminative stimuli and mediate generalization. When self-verbalizations are included in training, the student may be taught to verbalize the directions for performing a task or for responding correctly. Alternatively, a student may be taught to label salient characteristics of the task. For example, Lester might have been taught to name each task as he completed it rather than mark it on a checklist.

Picture prompts are another example of functional mediators. Picture-prompting procedures provide the student with pictures of each step in a chain of responses. The pictures become discriminative stimuli for correct responses. Once the student learns to follow the picture prompts in one setting, the prompts may be transferred to other settings in which similar responses are appropriate. Training students to respond to one set of pictures may facilitate their responding to novel pictures. Wacker, Berg, Berrie, and Swatta (1985), for example, found that students with severe disabilities who were taught to use picture prompts to complete vocational and domestic living tasks were able to generalize to novel pictures illustrating novel tasks.

Use General Case Programming

General case programming is a more precise method for identifying and sequencing optimal training examples. The first step in the procedure is to identify the range of possible stimulus conditions and correct responses. For example, Mr. Allison began training Mike to wash his hands by using general case–programming procedures. He identified stimuli that included different types of basins, soap dispensers, and drying methods. Response methods included pushing or pulling buttons or handles on soap dispensers and drying mechanisms as well as pulling towels off a roll.

Once the instructional situations are defined, examples are selected for training. Using a variety of training situations increases the probability that generalization will occur. In Mr. Allison's program, for instance, three different types of soap dispensers, faucet handles, and drying mechanisms were selected. Mike was trained to use the variety of soap dispensers and drying methods.

Negative examples must also be included in training. These are stimulus situations in which the trained responses should not occur. For example, Mr.

Allison taught Mike not to wash his hands in water used to clean dishes or in a water fountain.

Horner, Albin, and Ralph (1986) used general case–programming procedures to teach grocery-item selection to six young adults. Training sites were three grocery stores that had been surveyed to ensure that they were similar in size, availability of target products, and aisle layout. A fourth store was not trained but used as a generalization probe; it contained the same products as the other stores but different aisle, shelf, and product arrangements. Participants were taught to use picture-card cues to select 10 correct, or positive, grocery items and to reject 20 incorrect, or negative, grocery items. Following training, participants were able to select correctly the positive items in the nontrained store. Also, participants who had been trained using minimally different negative examples correctly rejected negative items.

General case–programming procedures become more important as students with severe disabilities move into community environments for work, domestic, and leisure activities. Community environments are fluid rather than stable. Over time, people, materials, and task requirements change. Students must be able to adjust to novel demands and situations in order to function independently within these environments.

Response Generalization

As previously mentioned, response generalization refers to a process in which a change in the rate of one behavior produces changes in other behaviors. An initial behavior is affected directly, such as through positive reinforcement, while other behaviors are affected indirectly. Generalization is evident in the indirect changes in the other behaviors.

Response generalization can refer to behavioral changes in any direction. In some instances, an increase in one type of behavior will produce increases in other behaviors. For example, Ingrid receives a reinforcer every time she makes eye contact with one of her peers. As the frequency of her eye contact increases, Ingrid also begins to smile and speak to the person at whom she is looking. Even though smiling and speaking are not reinforced directly, they may become more frequent because of the increase in eye contact. These are examples of desirable side effects. However, an increase in a desirable behavior (e.g., eye contact) can also be associated with an increase in an undesirable response (e.g., aggression). For instance, Ingrid could hit her peer rather than smile or talk to him.

Behavior change programs that serve to increase a target behavior may produce reductions in other behaviors. Functional communication is a clear example of this kind of relationship. *Functional communication training* is an approach for decreasing problem behaviors by increasing the rate of desirable communicative responses. For example, Janice was a 12-year-old student with autism. During meals she screeched loudly whenever she wanted more food. When Janice's teacher taught her to ask for more food by pointing to the item she wanted, Janice quit screeching.

Functional communication training begins with a functional analysis (see Chapter 3) of the problem behavior. The functional analysis should identify the motivations or causes of the problem behavior. These are usually interpreted as having communicative intent; that is, problem behaviors can often be identified as expressions of a person's desire to change the environment. For example, Janice's screeching behavior appeared to be an attempt to obtain a tangible item, food. Other behaviors can indicate a desire to receive more attention, discontinue an unpleasant activity, or create more excitement. These expressions are viewed accurately as functional communication—i.e., they serve to engage other people in performed desired activities.

When the communicative intent of a problem behavior is identified, an alternative communicative response is selected. In functional communication training, the communicative response must produce the same effect (e.g., obtaining attention, removing noxious activities, producing excitement) as was intended by the problem behavior; it also must be as effective as the problem behavior (i.e., it must be successful in manipulating the environment) and relatively easy for the person to perform. The alternative communication can be speech or a form of nonverbal communication. For example, the alternative form that Janice's teacher taught her met all three criteria: it had the same effect of obtaining more food and was effective and easy to perform. Every time Janice pointed, her teacher provided her with more food.

Teaching and reinforcing the pointing response gave Janice an alternative that she could use appropriately in situations when the problem behavior would occur. Since the alternative communication produced the same result that was intended by the problem behavior, the motivation (or cause) of the problem behavior was suspended, with the outcome being a concomitant and indirect reduction in the rate of the problem behavior. Functional communication training is a popular example of response generalization.

Response generalization that results from functional communication training is related to the notion of *response classes*. A response class is an instance in which two or more behaviors produce the same effect on the environment. Behaviors within a single response class are said to be *functionally equivalent*. In functional communication training, tantrums that are maintained because they produce attention may be functionally equivalent to a verbal or nonverbal request for attention. The tantrum and the request would be members of the same response class. Therefore, teaching a person to use an acceptable form of requesting attention should result in a generalized reduction in tantrums.

Response generalization also occurs when decreases in problem behaviors occur as a result of increasing the rate of a positive behavior that might not be in the same response class. Response generalization that occurs through the development of new, adaptive skills is viewed as an important means of decreasing the occurrence of tantrums, violent behavior, and stereotypy in persons with developmental disabilities.

To illustrate, Lisa caused may problems during leisure activities. She took toys from other students, hit the students, threw the toys, and rarely played with anything for more than 2 minutes. Mrs. Snodgrass, Lisa's teacher, developed a program to teach Lisa to play with toys appropriately. As Lisa learned to play with more toys, her previous inappropriate toy-play and aggressive behaviors during leisure activities stopped.

Response generalization may occur also in programs that are designed to reduce problem behavior directly. For example, behavior change plans that reduce repetitive, stereotypic behavior in people with autism or mental retardation have also produced increases in more desirable, task-related behaviors. This indirect effect of a behavior reduction plan is an example of response generalization.

Response generalization is essential for purposes of instruction and habilitation. It is impossible to teach every behavior that a person needs to learn in a behavior-by-behavior progression. There are simply too many behaviors that need to be acquired. Although many behaviors are taught directly, response generalization is depended upon for additional gains.

Imitation is a common example of learning through response generalization. Imitation training begins with a student being prompted to copy a demonstrated behavior. When that behavior is copied and learned, a behavior is modeled, and the student is again prompted to copy. Eventually, the student begins to copy the model without needing to be prompted to do so. Response generalization has taken place. This type of generalization is essential not only for imitation but also for language development and all other forms of complex responding.

Issues in Maintenance and Generalization with People with Disabilities

If behavior modification is to succeed, it must produce improvements in lifestyle for people who need assistance. The development of new skills and the reduction of problem behaviors should contribute to more productive, pleasant, and satisfying lives. Outcomes must generalize sufficiently to improve adjustment across relevant environments and circumstances. Several issues, guidelines, and limitations must be considered when planning for generalization and maintenance.

Several Forms of Generalization

An important issue in generalization is that there are several forms of generalization. As discussed earlier, generalization can refer to either stimulus generalization or response generalization. These are different processes with different outcomes that must be considered in efforts to increase independence and successful responding in community settings. A generalization in which the learning of one skill produces more efficient learning of a second, related skill may also be considered. For example, Alice, a 10-year-old student with developmental disabilities, is taught to identify the EXIT sign. It is likely that she will require fewer trials to learn the sign for the women's rest room. This phenomenon has been referred to as *learning to learn* and is a form of response generalization.

Stimulus generalization is the type of generalization most often researched and written about. It is related to stimulus control. Efforts to produce stimulus generalization are dependent upon the precision with which relevant antecedent stimuli are identified and manipulated. Sufficient preintervention planning and assessment must be done to determine the stimulus generalization that is desired and the relevant controlling stimuli in the generalization environments.

Stimulus generalization can have its limits. A common strategy for achieving stimulus generalization is to establish desirable responding in the target setting by providing stimuli (such as verbal or physical prompts) that are certain to result in the behavior and then to fade the stimuli so that other more naturally occurring stimuli come to control the desirable performances. For example, a job coach may provide verbal and physical prompts for a person with severe intellectual disabilities, with this guidance resulting in the person's satisfactory (even exemplary) performance of a task. The job coach may also be able to fade both the verbal and physical prompts over time so that they are barely perceptible. However, the job coach may be unable to remove herself completely. In other words, on-the-job responding by the person with disabilities might continue to be dependent on the stimulus control exerted by the job coach because naturally occurring stimuli on the job site do not become discriminative for durable, on-task responding. This example is representative of common limitations in generalization with people with developmental disabilities. It illustrates a need to maintain some level of support when people with disabilities experience the rigors and complexities of typical community settings.

The issue of maintenance of desirable responding raises similar cautions. Even when stimulus generalization occurs in a desirable way, there is no guarantee that the generalized responding will maintain. As discussed previously, maintenance is directly related to the schedules of reinforcement. If sufficient reinforcers are not available, the behavior will extinguish. Many typical environments are not designed to provide the level of reinforcers that may be required to sustain desirable performances exhibited by people with developmental disabilities. Therefore, it is frequently necessary to program some explicit reinforcement in order to maintain desirable responding. In the example just mentioned, the delivery of occasional reinforcement could very well be a key responsibility of the job coach.

The quest to produce generalized reductions in the rate of challenging behaviors, such as aggression or stereotypy, is another issue that has considerable importance. Many behavior modification plans that seek to reduce problem behaviors have failed to achieve generalization. Traditional behavior modification programs that rely on punishment or other forms of direct contingency management have had only limited success from the perspective of generalization. However, an encouraging answer seems to exist in teaching a functionally equivalent alternative behavior and then promoting generalization of that desirable response. For example, Durand and Carr (1991) used a strategy based on functional communication training with students with serious challenging behaviors and severe disabilities. The researchers not only were successful in producing relatively rapid reductions of the challenging behaviors but also found that these changes maintained over extended periods of time and across different school settings with just minor adjustments to the ongoing schedule of instruction. This strategy of teaching positive alternatives has the advantage of developing appropriate and adaptive behavior while concurrently reducing behavior problems. Of course, efforts to promote generalization of the desirable alternative behavior must be approached with the same precision and cautions that have been described for any other behaviors.

Summary

Generalization is a critical issue in effective behavior modification. Programming for generalization must be carefully considered and individualized for each learner. Some general guidelines include the following:

1. *Plan for generalization from the beginning of intervention.* Planning should include explicit objectives stated in terms of the desired generalization, such as a specification of the contexts and the behaviors that should be affected. Planning should also include careful assessment of the stimulus and reinforcement conditions that exist in the target environments.
2. *Provide intervention in relevant settings under naturally occurring*

conditions. As much as possible, perform the training in the target setting. The best way to insure that behavior change will occur in a particular setting is to provide the intervention in that setting, thereby avoiding possible problems with generalization. Usually, however, it is neither feasible nor practical to conduct a specialized intervention in each and every setting. In such circumstances, train in the context(s) in which the need or the problem is greatest. Then, make every effort to facilitate transfer to other settings.

3. *Make use of existing technology of generalization.* Make deliberate use of strategies for promoting generalization. Specific strategies are available for both stimulus generalization and response generalization, and these should be considered in any behavior change or teaching plan.
4. *For specific generalization objectives, attend to the functions of stimulus control (stimulus generalization), schedules of reinforcement (maintenance), and functional equivalence (response generalization).* As discussed in this chapter, there are principles that guide the processes of generalization. Recognition of these principles can help in the development of individual strategies for promoting generalization.
5. *For any concerns regarding important generalization objectives, be diligent in monitoring progress and be prepared to insert intervention procedures as necessary.* Generalization is not apt to occur without planned manipulations. Assurance of successful outcomes can be gained only with ongoing monitoring and a readiness to provide additional support when needed.

Study Questions

1. What are the three processes included under the term *generalization*? Provide a definition and example of each.
2. List four strategies for promoting stimulus generalization and provide an example of each.
3. List three strategies for promoting skill maintenance and provide an example of each.
4. Define *indiscriminable contingencies*. Provide an example.
5. Describe *functional communication training* and provide an example.
6. What role can data collection serve in programming for generalization?

Exercises

1. Daniel has a work/study job in which he delivers prepared meals to persons who are unable to make their own meals. He is supposed to work for

3 hours, but after 2 hours he consistently throws a tantrum that includes crying and throwing trays on the ground. His job coach has assessed this behavior and found that it functions as an escape response. Design a program for Daniel using the principles of response generalization.

2. Design a plan in which a delayed reinforcement procedure is used to increase the probability that a skill will maintain.

3. Mrs. Andrews' students were on a point system. Once a week, they could turn in their points to buy items in the school store. Mrs. Andrews used this opportunity to teach shopping skills. She had the students exchange their points for money that they used in the school store. However, when she took the students to a neighborhood grocery store, they were unable to select items or give their money to the cashier. Explain the students' behavior by using the principles of stimulus generalization. Describe two ways to remediate this problem.

4. Mitzi is learning to use a public bus to get to her job. Her teacher has faded prompts and reinforcers so that Mitzi is able to board the correct bus as long as her teacher is at the bus stop. However, when the teacher tries to fade her presence, Mitzi does not board any bus. Explain the limits of stimulus generalization.

Self-Application

1. You are interested in increasing the environments in which you can study effectively. You currently are able to study at the library but unable to study in your own residence. Describe possible differences between the two environments that might explain the discrepancy in your behavior and provide an intervention that will increase the probability that study behavior will generalize to your residence.

2. How would you use a functional mediator to help you sustain a diet in all environments?

3. Design a plan to help you maintain a newly learned skill, such as ballroom dancing, by using natural reinforcers.

SELF-MANAGEMENT PROJECT

1. Consider how you will program for maintenance and generalization of your targeted behavior for your self-management project. If applicable, plan for fading of the reinforcement schedule, use of natural reinforcers, use of functional mediators, or other maintenance and generalization strategies that will help you maintain your behavioral gains. Describe the maintenance and generalization strategies you will use.

References

Durand, V. M., & Carr, E. G. (1991). Functional communication training to reduce challenging behavior: Maintenance and application in new settings. *Journal of Applied Behavior Analysis, 24,* 251–264.

Horner, R. H., Albin, R. W., & Ralph, G. (1986). Generalization with precision: The role of negative teaching examples in the instruction of generalized grocery item selection. *Journal of the Association for Persons with Severe Handicaps, 11,* 300–308.

Wacker, D. P., Berg, W. K., Berrie, P., & Swatta, P. (1985). Generalization and maintenance of complex skills by severely handicapped adolescents following picture prompt training. *Journal of Applied Behavior Analysis, 18,* 329–336.

12

Designing a Behavior Change Plan

Mrs. Angus was a nursery school teacher who taught nine 4-year-old children. She worked hard to create an environment in which learning was interesting and even fun and had a variety of learning and play materials for the children. She also provided them with praise and smiles as they learned and cooperated. Since she was aware of the dangers of providing too much attention to misbehavior, she was circumspect in her reactions to children who misbehaved. Mrs. Angus was not implementing a formal behavior change plan. However, she had harnessed the principles of behavior and had used them on an ongoing basis with her students. As a result, she had a happy, cooperative classroom.

Mr. Billings also taught nursery school. He taught five children without handicaps and one child with language delays. The child with language delays had a number of severe behavior problems, including head banging, screaming, and toy throwing. Mr. Billings consulted with the school psychologist and the child's parents, and they decided that a formal behavior modification plan was needed. In it, the behaviors of head banging, screaming, and toy throwing were pinpointed for elimination; cooperative behaviors were targeted for strengthening. This formal behavior modification plan was designed for implementation by Mr. Billings and a classroom aide.

Both of these cases are examples of the use of the principles of behavior. The first case employed behavior modification as an ongoing tool for creating an optimal learning environment for the nursery school class. No one child was singled out, and no one behavior was targeted for change. However, application of the principles of behavior permeated the classroom setting. In the second case, one child was singled out for a formal behavior change plan. Behaviors were targeted, strategies chosen, and a plan was designed. This case is an example of the concentration of behavior modification procedures into a behavior change plan, targeting the behaviors of an individual student.

The principles of behavior can be used in an ongoing, naturalistic manner as a teacher manages a learning environment, a parent manages a home environment, a boss manages a working environment, or people manage their own lives. Informal application of these principles involves using them to maximize learning, progress, or production, without proceeding with prescribed steps of specific signals and reactions. The principles of behavior, therefore, are used but not in a rigidly controlled pattern. Although data collection and quantitative evaluation of data might not be involved, the principles are used systematically to meet goals. Informal application might be present in all phases of instructional, vocational, and interpersonal relationships. An individual who understands the principles of behavior can use them to structure interactions and achieve results in a less controlled way.

A formal behavior modification plan involves more rigid and data-based application of the principles of behavior. The process follows a set sequence. Specific strategies are assigned. Given certain circumstances and behaviors, certain responses or other efforts are prescribed. A formal behavior modification plan is likely to be used for specific behaviors that have been targeted for change and evaluation.

This chapter provides a brief discussion of the application of the principles of behavior in a natural, ongoing manner. However, it focuses on the design of a formal behavior modification plan to change specific, targeted behavior.

Informal Application

The principles of behavior describe laws under which behavior operates. Understanding how these principles operate can help teachers, parents, and instructors maximize their effectiveness in dealing with children. When applied to people's lives, these principles can help in establishing desirable patterns of behavior while eliminating undesirable ones. Individuals who are knowledgeable about the principles of behavior can apply these principles in naturalistic ways on an ongoing basis to optimize their own functioning and the functioning of others. Several examples of informal application are discussed in this section, which is not meant to be inclusive.

Strategies based on stimulus control can be optimized in the presentation and arrangement of instructional materials. Stimulus control can also be used routinely to evoke desirable behaviors and discourage undesirable behaviors. Stimulus fading and shaping can be used to teach skills. The design of entire curricula can be dictated by principles based on stimulus control.

Positive reinforcement can be used in a planned way to strengthen desirable behaviors. Praise, positive feedback, good grades, special privileges, and free time are examples of possible reinforcers that can be used systematically in classroom settings. Effective parents often make discerning use of praise, attention, special privileges, and favorite activities in order to build desirable behaviors in their children.

Modeling is a powerful method for effecting learning and behavior change. Teachers, coaches, instructors, and parents have intuitively noted the effects of modeling. People who are seeking to teach or otherwise influence the behavior of other people can use modeling in planned but natural ways to achieve goals. Limiting access to undesirable models becomes a consideration in naturalistic behavior change also.

Extinction can only operate if the reinforcer is no longer available. Teachers unaware of the principles of behavior often put a great deal of time and energy into attending to misbehavior and then are perplexed when the misbehaviors escalate. For example, teachers who are continually attending to the children who are out of their seats may notice that most of the children are out of their seats most of the time. Teachers who can place these minor disruptive behaviors on extinction often have more orderly classrooms than teachers who operate in ignorance of the role that extinction can serve.

Parents who are knowledgeable about the extinction principle can marshal it to prevent a myriad of low-level but annoying problems at home. Incessant demanding behavior and nagging are often the result of inadvertent reinforcement. Knowledge and application of extinction can rid a home of these unwanted behaviors.

Teachers, instructors, and parents who are knowledgeable about the principles of maintenance and generalization can work toward these goals as they teach and influence others. Chapter 11 elaborates specific methods for promoting generalization. These methods can often be routinely incorporated into instructional situations. For example, a parent who wishes to teach a child good table manners that will carry over to other environments will teach them to the child not only at Thanksgiving but also at other times. Teaching will occur in a variety of settings, including the home, restaurants, and friends' homes. By teaching table manners in diverse settings, generalization will most likely occur.

Informal application of behavior modification procedures can do much to enrich the learning possibilities of home, school, work, and social settings. The knowledgeable behavior analyst, whether parent, teacher, or psychologist, will take a behavioral world view and view behavior in its relationship to behavioral principles. Teaching, learning, and interacting with other people can be enriched through informal application of behavioral principles.

Formal Behavior Change

Behavior change efforts, however, might need to be formalized and evaluated quantitatively. The design and implementation of such a plan will proceed according to accepted steps, which include data collection and evaluation. The target subject can be a child or adult who has some diagnosis or problem, or the target subject can be an individual who is without handicaps and working toward specific behavioral achievements. With either population, behavior follows the same principles. Strategies based on the principles of behavior are organized into a prescribed plan, following a set process. The resulting plan can be called a behavior modification plan, behavior change plan, behavior management plan, or simply a behavior plan.

Formal behavior modification, therefore, follows a set process. Steps are carried out in a prescribed order, which begins when a behavior is targeted for change and ends with follow-up monitoring and, possibly, plan termination. The formal behavior change process is illustrated in Figure 12.1.

Pinpoint Behaviors

The first step of the behavior modification process is to pinpoint the behaviors for change. This process is described in detail in Chapter 2 and consists of targeting behaviors that are observable and measurable. Initial targeting might involve misbehavior. After a functional assessment is completed, additional adaptive behaviors might be targeted for strengthening, as appropriate replacements of targeted misbehavior.

Collect Data

After the pinpointing of behaviors for change, data collection procedures are designed and implemented. These procedures, discussed in detail in Chapters 2 and 3, involve measurement for quantity of and contextual information about the behavior. Baseline data collection takes place for a determined period of time—if possible, long enough to determine the baseline range of the behavior. If the behavior is serious and presents a danger, baseline might need to be curtailed. However, the subsequent plan might be inadequate and may need to be enriched as more information is collected. In cases of misbehavior, functional assessment data must be of sufficient quantity also, to provide hypotheses about factors promoting and maintaining the behavior.

Do Functional Assessment

After the collecting of data, a functional assessment is done, as described in Chapter 3. Possible functions of the misbehavior are listed, as well

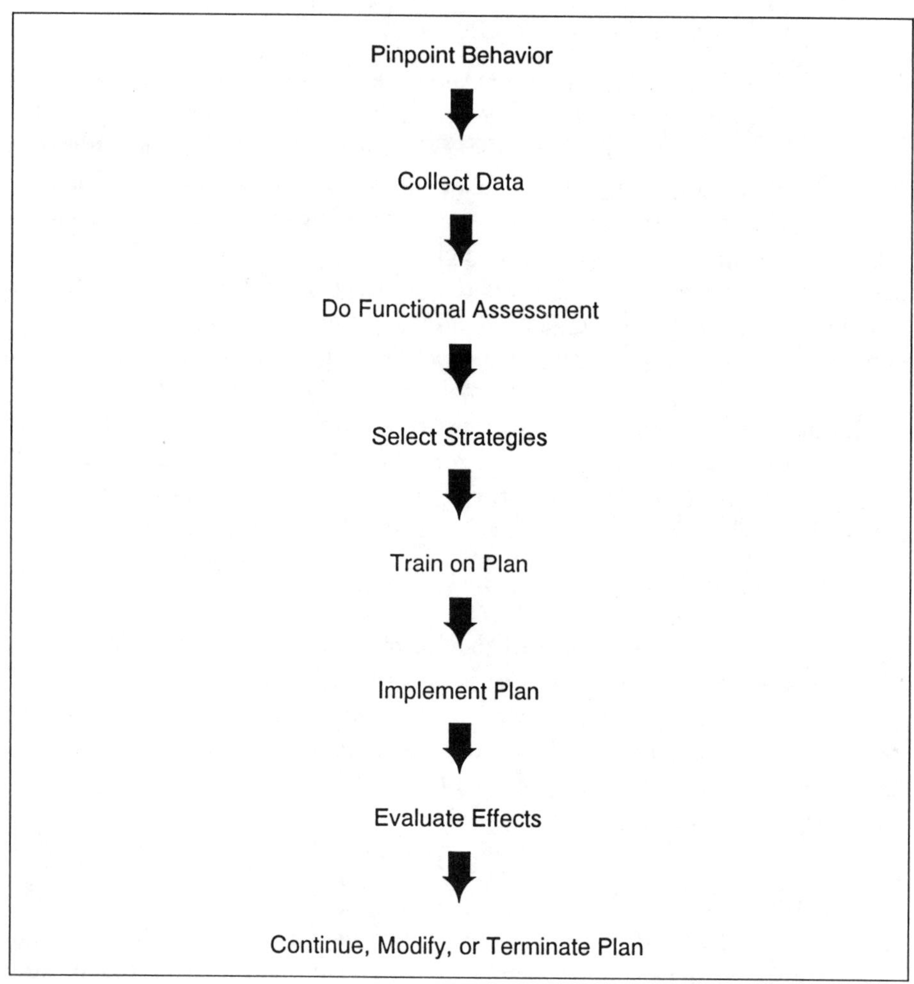

Figure 12.1 Flow chart showing the steps involved in a behavior change plan.

as stimuli or setting events that precede the behavior and seem to affect it. Functional assessments might also be done in cases of teaching new behaviors, to determine possible deterrents to skill acquisition. Once the functional assessment is done, intervention strategies can be selected.

Select Procedures

The functional assessment should be the basis for choosing strategies for a behavior change plan. It can be valuable in designing plans that build desirable behaviors and plans that eliminate or replace undesirable ones.

In cases of misbehavior, the functional assessment can provide a wealth of information on functions the behavior is serving for the individual. The functional assessment can also provide important information on factors related to learning, or failure to learn, new behaviors.

Strategies for behavior change often logically follow from information derived from the functional assessment. It pinpoints possible functions the targeted behavior serves, and each possible function has treatment implications. There are several basic approaches to dealing with functions of misbehavior. Any given behavior plan might use one or more of these approaches; and, within each approach, one or more of a variety of intervention strategies can be selected.

Teach Another Way

An important approach to behavior change is to identify the function the misbehavior serves and then teach the individual another way to fulfill that function. Giving the individual more acceptable means of having demands met can be a critical step toward lasting behavior change.

For example, Mary screams when she wants food. Clearly, she needs to be taught another way to ask for food. Johnny throws his work materials when having difficulty with math problems. He needs to be taught to ask for help with math. Mrs. Anderson screams at her students when they become too loud. She needs to learn another way to maintain a quiet classroom. Leonard bangs his head when he wants a break from work. He needs to learn another way to ask for a break.

Durand and Carr (1987) investigated the selection of intervention procedures for the self-stimulatory behavior of four children with developmental disabilities. A functional analysis revealed that these behaviors, which included body rocking and hand flapping, increased when difficult academic tasks were presented. The children were taught to ask for help, and the frequency of their self-stimulatory behavior subsequently decreased.

When teaching alternate responses, it is important to select an alternate response that is relatively easy to perform. Horner, Sprague, O'Brien, and Heathfield (1990), for example, compared the effectiveness of a high-effort response versus a low-effort response to replace an aggression response in a 14-year-old boy with moderate mental retardation. The researchers performed a functional analysis and determined that aggression served the functions of escaping from difficult tasks and of obtaining teacher assistance. They compared the effectiveness of a high-effort substitute response (typing a request for help) with the effectiveness of a low-effort replacement response (pressing a single key). While the high-effort response had no effect on the level of aggression, substantial decreases in aggression were reported after teaching the low-effort response.

There is no lack of strategies for teaching new behaviors. In fact, entire curricula fall under this category of intervention. Several procedures based on the principles of behavior and previously identified are highlighted.

Modeling

Modeling can be a valuable and effective means of teaching new behaviors. It can be used either alone or in combination with another strategy; and it can be done with symbols or by people such as teachers, instructors, or peers. Decisions must be made regarding what form the model will take, how often modeling will occur, whether or not the model's behavior will be reinforced, and whether the learner's behavior will be reinforced.

Shaping

Shaping is another effective way to teach new behaviors. In this procedure, decisions must be made regarding the breakdown of a behavior or task into steps, the initial criteria for reinforcement, the criteria for increasing the level required for reinforcement, the reinforcers to be used, the schedule of reinforcement, and the possible plans for fading.

Structured Instructional Procedures

Structured instructional procedures, such as systems of increasing prompts, decreasing prompts, and graduated guidance, might be used to teach specific tasks. They might also be used to teach such social skills as asking for assistance, greeting people, sharing, initiating conversations, obtaining social recognition, and solving social problems.

Stimulus Control Procedures

Stimulus control procedures are yet another means of teaching new behaviors. Providing distinct cues and then fading them as learning takes place might be a useful way to effect behavioral acquisition. Chapter 7 covers a variety of strategies that use stimulus control to teach new behaviors, such as the use of stimulus prompts and response prompts. Stimulus control procedures might also be critical when teaching a person to use behaviors under certain acceptable circumstances. For example, Albert talks excessively in class. He does not need to learn to be silent but, rather, to learn to talk at certain times only. Stimulus control procedures can be effective in providing Albert with cues for acceptable times to talk.

Positive Reinforcement

For any plan in which behaviors are taught or strengthened, the use of positive reinforcement might also be necessary. The target behaviors must be selected as well as the circumstances under which these behaviors will be reinforced. Positive reinforcers must then be chosen and arranged according to a schedule. These reinforcers should be as natural as possible but sufficiently potent to be effective. They can be chosen in a variety of ways (described in Chapter 4), such as from information gained from the functional assessment, from observation, from interviews, and from reinforcer sampling.

Chaining

Most human behavior occurs in chains. Behavioral *chaining* is the process of connecting simple behaviors into chains of more complex behaviors. Chaining can be used to teach complex sequences of behaviors by building small units of behaviors into sequences. Behavioral chains can be built by using stimulus control and positive reinforcement to link small units of behavior that are already in an individual's repertoire. Over time, the reinforcers can be faded, and the behaviors themselves can serve as conditioned reinforcers of preceding behaviors in the chain and as S^Ds for the next behavior in the chain.

For example, Glen was a young man with moderate mental retardation. He had behavior problems at home, which included task refusal, shouting, and cursing. A functional assessment revealed that these behaviors often occurred when Glen was asked to do a chore. Chaining was then used to teach Glen to complete a series of tasks each evening. He already had in his repertoire the component behaviors of performing household chores, but he did not have the overall skill of cooperatively performing a set of chores each day. So, each day, his schedule was written out for him; it included a list of his chores as well as some preferred activities. He was taught to check his schedule, perform an activity, cross the activity off the list, and proceed to the next activity. Glen's written schedule provided for stimulus control. Initially, he was provided reinforcers for completion of each activity on his schedule; eventually, these reinforcers were faded, and he was provided a reinforcer at the end of each evening for cooperatively following his daily schedule. The completion of each task served as the reinforcer for that task and as the S^D to return to the schedule and proceed with the next task. The chain of behaviors was reinforced with a favorite activity at the end of the evening.

In another example, Priscilla was a young woman with profound mental retardation and autism who could not use verbal language. She had a history of head banging whenever tasks were presented. Chaining was used to teach her to comply with a daily schedule. Instead of a written schedule, as used in Glen's case, a picture schedule was used in which photographs of Priscilla engaged in the tasks were posted in a sequence. Priscilla was initially provided with reinforcers after completing each task on her picture schedule. Eventually, she was offered a reinforcer at the end of the evening only, following completion of all the tasks on her picture schedule. As with Glen, the completion of each task became the reinforcer for the previous task as well as the S^D to check the schedule and begin the next task.

Satisfy the Function

Strategies might be selected that eliminate the need for problem behavior by providing the desired reinforcers or outcomes.

Free Provision

At times, the best approach in dealing with problem behavior is to determine what a person is trying to achieve by the misbehavior and then provide it for free. By providing an individual the item or event for free and in sufficient quantities, the individual can, in effect, satiate, and the misbehavior can lose its purpose. The targeted behavior will decrease in frequency at an even faster rate if it is put on extinction as well. This approach is particularly desirable when the functions the behavior serves are reasonable but the behavior itself is unreasonable.

A functional assessment might reveal that an individual is attempting to obtain attention, affection, food, help, or breaks from work. Free provision of these events or items can be either on an ongoing basis or according to a time schedule. For example, Elmer was a young man who had recently moved from an institution to a group home in the community. He had several incidents of severe aggression, including biting. Most of these incidents involved his attempts to get food. So, Elmer's behavior plan included a liberal snack schedule: he was offered a snack every 45 minutes. His aggression related to food snatching was soon eliminated.

For individuals whose behavioral functions are related to attention getting, it might be reasonable to provide praise, chats, or other social interactions on a regular basis. If attention is liberally supplied throughout the day, the individual learns that it is not necessary to misbehave in order to obtain attention.

It is not always reasonable to give free access to a desired item. To illustrate, a young man with autism often scratched his face, drew blood, and then smeared the blood on his face. Clearly, blood would not be provided to him. In such cases, it can be helpful to provide similar stimuli. For this young man, lotion was provided as a substitute for blood. At regular intervals throughout the day, he was given lotion to smear on his face.

In another example, Smith (1987) worked with a young man with pica. His pica consisted of swallowing hard, inedible objects such as paper clips, tacks, and bottle caps. Obviously, he could not be provided with a supply of these items to eat. Instead, he was provided with a snack pouch that contained crunchy foods such as granola, peanuts, and potato chips. His pica was rapidly reduced and eventually eliminated. Smith (1986) also eliminated rectal digging followed by finger sniffing in a young woman with autism by providing alternative scents for her to smell.

Contingent Availability

Rather than provide reinforcing events freely, it might be useful to provide them on a schedule of positive reinforcement. Targeted behaviors would be behaviors that can replace the misbehavior or that are desirable as goals in and of themselves. For example, Janet is a young girl with profound mental retardation who screams frequently for food and drinks. An effective intervention might be to implement a schedule of positive reinforcement that provides food and drinks for asking quietly for them. The desired reinforcers are provided contingent upon a behavior that is incompatible with and more appropriate than the misbehavior. In another example, Rebecca is a 10-year-old girl with a learning disability. She frequently stops working in order to talk with her teacher. Her teacher might arrange a schedule of reinforcement under which special chats with Rebecca are provided contingent upon task completion.

Durand, Crimmins, Caulfield, and Taylor (1989) selected treatment strategies for 14 students with severe developmental disorders and problem behaviors. These were based on the reinforcers that were maintaining the problem behaviors. Thus, if problem behaviors were maintained by social attention, social attention was used effectively as a reinforcer for task performance. If problem behaviors were maintained by negative reinforcement (escape from a task), breaks from a task were effective as reinforcers for task performance. The researchers found that reinforcers that are functionally related to a problem behavior can serve as effective reinforcers for desirable behavior.

Eliminate the Function

In some cases of misbehavior, it is possible to eliminate the behavior's function altogether. Often, the behavior serves the function of escaping from a certain task, event, or environment. Johnny, for example, hits his classmate when his classmate yells. The function of his aggression is to escape from the yelling. Amy, a child with a learning disability, cries when given math assignments. The function of her crying is to escape from math, a subject that is difficult for her. It might be desirable to identify the reasons an individual is attempting to escape and then provide remedies. By providing remedies, the individual will no longer need to engage in escape-related behaviors. The escape function, then, can be eliminated or its effects can at least be mitigated. There are several strategies that can be used to eliminate or mitigate the reasons for escape.

Eliminate Negative Reinforcer

It might be useful to eliminate a negative reinforcer. For example, Johnny hit other children in attempts to escape a child's screams, a negative reinforcer. Johnny was removed from his classroom, in which there were many children with so-called emotional problems, and placed into a classroom with children without such problems. In Johnny's new classroom, there was no screaming. So, Johnny no longer needed to hit others in order to escape from some child's screaming.

Negative reinforcers can be more pervasive than some child's screaming. The nature of tasks or activities, the spacing of activities, and the nature of social interactions can also serve as negative reinforcers from which an individual attempts to escape. For example, a first-grade boy with hyperactivity who is required to stay in his seat and do schoolwork quietly all day may attempt a variety of escape behaviors to avoid what for him is an intolerable situation. A teenager who lives in a home full of discord might engage in escape-related behaviors, such as staying out late.

If a misbehavior serves the function of escape, it might be necessary to evaluate all aspects of an environment to determine what events or interactions are serving as negative reinforcers. Changes in the environment might then be needed to create a situation that is less conducive to escape-motivated behavior.

Revise Goals

Goal revision can eliminate the need for escape behavior. Amy's case provides a good example. Amy was escaping from doing math assignments by crying. She was given a math assessment that determined that her math goals were too difficult for her to achieve. Her teacher was teaching multiplication, and Amy had not yet mastered the concept of addition. So, instead of trying to teach multiplication to Amy, the teacher began to teach her addition. When Amy was provided with math instruction on a more appropriate level and her math goals were changed, her crying ceased. She no longer needed to escape from math.

Revise Methods

If a misbehavior serves the function of escape from a task, instructional procedures must be reviewed to determine whether they are appropriate for the learner. It might, therefore, be necessary to change the instructional methods. For example, instead of teaching Amy math with paper and pencil, it might be more appropriate for the teacher to use manipulative objects, such as rods and blocks. Instead of just verbal instruction, more blatant use of stimuli might be needed, such as modeling. With instructional methods mitigating the difficulty of math concepts, Amy will no longer need to escape from the task of doing math assignments.

In another example, Weeks and Gaylord-Ross (1981) noticed that higher rates of problem behavior occurred when three children with severe handicaps were presented with difficult tasks. A functional analysis suggested that the function of their problem behaviors was to escape from the demand situation. The researchers changed the instructional procedures so that the children could perform the tasks with few or no errors. The revised instructional strategy resulted in an elimination of problem behavior during visual discrimination tasks. This study provides a demonstration of the modification of problem behaviors through changes in the curriculum.

Eliminating the functions of a misbehavior can be accomplished by small changes in the environment, as in Amy's case. In other instances, sweeping changes might be needed, as in Johnny's case. Much of Johnny's aberrant behavior was escape motivated. By taking him out of a segregated special-education class for children with emotional disturbances and placing him in a class with children without handicaps, many of the events that triggered his escape behavior were no longer present. Johnny made significant strides in social development when the setting events and consequences for his bizarre behavior were eliminated.

Mitigate Effects

As already mentioned, it is possible in some cases to eliminate the reason for an escape behavior by changing the task, the environment, or other aspects of the setting. If it is not possible to eliminate totally the reason for an escape behavior, it might be possible to lessen, or mitigate, the effects. For example, Albert cried, screamed, and hid under the bed during thunderstorms. Although it was not possible to eliminate thunderstorms, it was possible to mitigate the effects of thunderstorms. Whenever they occurred, Albert's mother provided Albert with extra attention, special snacks, and an opportunity to engage in favorite play activities. These special provisions helped mitigate the effects of the thunderstorms. They eliminated Albert's need to escape from thunderstorms by screaming and hiding under the bed.

Provide Motivation

A functional assessment might reveal that desired target behaviors are not sufficiently reinforced. In order to strengthen these behaviors, it might be necessary to use positive reinforcement. For example, Janey works too slowly. A DRH schedule of positive reinforcement might be used to increase her productivity. Mark has a high frequency of disruptive behavior in the classroom, and this behavior might be obtaining more teacher attention than his cooperative behavior. In order to strengthen his cooperative behavior, it might be necessary to use positive reinforcement. In any behavior change plan in which desired behaviors are targeted for strengthening, the use of positive reinforcement might be necessary. A functional assessment can reveal possible reinforcers and so can reinforcement sampling, interviews, observations, and reinforcement inventories.

Group contingencies might be applicable in classroom settings. These involve scheduling positive reinforcement for members of a group, such as a classroom of students. Group contingencies can take several forms. One type of group contingency involves providing reinforcers for all members of a group if each member meets specific criteria. For example, if all the children in a math group bring in their math homework, all the children are given an extra 10 minutes of recess.

Another type of group contingency requires that a group as a whole meet a specific criterion. For example, the math group as a whole must have completed a total of 100 homework problems in order to have extra recess. In this type of contingency, the contribution of individual members is not important.

A third type of group contingency requires that a specific member of a group meet a specific criterion in order for the group as a whole to receive a reinforcer. For example, the requirement might be that Angela complete her homework in order for the group as a whole to get 10 extra minutes of recess.

Group contingencies have the advantage of using peer pressure to change behavior. They can also promote cooperation among members of a group, since the fate of the group in dependent on the behavior of certain or all members of the group. Group contingencies must be used only with careful consideration, to prevent undue pressure being placed on children who cannot handle such pressure either academically or socially.

Rearrange Stimulus Control and Setting Events

A functional assessment might reveal that certain misbehavior is under the control of environment stimuli. These stimuli might be immediate antecedents, or they might be setting events. The design of a behavior modification plan must take into account the role that environmental stimuli and setting events play. Interventions might be required that eliminate certain stimuli, introduce S^Ds for more acceptable behavior, or change or mitigate the effects of certain setting events. Alternatively, the plan might need to target behaviors that promote more acceptable responses to stimuli or setting events that cannot be changed or mitigated.

Eliminate Stimuli

Certain stimuli might serve as S^Ds for the reinforcement of targeted misbehavior. One method for decreasing the frequency of a misbehavior is to eliminate the stimuli that serve as S^Ds for that behavior. If the teacher, for example, speaks harshly to Roger, he is very likely to become aggressive. Harsh tones can be eliminated, and in doing so, an S^D for aggression is eliminated. This intervention can contribute to the elimination of Roger's aggression. In another example, if Alberta screams when her classmate grabs her lunch, eliminating the grabbing of Alberta's lunch will eliminate an S^D for screaming.

Introduce Stimuli

An intervention plan that purposefully introduces new stimuli to serve as S^Ds for acceptable behavior might be helpful. This intervention plan should also incorporate the use of positive reinforcement, so that the new stimuli will assume the role of S^Ds for acceptable behavior. For example, both Glen's written schedule and Priscilla's picture schedule were arranged as S^Ds for on-task behavior. Used in conjunction with positive reinforcement, these schedules assumed the role of S^Ds.

Touchette, MacDonald, and Langer (1985) examined the relationship between problem behaviors and environmental stimuli by using a scatter plot (see Chapter 3). The scatter plot indicated the time periods when problem behaviors occurred. Intervention consisted of scheduling the kinds of activities that were associated with absence of problem behavior during the time periods when problem behavior typically occurred. Concurrently, activities associated with high rates of problem behavior were eliminated from the daily schedule. For example, when the aggressive behavior of one young woman in the study occurred during group participation but not during individual instruction, her schedule was revised, with group participation being eliminated and individual instruction and activities being assigned instead. A young man's self-injury was reduced by rescheduling also. Supervision by an assistant with whom the man's rates of self-injury were low replaced supervision by an assistant associated with the man's high rates of self-injury. This study provides a clear demonstration of the rearrangement of environmental stimuli, based on an environmental assessment, to eliminate problem behavior.

Manipulate Setting Events

A variety of events can serve as setting events for misbehavior. Gardner, Cole, Davidson, and Karan (1986) provide a model for the assignment of interventions based on setting events. Their model suggests that strategies can involve directly eliminating the antecedent stimuli or setting events, neutralizing their effects, or intervening to change an individual's response to those events.

Elena's parents, for example, occasionally promise her an activity and then, at the last moment, change their minds. This situation, in turn, serves as a setting event, with Elena likely to have a tantrum when her parents approach her. An obvious intervention strategy in this case is for Elena's parents to cease making promises they cannot keep.

Some setting events cannot be eliminated, but their effects can be mitigated. For example, Jim's misbehavior is often affected by the setting event of his allergies. If Jim's allergies are causing him physical discomfort, he is likely to become self-injurious when asked to do schoolwork. It might be possible to eliminate the setting event for Jim's misbehavior by the use of allergy medicine. However, if medication does not work, the effects of the allergies can be mitigated by keeping Jim home, rather than sending him to school when he is ill.

At times, it is impractical or undesirable to eliminate or mitigate the effects of a setting event. In these cases, it might be necessary to teach an individual a more acceptable way to react to the setting event. In Elena's case, for example, teaching her a more acceptable way to react to disappointments might be very effective. Social skills training, including the use of instruction, modeling, rehearsal, and positive reinforcement, can be effective in teaching a variety of social skills for dealing with setting events that typically result in destructive or maladaptive behavior.

Put on Extinction

If a misbehavior continues to serve its function, all other aspects of a behavior change plan can prove futile. A behavior change plan, therefore, must include a strategy for placing targeted misbehavior on extinction. For example, if a behavior has been maintained by reprimands or long, drawn-out explanations, it is necessary to eliminate reprimands following the occurrence of the behavior. If a child's misbehavior has been maintained by attempts to placate the child (with cuddling, favorite treats, or favorite toys, for instance), these consequences must no longer immediately follow the misbehavior. If a behavior somehow allows a child to escape from or avoid an undesired activity or event, this escape hatch must be closed.

As a rule, if a misbehavior results in some positive reinforcer, such as provision of attention, food, cuddling, favorite objects, or other demanded items or events, the extinction procedure must no longer provide these events directly after the misbehavior occurs. If a misbehavior results in the opportunity to escape from or avoid some event, extinction must consist of continuing to present the activity or event. The following case illustrates an extinction procedure.

Shirley is a 5-year-old girl who has tantrums in her kindergarten class. She cries and screams each day at nap time. When Shirley has tantrums, the teacher sits with her and allows her to do special activities while the other children must lie on their mats. Shirley's tantrums, therefore, seem to serve two functions: they allow Shirley to escape from lying on a mat, and they provide her with extra attention and special activities. If the teacher wants to eliminate Shirley's tantrums, she will have to place them on extinction. She can no longer allow Shirley to get off her mat nor provide her with special privileges as a result of her tantrums.

Combine Strategies

Any given behavior change plan might need to include a variety of strategies, such as instruction in more adaptive behavior, modeling, stimulus control procedures, positive reinforcement, and extinction. When combining strategies, it is important to insure that the methods can logically coexist, with one strategy not contradicting or otherwise interfering with another. For example, if free provision and positive reinforcement are used in a plan, avoiding satiation is important. Equally important is the use of any strategies necessary to augment the methods already selected for use. For example, if stimulus control procedures are being used, it might be imperative to use positive reinforcement also, to establish the stimuli as discriminative stimuli; or, if positive reinforcement is being used to effect more acceptable behavior, it might be imperative to place the targeted misbehavior on extinction also. Likewise, if extinction is used on a targeted misbehavior, it might be imperative to provide other means of obtaining reinforcers also.

A Model for Strategy Selection

Donnellan, Mirenda, Mesaros, and Fassbender (1984) present a model for analyzing the functions of aberrant behavior and for selecting strategies for behavior change based on those functions. Their model focuses on the communicative intent of the aberrant behavior; that is, a misbehavior is assumed to have a communicative intent if an individual is performing it. Once that intent, or function, is understood, interventions can be selected. Table 12.1 provides a summary of their model for selecting interventions based on motivational sources and communicative intent.

Kearney and Silverman (1990) used a functional model of assessment to treat seven children or adolescents, aged 9 through 16, who either had difficulty going to school or refused to go to school. The variables associated with school refusal were evaluated through the use of the *School Refusal Assessment Scale.* Motivating conditions were assessed, including escape from aversive social situations, attention getting, tangible reinforcement, and reluctance to leave home. Treatment strategies were selected based on the motivating conditions as revealed by the assessment scale. The researchers reported that six of the seven participants began full-time school attendance following intervention based on the functional assessment.

Table 12.1 Summary of Motivational Sources, Possible Communicative Messages, and Related Interventions

		Intervention Procedures		
Motivational Source	*Possible Communicative Message(s)*	*Teach Replacement Communicative Response*	*Functionally Related Alt-R Procedures*	*Manipulation of Antecedent Conditions*
I. Positive Reinforcement: *Attention* maintains behavior	"Pay attention to me." (general) "Hello!" (greeting) "Look at me, I'm silly." (humor) "Play with me." "Look at ________." (comment) "Help me."	[Teach a variety of means for requesting/soliciting attention, depending on context (e.g., tap on arm, greeting sign, "Play," "Help," etc.)]	Use attention to reinforce already occurring alternative responses Direct instruction and social reinforcement of new alternative responses	Alter environment to provide non-contingent attention
Material reinforcers (e.g., food, objects) maintain behavior	"I want ________."	Teach manual sign for desired object/food	Use desired materials to reinforce already occurring alternative responses Direct instruction and material reinforcement of new, alternative responses	Alter environment to provide non-contingent access to material reinforcers
II. Negative Reinforcement: *Termination* of an aversive stimulus or situation maintains behavior	"I don't want to do this anymore." "Stop!" "No!" "I don't understand; I want out!"	Teach manual/gestural sign to terminate activity/escape	[Reinforce already occurring alternative responses with escape]	Alter context to decrease/eliminate aversiveness: simplify tasks; increase preference value of tasks; decrease or alter instructional demands; alter instructional procedures

Table 12.1 Summary of Motivational Sources, Possible Communicative Messages, and Related Interventions *(continued)*

		Intervention Procedures		
Motivational Source	*Possible Communicative Message(s)*	*Teach Replacement Communicative Response*	*Functionally Related Alt-R Procedures*	*Manipulation of Antecedent Conditions*
III. Extinction/Frustration: Previously available reinforcers are no longer available	"Help me." "I'm frustrated." "Why can't I have . . . ?" "You used to give it to me; I want it now."	[Teach communicative means for obtaining desired reinforcers and/or for enlisting aid to obtain reinforcers]	[Reinstate previously available reinforcers contingent on occurrence of alternative response]	[Alter environment to provide previously available reinforcers: alter instructional procedures, provide richer reinforcement schedule, etc.]
IV. Arousal induction/sensory reinforcement: Behavior provides sensory stimulation that is intrinsically reinforcing	"I'm not getting the input I want." "I'm bored."	[Teach communicative means to obtain sensory input, e.g., request for sensory activity]	Provide reinforcing sensory input through alternative activities Direct instruction and reinforcement of alternative behaviors	Alter environment to provide more sensory input and stimulation: enrich environment and curriculum
V. Arousal Reduction: Behavior maintained by termination of aversive overstimulation—i.e., behavior "blocks out" excess sensory input	"I'm anxious/tense/excited/nervous/overwhelmed, etc." "Help me."	[Teach alternative communicative means for expressing distress/enlisting aid]	Provide and reinforce alternative means of removing the aversive effects of overstimulation: vigorous exercise; relaxation response	Alter environment to decrease environmental stimulation and demands

(continued)

Table 12.1 Summary of Motivational Sources, Possible Communicative Messages, and Related Interventions *(continued)*

		Intervention Procedures		
Motivational Source	*Possible Communicative Message(s)*	*Teach Replacement Communicative Response*	*Functionally Related Alt-R Procedures*	*Manipulation of Antecedent Conditions*
VI. Respondent Conditioning: Behavior originated from association with a traumatic event (e.g., loud noise, pain) that triggers the behavior Behavior is then maintained by positive or negative reinforcement	"I'm scared/afraid." "This is a bad habit that I can't control." "I want ________ to stop." "Help!"	[Teach communicative means to express distress or enlist assistance]	Reinforce gradual tolerance of trigger stimulus: systematic desensitization [Direct instruction and reinforcement of alternative responses to trigger stimulus]	[Alter environment to preclude occurrence of the trigger stimulus]
VII. Physiological: Behavior is the product of an aberrant physiological process	"I hurt." "I'm tired."	[Teach communicative means to express distress]	Not applicable	Not applicable

Adapted by permission of the *Journal of the Association for Persons with Severe Handicaps* from Anne M. Donnellan, Patricia L. Mirenda, Richard A. Mesaros, and Lynette L. Fassbender (1984), "Analyzing the Communicative Functions of Aberrant Behavior," *Journal of the Association for Persons with Severe Handicaps*, 9 (3), 201–212.

Program for Maintenance and Generalization

Whether a behavior modification plan is formal or informal, measures should be taken to promote maintenance and generalization. Teachers and parents have the privilege of having children for only limited periods of time, during which teaching and guidance can take place. The goal of teaching and guiding children must be to prepare them for when they are no longer in the learning environment. Special care must be taken to incorporate maintenance and generalization technology into behavior change efforts. These procedures are described in detail in Chapter 11.

When teaching or working with individuals with such severe learning handicaps as profound mental retardation or severe developmental disabilities, maintenance and generalization goals might be more modest. The complete independence of these individuals might not be realistic. Maintenance and generalization goals must, therefore, take into account the characteristics of the learner. Generalization must be pushed to the limit but not at the expense of leaving the learner without necessary behavioral supports.

Criteria for Behavior Change Plans

Certain criteria might be helpful in determining whether an intervention plan is suitable for application. Behavior change agents can choose their own criteria and then evaluate the plan against those criteria prior to implementation. The following criteria might be important considerations when developing a formal behavior change plan:

1. Is the plan nonaversive? A behavior modification plan should exclude the use of punishment procedures involving painful or harmful stimuli.
2. Is the plan based on a functional assessment? Targeted behaviors as well as intervention strategies should follow from a functional assessment. If functions for a misbehavior are identified, the plan should seek to replace the misbehavior or to eliminate the need for its functions.
3. Are the methods selected based on the principles of behavior? Any method chosen for behavior change is likely to work if the principles of behavior and their application in a particular setting have been carefully analyzed. For example, Jim needs to learn to complete his work assignments. The principle of positive reinforcement suggests that if task completion is reinforced, its frequency will increase. Therefore, the use of positive reinforcement with Jim is based on a principle of behavior. On the other hand, providing Jim with extended counseling and encouragement following each incomplete assignment is not consistent with the principles of behavior as applied to Jim's

targeted behavior, task completion. In fact, such methods might be expected to exacerbate the problem.

4. If a combination of methods is used, can these methods coexist with coordinated effects? As discussed earlier, some strategies might actually interfere with other strategies. Thus, the possible effects of each strategy must be considered, as well as a strategy's interactive effects with other strategies used. Strategies must be chosen with regard to coordinating their effects.
5. Can the plan be implemented given the resources available? Availability of staff, parents, instructional materials, reinforcers, and appropriate models are examples of the kinds of resources that might be necessary to implement a behavior change plan. If the plan cannot be implemented with available resources, either the resources must be procured or behavior change cannot take place.
6. Are naturalistic and unobtrusive procedures and reinforcers used as much as possible, with contrived procedures implemented only if deemed necessary? For example, if verbal praise in a classroom setting is enough to motivate a child to work quietly, there would be no reason to use food treats. However, if a disruptive behavior is severe and social attention is not a potent reinforcer, such tangible reinforcers as food or activities might be imperative.
7. Are maintenance and generalization goals appropriate for the learner and programmed for accordingly?

Applications

Case 1: Informal Behavior Modification

Mr. Huott coached swimmers aged 5 through 18 on a small swim team. He made extensive but informal use of behavior modification in order to motivate and teach his swimmers. They were taught swimming techniques through shaping, chaining, modeling, and, in some cases, graduated guidance. Training procedures depended heavily on stimulus control. In order to standardize coaching, swimmers were taught to respond to electronic cues that dictated their workouts. Their achievements and efforts were strengthened through positive reinforcers, such as praise, public recognition, ribbons, trophies, and other awards. Disciplined, accomplished swimmers were promoted as models for less accomplished athletes; and the achievements of these swimmers were publicly recognized, promoting modeling through vicarious reinforcement. Swimmers were encouraged to engage in self-management through self-monitoring of their progress. Swimmers with poor sportsmanship were taught, through verbal instruction and modeling, acceptable ways of interacting with teammates and the coach. Disruptive behaviors were typically placed on extinction: swimmers were simply directed to proceed with their assignments and not allowed to avoid practice as a result of their misbehaviors. Mr. Huott's swim team, therefore, made extensive and purposeful use of strategies based on the principles of behavior.

Case 2: Formal Behavior Modification

Archie was an 18-year-old boy with moderate mental retardation. He had a part-time job at a printing company, where he collated materials and put covers on books. Archie had a history of screaming and making threats at work. As a result of these behaviors, he would be sent to the break room to calm down, or he would be sent home.

Baseline data were collected on Archie's behaviors, and a functional assessment was done. From information gathered from this functional assessment, it appeared that the functions of Archie's behaviors were to avoid both work and transitions. The discriminative stimuli for his misbehaviors appeared to be verbal instructions from his supervisor to return to work or to change tasks. A strategy was then developed to eliminate these stimuli. A written schedule was used so that it could become the S^D for working, instead of the supervisor's verbal instructions. A schedule of positive reinforcement was also implemented. If Archie completed his scheduled work tasks quietly each day, he was offered a choice of several reinforcers. In addition, social skills training was implemented to teach Archie to accept interruptions in his work as well as abrupt transitions in tasks. This training involved verbal instructions, modeling, practice, and positive reinforcement. Yelling and threats were placed on extinction. If these occurred, Archie's supervisor simply directed him back to his schedule; he was no longer allowed to leave work as a result of misbehavior.

Case 3: Formal Application

Nina was a four-year-old child with a language delay who attended nursery school. She had severe tantrums in her classroom, during which she would scream, yell, stomp her feet, and occasionally bite her classmates. Baseline data were collected on these behaviors, and a functional assessment revealed that her tantrums typically occurred when she was prevented from taking a toy from a classmate. At such times, the teacher would often intervene, speak soothingly to her, and on occasion provide her with the toy she wanted or another toy or with a special activity. Thus, the functions of Nina's misbehavior appeared to be the obtaining of attention, toys, or preferred activities.

Nina's intervention plan consisted of several strategies. She was taught to share by the use of symbolic modeling (stories about children sharing). Vicarious reinforcement was also used, as Nina's classmates were praised enthusiastically for sharing. Additionally, Nina was taught how to ask nicely for a desired toy and how to wait her turn if the toy was unavailable. Nina's waiting was reinforced with praise from the teacher and occasional permission to engage in favorite activities. Her tantrums and aggression were put on extinction. If she had a tantrum, she was prevented from biting another child and redirected back to her own activity. She was no longer provided with extra attention, favorite toys, or favorite activities following a tantrum.

Case 4: Formal Behavior Modification

Lonnie, who had mild mental retardation, worked at a manufacturing firm. Occasionally, a co-worker would need to share Lonnie's work space, and Lonnie would curse at the co-worker and refuse to make room at the work table. So, Lonnie had to be taught another way to respond to a co-worker's need to share work space. Social skills training was provided to teach him to smile at a co-worker and make room at the work table. A combination of verbal instructions, modeling, practice, and praise were used to teach Lonnie to share his work space. Eventually, the training and praise were faded out. Natural reinforcers, such as the positive responses from Lonnie's co-workers, continued to maintain Lonnie's sharing behavior.

Summary

Behavior modification can be used informally or formally. Informal application involves using the principles of behavior in an ongoing manner in teaching, parenting, or interpersonal situations. Teachers and parents who are cognizant of the principles of behavior find them invaluable for teaching and motivating children.

Formal application of behavior modification is accomplished through a behavior change plan. Plan development follows a prescribed order: behaviors are targeted for change, data are collected, a functional assessment is done, and strategies are selected. Selection of strategies is based on the functional assessment.

A variety of procedures can be used to promote more acceptable behavior and to eliminate maladaptive behavior. These strategies can be used to teach more acceptable behaviors, to eliminate the need for a misbehavior, to eliminate cues that serve as S^Ds for a misbehavior, to eliminate or mitigate the effects of setting events, and to render misbehavior functionally ineffective. Strategies can be used alone or in combination in order to meet behavioral goals.

It is important that behavior change experts or teams adopt certain suggested criteria for plan development. These criteria deal with the principles on which the strategies are based, the strategies' use in combination and the strategies' feasibility in applied settings.

Study Questions

1. Explain the difference between informal and formal uses of behavior modification. Give an example of each.
2. List the steps in a formal behavior modification plan.
3. List four strategies that can be used to teach new behaviors.
4. Describe two types of group contingencies.
5. Give an example of chaining.
6. Describe two procedures for eliminating the function a behavior serves.
7. Give an example of how strategies based on stimulus control might be used to eliminate a misbehavior; to encourage a more adaptive behavior.
8. What are two ways to deal with setting events for misbehavior?
9. List five criteria for a formal behavior modification plan.

Exercises

1. Mrs. Caron has lost control of her nursery school class. She spends most of each morning reprimanding children, imploring them to come to circle time, intervening in their fights and, cleaning up their messes. How might Mrs. Caron make informal use of the principles of behavior to bring some order to her class?

2. Gloria is a 10-year-old girl with profound mental retardation and a high frequency of self-injury. She bangs her head and scratches her skin. A functional assessment suggests that her self-injury serves the function of obtaining attention, avoiding tasks, and getting favorite snacks and activities. Design a behavior modification plan for Gloria. Include targeted behaviors, data collection procedures, and intervention strategies.

3. Michael is a 13-year-old boy with mild mental retardation. He refuses to do homework or help with household chores. When given an instruction by his parents, he curses, stomps his feet, and yells. They then typically send him to his room, where he remains, listening to records, for about 30 minutes. When he leaves his room, he watches television. Design a behavior modification plan for Michael. Include targeted behaviors, data collection procedures, and intervention strategies.

4. The children in Mrs. Allen's fourth-grade class do a great deal of talking during math class and often do not complete their assignments. Design a group contingency to encourage completion of math assignments.

References

Donnellan, A. M., Mirenda, P. L., Mesaros, R. A., & Fassbender, L. L. (1984). Analyzing the communicative functions of aberrant behavior. *Journal of the Association for Persons with Severe Handicaps, 9,* 201–212.

Durand, V. M., & Carr, E. G. (1987). Social influences on "self-stimulatory" behavior: Analysis and treatment application. *Journal of Applied Behavior Analysis, 20,* 119–132.

Durand, V. M., Crimmins, D. B., Caulfield, M., & Taylor, J. (1989). Reinforcer assessment I: Using problem behavior to select reinforcers. *Journal of the Association for Persons with Severe Handicaps, 14,* 113–126.

Gardner, W. I., Cole, C. L., Davidson, D. P., & Karan, O. C. (1986). Reducing aggression in individuals with developmental disabilities: An expanded stimulus control, assessment, and intervention model. *Education and Training of the Mentally Retarded, 21,* 3–12.

Horner, R. H., Sprague, J. R., O'Brien, M., & Heathfield, L. T. (1990). The role of response efficiency in the reduction of problem behaviors through functional equivalence training: A case study. *Journal of the Association for Persons with Severe Handicaps, 15,* 91–97.

Kearney, C. A., & Silverman, W. K. (1990). A preliminary analysis of a functional model of assessment and treatment for school refusal behavior. *Behavior Modification, 14,* 340–366.

Smith, M. (1986). The use of alternate sensory stimuli in the community-based treatment of the self-stimulatory behavior of an adult disabled by autism. *Journal of Behavior Therapy and Experimental Psychiatry, 17,* 121–125.

Smith, M. (1987). Treatment of pica in an adult disabled by autism by differential reinforcement of incompatible behavior. *Journal of Behavior Therapy and Experimental Psychiatry, 10,* 285–288.

Touchette, P. E., MacDonald, R. F., & Langer, S. N. (1985). A scatter plot for identifying stimulus control of problem behavior. *Journal of Applied Behavior Analysis, 18,* 343–351.

Weeks, M., & Gaylord-Ross, R. (1981). Task difficulty and aberrant behavior in severely handicapped students. *Journal of Applied Behavior Analysis, 14,* 449–463.

13

Plan Implementation

Jim was a 9-year-old boy who had been diagnosed as having a learning disability and behavior problems. He had several problems at school, such as refusing to do most of his classroom assignments, bullying other children, and running from the classroom. So, the school psychologist and Jim's teacher held meetings and decided to design a formal behavior change plan for Jim. A functional assessment was done and a plan developed. The goals of the plan were to increase Jim's compliance with classroom tasks, to encourage him to remain in the classroom, and to decrease the frequency of his negative interactions with other children. The plan included curriculum changes in his math and reading programs, a schedule of positive reinforcement to increase his compliance with the programs, and social skills training to teach him more acceptable ways of interacting with other children.

Following the plan-development meetings, several tasks remained for the psychologist and Jim's teacher. The plan needed to be put into writing, the teacher trained, the plan implemented, and follow-up monitoring and evaluation done. This chapter explores the implementation, monitoring, and evaluation of formal behavior change plans.

Plan Preparation

In many cases, there is more than one individual actually implementing a behavior change plan. In classroom settings, a plan may be implemented by one or more teachers, by a classroom aide, or by support personnel, such as language therapists and occupational therapists. At home, a plan may be implemented by one or both parents, or by siblings, grandparents, or a child-care worker. For older students, an instructor at school or a supervisor or co-worker at work might implement a plan. For individuals with severe disabilities, staff at a group home or a job coach at work might do this. A written plan is essential to insure that all individuals involved in plan implementation have a written record of what the plan entails.

The written plan must include specific instructions for all procedures contained in the plan. It must precisely explain all strategies to be used. Details must be provided so that consistent implementation is possible. Although all strategies cannot be covered in this chapter, broad classes of strategies are covered in terms of plan write-up.

Positive Reinforcement

If positive reinforcement procedures are included, the plan should state the behaviors targeted for reinforcement. Specific behavioral descriptions must be defined and provided. For example, Jim's plan defined remaining in his assigned location and separating newspapers as the targets for reinforcement. In another example, Anita was a young girl with frequent head-banging and screaming behavior. She was nonverbal also. Anita had a number of behaviors targeted for reinforcement, including keeping her hands on her tasks, following directions, beginning her work, working quietly, completing her tasks, participating in recreational activities, smiling, and using gestures or signs to communicate. Her written behavior plan included a list of these behaviors, which were targeted for reinforcement.

The behavior plan must also specify the schedule of reinforcement. For example, Margaret was a 16-year-old girl with mild mental retardation. She had a part-time job making computer cables. Her accuracy was excellent, but she worked slowly. Her plan included and described a fixed ratio schedule of positive reinforcement. For every 30 computer cables she constructed, she was given a 10-minute break to read a favorite magazine.

The behavior plan, additionally, must specify the reinforcers that are to be used. In some cases, there will be one specific reinforcer. A child's cooperative behavior, for instance, may be rewarded with a weekly trip to a favorite ice cream parlor. However, some plans may designate a variety of reinforcers. In these cases, the plan should describe the types of reinforcers to be used and give examples of each. For instance, Jim, mentioned earlier, may be on a Variable Interval 15-minute schedule. His reinforcers may be sensory, activity, and food reinforcers. If so, his plan must describe each category of reinforcers and provide examples.

Stimulus Control

All stimulus control procedures in a behavior change plan must be described as well. If certain types of prompting systems are to be used, they must be described. If stimulus prompts are to be used, they too must be described. If the plan includes strategies related to scheduling of activities, types of activities, or manner of presentation of activities, specific directions must be included. Any procedures designed to promote stimulus discrimination or stimulus generalization must be described.

Instructional Procedures

Any instructional procedures that seek to impact on the targeted behaviors should be included also. The plan should include descriptions of the behaviors targeted for change by the instructional procedures, as well as descriptions of those procedures.

Responses to Problem Behavior

If the behavior plan targets a problem behavior, the plan must describe exactly how to respond to the target behavior's occurrence. If the behavior is to be put on extinction, a description of the extinction process must be included. If the behavior is dangerous and must be managed in a way to prevent injury or property destruction, this procedure must be described as well.

Plan Changes

After implementation of the behavior plan, it might be necessary to change aspects of it. Any changes should be put in writing. The written description of the behavior plan should always be consistent with the strategies that are actually being implemented.

Training

It is important that anyone who might implement a behavior modification plan be well trained on that plan. In a classroom, the teacher, teacher aides, or even such support personnel as speech and language therapists may need this training. If the plan is to be implemented at home, parents need training and so do other relatives or caretakers, such as siblings, grandparents, and babysitters.

A certain amount of basic information must be conveyed in training. Initially, it is advisable for the person(s) implementing the plan to have general training in behavior modification. This general training can provide an orientation to the principles that underlie any specific procedures that might be involved in an individual's plan.

Specific training then needs to be done on the behavior modification plan.

The person needs to be taught the purposes of the plan and how to carry out each of the strategies. Once the plan is explained to the implementer, training can continue in the actual setting. It is helpful to have follow-up training in the actual setting to insure that the implementer is carrying out the plan correctly. This follow-up training can involve the trainer observing the implementer, giving feedback, and possibly modeling implementation as well. An example follows.

Susie was a young girl with severe behavior problems, including aggression toward other people. The school psychologist, an expert in behavior modification, gave Susie's teacher and a classroom aide general training in behavior modification. They then worked together to develop a behavior modification plan for Susie. The teacher and the classroom aide were then trained on the plan by the school psychologist, who spent time in the classroom demonstrating how to carry out procedures in the plan, observing the classroom staff, and giving them feedback. This training and follow-up process insured that the behavior modification strategies were implemented as designed.

Plan Implementation

Training is naturally followed by plan implementation. Once a plan is developed, it is important to have all personnel trained on all aspects of the plan. It is also important to have any necessary materials available. The plan should then be implemented in its entirety.

To illustrate, Susie's behavior modification plan included a schedule of positive reinforcement, stimulus control procedures involving charts and signs, and an extinction procedure. Additionally, it was determined that her classroom tasks had been too difficult, so a change was necessary in her math programming. Staff needed to be trained on all aspects of the plan, and other materials and adaptations were involved. It was necessary to assemble reinforcers and to create the signs and charts. It was also necessary to consult with the math curriculum specialist to make the adaptations in Susie's math program. All of these tasks needed to be accomplished prior to plan implementation.

It is generally not advisable to implement only parts of a behavior modification plan because implementing parts out of context from the whole plan can be ineffective at best and harmful at worst. For example, if Susie's teachers simply implemented extinction without also beginning the schedule of positive reinforcement, Susie's problem behavior could initially escalate, creating even more problems. Without the changes in her math program, she might continue to misbehave during difficult math assignments, despite the fact that reinforcers are available for her compliance. If the schedule of positive reinforcement is implemented without extinction, misbehavior would continue to be reinforced, possibly defeating any gains made by using positive reinforcement for acceptable behavior. If the stimulus control procedures are not in place, progress might be hampered.

Follow-Up Monitoring

Follow-up monitoring of a behavior modification plan is essential. This involves assessing the accuracy of plan implementation and determining the effectiveness of the plan itself. Measures of these two outcomes are necessary to make sound decisions regarding future training needs or programming needs. The first of these two factors to consider is plan accuracy.

Plan accuracy is critical to plan success. If the behavior modification procedures are not implemented as designed, the plan can fail. For example, if a positive reinforcement schedule is planned as a Fixed Ratio 10 with tangible reinforcers, and the job coach decides to use only praise as a reinforcer, then expected progress might not occur. If, in another example, the extinction procedure is not fully implemented, and the teacher continues to give the child counseling and reprimands each time he calls out of turn, the child's undesirable behavior might be expected to continue. It is necessary, therefore, to insure accuracy of implementation.

There are several ways of determining accuracy. One method is observation. Observational checks are possible when someone well trained on the plan can observe the implementers and determine accuracy of plan implementation. In some cases, this observer might be the person who designed the plan. In Susie's case, for example, the school psychologist once a week assessed implementation of the plan by the teacher. The teacher, in turn, assessed the classroom assistant. Formal checks can be made by observing implementation over a period of time (e.g., 2 hours) and recording whether or not each step of the plan is performed correctly.

If a formal reliability check is done, the observer can determine the number of steps performed correctly. This number can then be used to calculate the percentage of steps performed correctly, as illustrated in Figure 13.1.

$$\frac{\text{No. of steps done correctly}}{\text{Total no. of steps}} \times 100\% = \%\text{ of steps done correctly}$$

Figure 13.1 The formula for computing the percentage of steps in a behavior plan that are performed correctly.

An example of a reliability checklist is given in Figure 13.2. For each step of the behavior plan, the observer recorded whether it was performed correctly, incorrectly, or not at all.

It may not always be possible to have implementation assessed by an independent observer. In some cases, a parent, a classroom teacher, a job coach, or other instructor might not have ongoing access to a school psychologist or other outside consultant who can provide this service. An alternative method of assessment is through data collection on various aspects of plan implementation. The implementer can periodically review the data to determine accuracy.

An example of a data collection sheet that is useful for this purpose is a reinforcement data sheet. To illustrate, each time Susie's teacher gave Susie a reinforcer, the teacher recorded the time, the reinforcer, and the target behavior. This data allowed her to review the positive reinforcement aspect of plan implementation at the end of the day. She checked the sheet to insure that reinforcers were delivered as scheduled.

Antecedent-Behavior-Consequence (ABC) sheets can be used also to review plan accuracy. For example, Susie's teacher had a difficult time with putting Susie's behavior on extinction. By using ABC sheets to record her responses to each of Susie's tantrums, the teacher could review these records at the end of the day to assess whether she responded according to the plan. The two entries shown in Figure 13.3 represent two incidents of Susie's tantrum behavior and the manner in which the teacher responded to the tantrums. According to the plan, there was to be no direct discussion of the tantrum with Susie; rather, she was to be directed back to task.

From a review of these entries, the teacher could see that she needed to improve her implementation of the extinction process. Susie was still receiving a great deal of attention for her misbehavior.

Plan implementers can also use self-check lists to assess reliability. For example, Mr. Smith needed to post Jimmy's schedule for him each day and occasionally forgot to do this. On days when his schedule was not posted, Jimmy was obviously more noncompliant. So, Mr. Smith began his own daily checklist and put a check on it each day after he posted Jimmy's schedule. This checklist served as a reminder to Mr. Smith and also provided him with a record of that aspect of plan implementation.

If plan implementation is not being reliably performed, retraining should be done. A teacher or parent may need more training on how to carry out a plan, for certain behavioral procedures are easy to design but difficult to perform. The extinction process provides a good example. It is fairly easy, for instance, to determine on paper that spitting should be ignored, but it is another matter altogether for a teacher to ignore it when it happens. Continued

Program Checklist

Student	Jane Doe
Instructor	Alan Craig
Site	Elton Dept Store
Evaluator	M. Felder
Date	4-12-92

C = Step done correctly
SI = Step done incorrectly
ND = Step not done
N/O = No opportunity to observe

86 % implemented

Program Steps	Rating/Comments
1. Reinforcer delivered every 60 minutes ± 10 minutes for target behavior	C
2. Reinforcers varied	C
3. No reinforcers within 15 minutes of tantrum	N/O
4. Jane participated in choosing after-work, non-routine activity reinforcer	N/O
5. Jane praised about every 15 minutes	C
6. No praise within 10 minutes of tantrum	N/O
7. Jane wrote out schedule with counselor in morning	ND
8. Jane either purchased coffee before work or spent 5–10 minutes with staff having coffee, chatting on non-work topics	C
9. Non-dangerous behaviors ignored, Jane redirected	N/O
10. Nonaversive physical management used as required by staff trained in nonaversive physical management	N/O
11. Jane told of upcoming events day or two in advance, not several weeks in advance—not told of unsure plans	C
12. Reinforcer data kept promptly	C
13. ABCs on aggression, destruction	N/O

Figure 13.2 A sample reliability checklist form.

Date	Time	Antecedents	Behavior	Consequences
2/16	10:00 am	Began spelling test	Susie starts to scream	I told her why it's important to take the spelling test
2/17	2:30 pm	Told recess is over	Susie runs off, cries, refuses to come in from recess	I told her she needs to cooperate and can have a longer recess tomorrow

Figure 13.3 Two ABC entries used for evaluation of correctness of plan implementation.

training and follow-up support can help teachers, parents, and other instructors learn to implement procedures that at times can be difficult.

Progress Expectations

Learning new skills and eliminating undesirable behaviors can take time. The length of time it takes to learn a new skill or to eliminate an undesirable behavior depends on the skill itself, the characteristics and the behavioral history of the learner, the methods employed, and the instructional environment. A common error in behavior change planning is to expect success too soon and when it is not realized, to abandon or change a plan prematurely. In some cases, a behavior change agent might even use lack of progress as justification for the use of punishment, when in fact the nonaversive procedures were implemented only for a matter of days. The following factors are among those that must be carefully weighed when determining reasonable goal times.

Behavior to be Changed

Some skills are obviously more complex and difficult to learn than others. For some skills, learning is almost instantaneous. For example, a child is shown once how to open a gate and then performs the skill successfully. A child might be taught to ride a bicycle within one week and to tie shoes within two weeks. To be taught to read, however, might require several months. When determining reasonable progress periods, it is therefore important to consider the complexity of the skill.

Characteristics of the Learner

Learner characteristics will determine the amount of time for skill acquisition. If a skill is being taught to a child without learning handicaps, the acquisition time is probably known. For example, it is known that most children without learning handicaps acquire fairly fluent language by 3 years of age. If the learner has a learning handicap, skill acquisition can take much longer than average. Success will be seen over a greater period of time. Attempting to rush the process and ignoring the needs of the learner can result in a situation that is discouraging for both the teacher and the student.

In attempts to change behavior patterns, characteristics of the learner are critical in determining the amount of time needed for success. Consider tantrum elimination in a 4-year-old child. A child this age without handicaps will have a different time-to-success period than a child the same age with language or developmental delays.

Behavioral History

The amount of time needed to change behavior will be affected by a person's behavioral history. An undesirable behavior that has been in the individual's repertoire for years might take longer to eliminate or change than a behavior that has recently appeared. In cases of targeted misbehavior, the reinforcement history will be a determining factor also in time-to-success. Effects of past reinforcement history on the extinction process are discussed in Chapter 5. Suffice it to say that the length of reinforcement history, the potency of reinforcers, and the reinforcement schedule itself will all affect the time it takes for a behavior change plan to succeed.

Methods Employed

The behavior change strategies will affect the time-to-success. For example, it might be possible to teach a new behavior to a young child more quickly with food treats than with praise as a reinforcer; however, a classroom teacher or a parent might prefer to take a little longer and avoid using food reinforcers with a child. A social skill might be taught more quickly using a formal social skills–training package, but an instructor might decide to use less formal methods and take a little longer to teach the skill.

Instructional Environment

A myriad of other factors affect time-to-success. The instructional environment itself has many possible detractors, inhibitors, or encouragers for learning. In any given case, the behavior change agent must make a careful assessment of the environment and then assess the environmental conditions and weigh their possible impact on time-to-success.

Conclusions

Knowledge of child development, of the impact of handicapping conditions on learning rates, and of typical courses of training and treatment is necessary to evaluate whether success is occurring at a reasonable rate. Misbehavior, such as tantrums, spitting, aggression, task refusal, and self-injury, can take days or months to eliminate in children with developmental disabilities. Even children with milder impairments or simply with behavior problems can take weeks or months to relearn more acceptable ways of behaving. Some indication of progress might be seen within the first several weeks, with gradual or rapid progress thereafter. Failure to project time-to-success accurately can create a premature abandonment or change of the behavior plan or, to the contrary, the use of a plan far beyond any reasonable expectations of success.

Effectiveness Evaluation

Behavior modification is a systematic approach to behavior change. Part of the system involves ongoing evaluation of the effectiveness of the procedures. The quantitative aspects of behavior modification permit a precise determination of its success. There are several means of evaluating the effectiveness of a behavior modification plan.

Baseline Versus Treatment

A straightforward way of assessing effectiveness is to compare baseline data with treatment data. If circumstances permit, it is always advisable to take baseline data prior to plan implementation. Data should continue to be collected throughout plan implementation. Baseline data can then be compared with treatment data.

Generally, if treatment data is outside the baseline range, the plan is considered effective. The baseline range is the lower and upper limits of the baseline data. For example, if during baseline-data collection of Marvin's stealing behavior, stealing occurred as infrequently as 10 times per day and as frequently as 20 times per day, the range would be 10 to 20 times per day. Figure 13.4 displays Marvin's baseline data.

Figure 13.5 displays Susie's data during baseline and during treatment. Since treatment data is generally outside the baseline range, it can be assumed that the plan is having an effect on her behavior.

If the treatment data is not entirely outside the baseline range, judgments must be made about plan effectiveness. The trend of the data can then be taken into consideration. Figure 13.6 provides a graph of Margie's cursing behavior. Her treatment data do not fall completely outside the baseline range. However, there is definitely a trend indicating a decline in frequency of her behavior.

It is also necessary to consider whether other factors in the environment, outside the behavior modification plan, impacted the behavior, such as use of a behavior modifying drug.

If the treatment data are well within the baseline range, it should probably be said that the plan is not effective. Figure 13.7 shows data for Michael, who is on a behavior change plan to decrease the frequency of his hitting other children. Michael's treatment data are well within the baseline range. Therefore, it appears that Michael's plan is not having an effect on his targeted behavior.

An alternative, or adjunct, to inspecting the graphs visually is to compute averages. The average computed for the baseline can be compared with the average computed for the treatment period. Differences in averages should be interpreted conservatively because the differences might be so small as to be of no significance. Johnny's data reveal that prior to a self-management plan for study behavior, his average test score in math was 70. After implementation of his self-management plan, his average rose to 85. This difference probably suggests that Johnny's self-management plan was having positive effects.

Teacher/Parent Reports

Reports of teachers, parents, or other people who work with an individual can be used to assess the success of a plan. For example, a teacher might report that a student is generally more cooperative. The parents of a

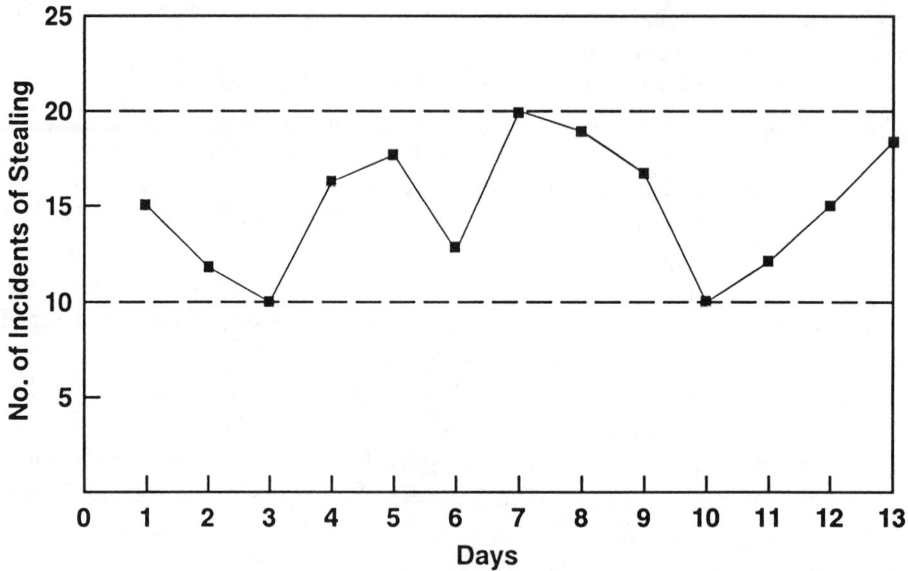

Figure 13.4 Marvin's baseline data, with range bordered by horizontal dotted lines.

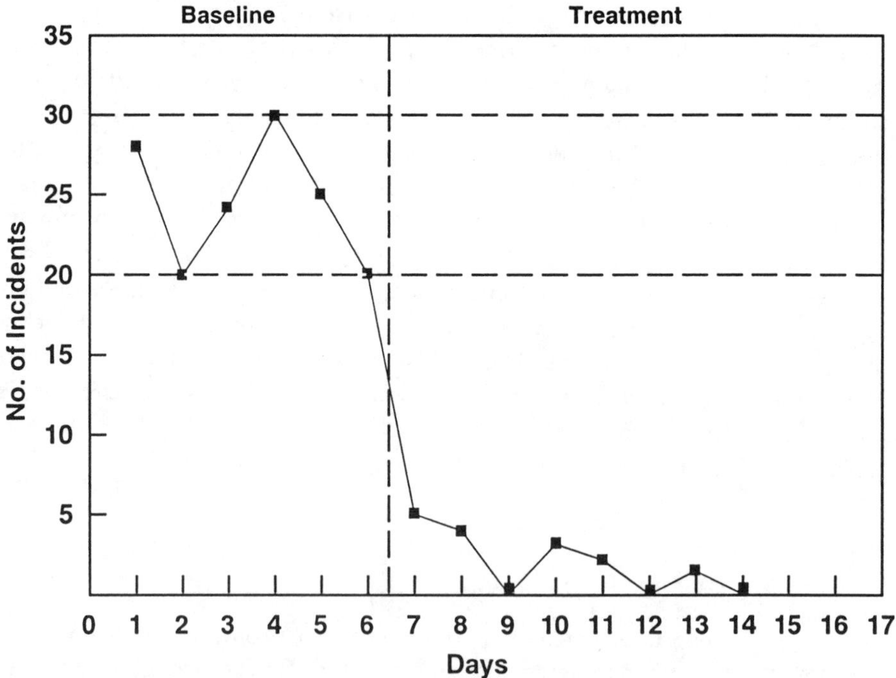

Figure 13.5 Susie's data during baseline and treatment, with baseline range bordered by horizontal dotted lines.

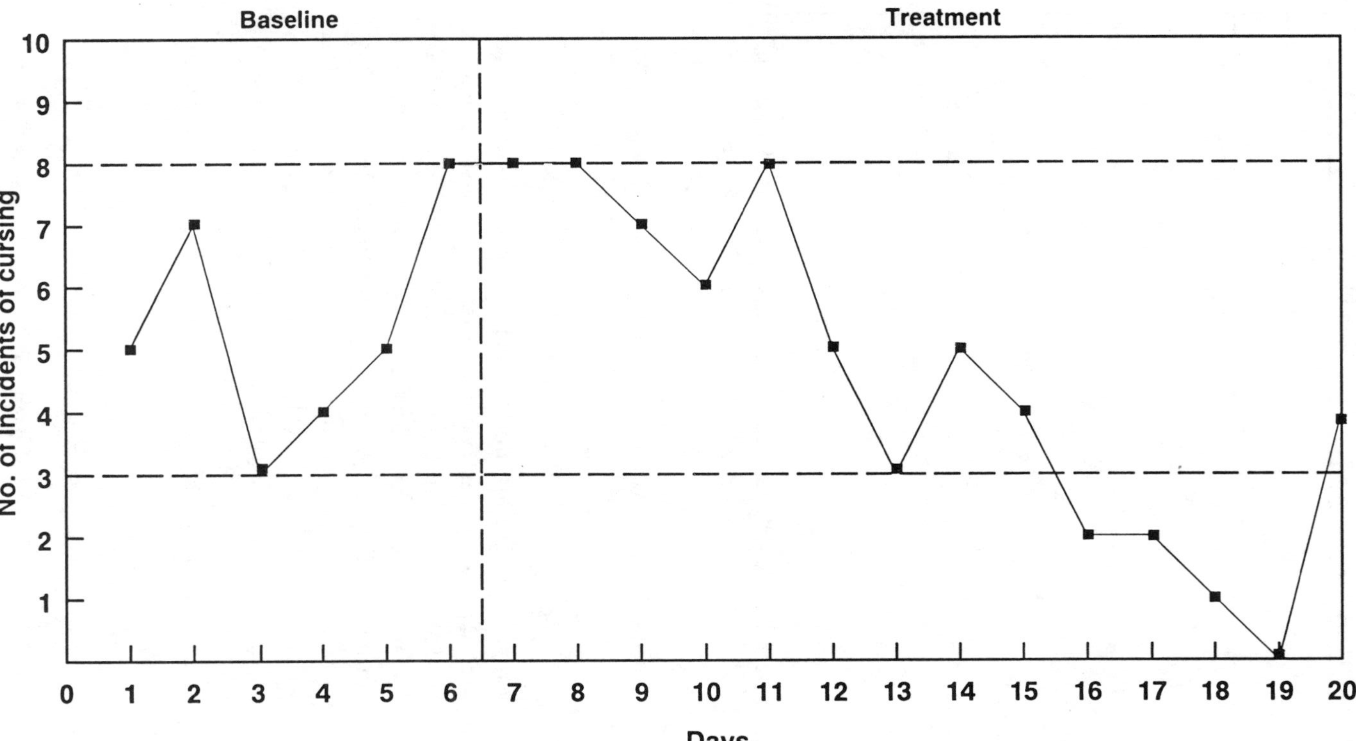

Figure 13.6 Margie's data during baseline and treatment, with baseline range bordered by horizontal dotted lines.

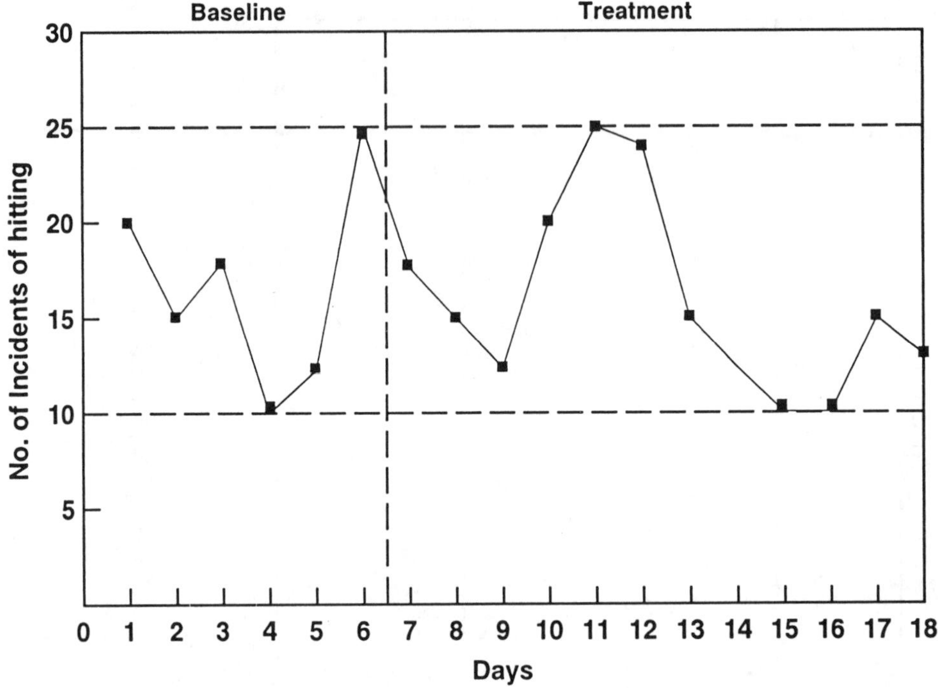

Figure 13.7 Michael's data during baseline and treatment, with baseline range bordered by horizontal dotted lines.

child might report that they are getting along much better with the child. An employer might report that a worker is doing a better job. Anecdotal reports that are not based on data must be interpreted with caution. These reports should not be the only measure of a plan's effectiveness. However, when taken together with the quantitative data, anecdotal reports are worth consideration.

Anecdotal reports can be especially helpful in assessing changes in factors that are not directly measured quantitatively. Susie's teacher, for instance, took data on the number of tantrums Susie had each day. Since there was no quantitative measure of the intensity of these tantrums, the teacher's report, although it might be inaccurate and even biased, can provide some information on their intensity.

Other Outcome Measures

Occasionally, other forms of data can be used to assess the effectiveness of a behavior plan. Archie's case provides an example of how outcome measures can be used to do this. Archie was a 15-year-old boy with a learning disability who participated in a work-study program. His productivity was very low, and he often talked loudly while working. The manager of the store where Archie worked was seriously thinking of firing him. However, after Archie's teacher developed and implemented a behavior modification plan to increase Archie's productivity and decrease the frequency of his loud talking at work, the manager became satisfied with Archie's progress and continued to employ him. The manager's expressed satisfaction and the fact that he continued to employ Archie are both outcome measures suggesting the success of the behavior modification plan.

Martin's case provides another example of the use of an outcome measure to evaluate a plan's effectiveness. Martin was a 22-year-old young man with normal intelligence and severe autism. He lived in an apartment with another young man with autism and was provided drop-in supervision from a trained residential counselor. When a neighbor complained that Martin was banging on the walls at night, a self-management plan was implemented to help Martin eliminate this behavior. The plan was successful, as indicated by the neighbor reporting that he no longer heard the banging at night.

In another example, Robert was a 14-year-old boy with mild mental retardation and serious aggression towards other people. His aggressiveness toward his teachers at school resulted in several teachers requiring medical attention. After a behavior modification plan was implemented to help Robert eliminate his aggressiveness, one outcome measure was the elimination of injuries requiring medical attention.

After Success: The Next Step

If the behavioral data and other relevant outcome measures suggest that a plan is effective, it is important to determine the next step. There are several possibilities, including continued implementation of the plan, fading, or changing the plan in some manner. The decision as to which procedure(s) to use next is based on the data in comparison with baseline and initial goals.

It might be advisable to continue to leave all components of the plan in place. Several factors that will influence this decision include the length of time the behavior has been a problem, the severity of the behavior problem, the risks associated with the behavior, and the availability of naturalistic cues and consequences to replace the contingencies provided in the behavior plan. An additional factor to consider is the nature of the strategies employed. If the behavior has been a problem for a long period of time, it might be inadvisable to make changes in a successful plan too soon. The following example is a case in point.

Eileen was a 15-year-old girl with profound mental retardation. Behavior modification was used to help eliminate her hand sucking, which had been a problem since her early childhood. The data revealed a significant decrease in this behavior within 2 months of implementing a behavior plan. Although there might be a great temptation to consider Eileen's hand sucking cured, it must be remembered that this behavior had occurred at a high frequency for almost 10 years. Two months of good data might be a premature point to withdraw a successful behavior plan.

In another example, Betty was a 10-year-old girl who only recently had begun crying in class. After a behavior modification plan was developed, Betty's crying behavior was eliminated. Since her behavior had been fairly new and since the plan was almost immediately effective, it appeared that termination of the plan was a realistic goal.

The severity of the target behavior or the risks inherent in the behavior might also dictate leaving a successful plan in place. For example, Arnold had serious problems with pica. At one point, he was hospitalized and needed surgery after eating several metal objects. His physician warned that Arnold would probably die if he continued his pica behavior. Behavior modification procedures were then used and were successful in eliminating Arnold's pica. Although it might have been possible to withdraw the behavior plan, the risks of the target behavior, pica, were great and presented a clear danger to Arnold's life. As a result of this danger, the plan was continued as a permanent part of his programming.

In another example, Donnie was a 4-year-old boy with the annoying behavior of interrupting his mother while she was talking on the telephone. She tried behavior modification procedures and within several days Donnie's problem behavior was eliminated. Since the behavior did not pose a risk to Donnie or to other people, it seemed appropriate to terminate the plan after it was successful.

Any decisions regarding plan withdrawal must take into consideration the original functions served by the target behavior and how those functions will be served if the plan is withdrawn or faded. If the individual can continue to have the functions served despite the withdrawal or fading of the behavioral plan, the plan might no longer be needed. This may also be the case if the plan allowed for strengthening new behaviors that will be reinforced in more natural ways. The role of stimulus control procedures and modeling must also be taken into account in regard to plan withdrawal. If environmental manipulations are withdrawn, will cues for appropriate behavior remain? If not, are they needed?

The availability of natural contingencies can help determine whether functions can be served after plan withdrawal. For example, Jimmy's teacher implemented a behavior modification plan to teach Jimmy to cooperate with his peers. The plan was successful, and Jimmy began to make friends. Since these friends provided natural reinforcers for Jimmy's cooperative behavior, the artificial arrangements set up by the teacher were no longer needed and could be withdrawn.

In another example, Sara was an 18-year-old girl with mental retardation who worked in a factory with the assistance of a job coach. She was nonverbal and could not count. She was paid every two weeks but did not have a good understanding of her paycheck. Her low productivity was increased by providing her with tangible reinforcers on a fixed ratio schedule. If these tangible reinforcers are faded or withdrawn, natural contingencies (such as the paycheck) would not be sufficient substitutes. Sara's work behavior would in effect be placed on extinction by the removal of the tangible reinforcers. In Sara's case, the behavior modification procedures might need to continue indefinitely.

It might be possible to fade certain aspects of a plan without totally eliminating the stimulus cues, reinforcers, or other strategies employed. As discussed in Chapter 11, it might be possible and desirable to thin a reinforcement schedule. For example, Betty was originally provided with reinforcers on a Fixed Ratio 5 schedule. This schedule was gradually thinned to a Fixed Ratio 50, and her productivity remained high. In another example, Sandy's productivity began to decline when her Fixed Ratio schedule was changed from an FR 10 to an FR 15. Continued thinning of her schedule would have cost Sandy her job.

In some cases, fading of cues is possible. Ellen, for example, initially needed a great deal of verbal instruction and self-instruction to learn to drive a car, but after several weeks, these cues could be gradually faded. On the other hand, Johnny, a young man with a learning disability, needed pictorial cues showing him how to assemble a computer cable (the task of his part-time job), and whenever he failed to follow the picture cues or if they were not in place, Johnny made errors in the assembly. For Johnny, fading of his pictorial cues was not advisable.

If a behavior modification plan is faded or withdrawn, it is important to keep data for a reasonable period of time to insure that the behavioral gains are not lost. If the progress is not maintained, or if there are behavioral setbacks, it might be that the plan or aspects of the plan were prematurely withdrawn or faded.

Plans Without Progress

Sometimes, behavior modification procedures will not bring about a desired change nor result in progress. Failure to progress will be evident by inspection of the data. If the data do not reveal a change in the desired direction, it is necessary to review the procedures and their implementation.

Ellen's behavior modification program, for example, might fail to increase her productivity at work. Prior to the development of her plan, Ellen was completing 30 units of work a day, and she continued to average 30 units of work daily after implementation of the plan. Jimmy's tantrum behavior might also remain unaffected by his behavior modification program. During baseline, Jimmy averaged four tantrums a week, and his tantrum behavior remained constant despite implementation of his behavior modification program. Additionally, Sarah might continue to avoid exercising despite the elaborate self-management plan she has devised. Prior to the development of her self-management plan she was not exercising at all, and she continued to avoid exercise afterward.

There are several factors to consider when an individual fails to progress. Pinpointing relevant factors will suggest remedies for a plan that is not resulting in progress.

Plan Implementation

The first factor to consider is the reliability of plan implementation. If a plan is not implemented as designed, failure can be expected. In fact, a common cause of failure to progress is failure to implement fully the procedures.

If a plan has been based on a functional assessment, the result is a set of procedures that must be carried out simultaneously in order to effect behavior change. Implementing 50 percent of the plan will not typically result in a 50 percent change in the target behavior. Implementing only part of a plan may, in fact, result in no change. In some cases, a deterioration in behavior might even occur. Angie's case provides a good example of problems created by failure to implement a behavior plan correctly.

Angie was a young woman with a developmental delay who had a history of shrieking. A functional assessment revealed that she often was given favorite items as a result of her shrieking, in order to quiet her. So, in effect, her shrieking was actually being reinforced. A behavior plan was then developed that involved positive reinforcement for Angie's speaking quietly. Her shrieking was placed on extinction; her teacher was to ignore it. However, Angie's shrieking did not improve after plan implementation and, in fact, became more frequent. A close evaluation revealed that the teacher implemented the plan only occasionally. Also, classroom assistants were untrained and never implemented the plan in the teacher's absence. Angie was, in effect, on no consistent plan, and her behavior continued to worsen, thereby convincing the classroom assistants that behavior modification did not work. Indeed, behavior modification does not work unless it is consistently used.

A formal reliability check can be performed to determine the percentage of plan steps that are being implemented correctly. If the percentage falls short of 100 percent, lack of implementation can be the cause of lack of progress. If a plan has not been fully implemented, it needs to be. The effectiveness of the procedures cannot be evaluated without full implementation. Retraining or additional training might, therefore, be necessary. The common conclusion, already expressed, that behavior modification does not work is often reached by people who do not fully implement the procedures.

Functional Assessment

An incomplete functional assessment is a second factor that can result in failure to progress. If all of the functions a behavior served are not identified and addressed, it is likely that the maladaptive target behavior might persist. Sam's behavior modification plan, for example, targeted his aggression, and the functional assessment revealed that aggression served the function of obtaining attention. His behavior modification plan thus consisted of a reinforcement schedule that provided ample attention for more acceptable behavior. However, when this procedure was fully implemented, his aggression persisted.

Sam's functional assessment had been incomplete. His aggression was caused also by his attempting to escape from difficult tasks in the classroom. Since this aspect of Sam's behavior was not addressed in his behavior change plan, his aggression remained a problem. Once this function was identified, new procedures were added to Sam's plan. His curriculum was revised so that his tasks were not so difficult. Additionally, he was given communication training to teach him to ask for help when having a problem. Following these modifications, Sam's aggression was significantly reduced.

Thus, if a plan is fully implemented and maladaptive behaviors persist, a more thorough functional assessment may be necessary. The behavior change plan must then be revised to account for the newly identified functions.

Sufficiency of Procedures

A third factor that can result in failure to progress is insufficiency of procedures. A behavior change plan might not include enough strategies to effect behavior change, and it might be necessary to include more strategies. An example of a behavior modification plan with insufficient strategies follows.

Eileen was a 10-year-old girl with a learning disability. She often refused to do her work and screamed at the teacher. Her behavior change plan consisted of providing her with positive reinforcers for completing her work and working quietly. Additionally, screaming was placed on extinction; the teacher provided no response to her screaming. Eileen was also taught to ask for assistance when having difficulty with a task, since a function of her behavior was to escape from difficult tasks. Her screaming behavior persistent, however. So, the teacher decided to add a modeling component to Eileen's behavior change plan. She began very obviously to praise the children sitting near Eileen for working quietly. This added strategy made the difference; with modeling, Eileen's behavior began to improve.

Reinforcement Schedules

Another factor that might lead to an individual's failure to progress is the density of the schedule of positive reinforcement. If desired behaviors are not increasing in frequency, the reinforcement schedule might be at fault. If the schedule is too thin (i.e., if reinforcers are not scheduled frequently enough), desired behaviors might not undergo strengthening.

Clara, for example, was a young woman with moderate mental retardation who worked part-time stamping documents at a printing company. Her productivity at work was very low; she took almost 3 hours to complete 100 units of work. When a reinforcement schedule was implemented that provided a reinforcer for every 100 units of work Clara completed, her productivity remained low. However, when the schedule was changed to a Fixed Ratio 20, Clara's rate improved sufficiently to please the manager.

In Clara's case, the type and density of the reinforcement schedule used were not appropriate. Since the rate of her behavior was the issue, with the targeted goal being a higher rate, it might have been more effective to use a DRH schedule rather than an FR schedule.

In another example, Donnie was an 11-year-old boy with an educational diagnosis of emotional impairment. He frequently cursed and made verbal threats at other people. He also often refused to participate in classroom tasks. A functional assessment revealed that his behavior served the functions of obtaining attention, preferred activities, and escape from tasks. A behavior change plan was then designed that included a DRO schedule of reinforcement for any behavior other than cursing or threatening. Preferred activities and attention were used as reinforcers. However, Donnie continued to resist tasks.

In Donnie's case, a DRO schedule was not the best choice. Even though teachers were providing him with reinforcers when he was not engaging in cursing or threatening, Donnie could be sitting without working and, because he was not cursing or threatening, be given reinforcers while on the DRO. His reinforcement schedule was, therefore, changed to a Variable Interval schedule of reinforcement, under which a variety of desirable target behaviors were reinforced, including his participating in tasks. Once Donnie began receiving reinforcers for acceptable behaviors, rather than for an absence of maladaptive behaviors, his task participation increased and his problem behaviors decreased.

Type of Reinforcers

An individual's failure to progress can also be due to failure to use potent reinforcers. Often, the events or items chosen as reinforcers actually do not function as reinforcers; that is, they do not serve to increase the frequency of the desired behavior. Rather than conclude that the reinforcers need to be more potent, novice behavior analysts often conclude that positive reinforcement does not work. When a reinforcement schedule does not appear to be working, it is necessary to reconsider the choice of reinforcers. For example, if praise is being used as the only reinforcer, tangible reinforcers or activity reinforcers might be necessary. If activities are used as reinforcers, it is important to evaluate their potency continually. If tangible reinforcers are used, they also need to be examined for effectiveness. What is reinforcing for one individual might not be reinforcing for another.

Satiation might also occur, thereby weakening or eliminating the positive effects of a reinforcement schedule. Charlie, for example, loved chocolate, so his teachers provided him with chocolate on a Fixed Ratio schedule for work completion, in which he earned chocolate pieces about every 15 minutes. By the end of 2 hours, Charlie was satiated on chocolate, and it lost its value as a reinforcer.

As the outset of program planning, it is important to complete a thorough inventory of possible reinforcers for an individual. In the course of plan implementation, it is necessary to assess continually the effectiveness of the reinforcers used and to make adjustments and changes if these reinforcers appear to be losing their effectiveness.

Extinction

Yet another factor that can result in one's failure to progress is a faulty extinction process. Extinction can be difficult to implement. If a targeted misbehavior persists, the purity of the extinction process must be examined. It is possible that the behavior is continuing to be reinforced. Close examination of actual instances of the misbehavior must, therefore, be undertaken to ferret out sources of inadvertent reinforcement. The case of Jill provides a good example of an impure extinction process.

Jill's classroom teacher was dismayed that Jill continued to throw her work materials despite a behavior change plan that included positive reinforcement for her working, with more varied and preferred tasks as work assignments and more help and assistance with task completion. A close look at Jill's case revealed that the extinction component was not pure. Although the teacher continued to direct Jill to her work after she had thrown the materials, the teacher still responded to the behavior in ways that could be reinforcing. After Jill would throw her materials, the teacher would make eye contact with her, look extremely displeased, and shake her head. The teacher was actually providing reinforcement for Jill's behavior in the form of eye contact and facial gestures. The teacher thus needed additional training on how to react when Jill threw her materials; and once the teacher learned to react without showing any sign of annoyance, Jill's behavior began to improve.

Pitfalls

Behavior modification can be a powerful tool for behavior change. However, behavior change often does not come easily. It can require a great deal of expertise, patience, and resources. There are a number of pitfalls to avoid when attempting behavior change. To the extent to which these pitfalls occur, behavior change will be hampered.

Lack of Expertise

An effective behavior change plan can require a great deal of expertise to develop, to provide training on, and to implement. Many behavior problems can be solved by teachers and parents. However, lack of knowledge of behavioral principles can thwart them in their efforts. Thus, it is necessary that teachers and parents who are confronted with behavior problems that might be associated with learning or other disabilities be familiar with the principles of behavior modification. Their familiarity must be sufficient for them to use the principles in positive ways and to avoid inadvertently encouraging behaviors they wish to eliminate.

More severe behavior problems, such as high frequency self-injury, aggression, and property destruction, might require the expertise of a professional in behavior modification. Failure to have knowledgeable input into the development of a behavior change plan can doom the plan and targeted individual to failure.

Lack of Sufficient Resources

A behavior change plan might dictate sweeping changes in a person's environment. These changes might involve resources not currently provided or the need for more adult attention. For example, a teacher might have 25 students in a classroom, and Jeffrey, one of these students, might need additional teacher attention if his behavior problems are to be solved. Changes in his curriculum might also be needed. In another example, Janet is a young woman with profound mental retardation, whose classroom task consists of stuffing and unstuffing envelopes most of the morning. Her behavior change plan might require a variety of more meaningful tasks. It also might call for more integration with people without her handicapping condition and severe behavior problems who can serve as models for her. Additionally, the plan might call for a variety of reinforcers not currently available at school.

Failure to provide sufficient resources for a behavior change plan can be a pitfall that dooms the plan to failure. So, when a behavior is initially targeted, teachers, parents, or other people in decision-making roles must make a realistic assessment of the environment and the target behavior. If it is important to change a target behavior, a commitment is needed to provide sufficient resources for behavior change.

Resistance to Change

It is easy for one individual to impose behavior change on another individual. It is not so easy to change one's own behavior in order to produce change in other people's behavior. Behavioral procedures, including schedules of positive reinforcement and extinction procedures, can be difficult to implement. In many settings in which behavior change plans are needed, there are often relatives, staff, or other people who are resistant to changing their own behaviors for the sake of the individual who needs a plan. Resistance to change must be recognized and eliminated. Without full cooperation from all key people, a behavior change plan will not enjoy full implementation, and the individual in need of behavior change will be deprived of full success.

Insufficient Follow-Through

Behavior change can take time. Lack of sufficient follow-through can sabotage an otherwise effective plan. One pitfall to success is giving up a plan too soon. Maladaptive behaviors might have been present for years, and their elimination can take more than a few days. A good behavior change plan can take weeks or even months to effect behavior change. If a plan is terminated either unintentionally through neglect or intentionally through premature fading, success may not be realized. So, it is important to provide sufficient follow-through to allow the procedures to take effect.

Last-Resort Technology

Behavior modifiers often use punishment as a last-resort technology. Failure to progress becomes justification for the use of punishment. Research literature gives a variety of examples of punishment purported to reduce the frequency of problem behaviors successfully. However, punishment is often used without the benefit of a well-designed behavior plan based on a functional assessment and fully implemented. When an individual's progress is limited, instead of reexamining the functional assessment; the plan implementation; the strategies, reinforcers, and schedule(s) used; and other pertinent factors, the behavior modifier concludes that positive procedures do not work. This conclusion leads to the application of punishment procedures.

Applications

Case 1

Ariel was a 6-year-old girl with a developmental disorder who was in a regular classroom in a public school, with full-time help from a classroom aide. Ariel had several severe behavior problems, including biting and hitting other children. So, a behavior modification plan, based on a functional assessment, was developed for her by the school psychologist, a classroom teacher, and the aide. The school psychologist put the plan into written form, describing all procedures in detail.

The teacher and Ariel's aide were trained by the school psychologist in plan implementation. The school psychologist spent additional time in the classroom, observing implementation and providing the classroom staff with feedback. Since the teacher had difficulty with implementing extinction, the school psychologist worked with Ariel and modeled the extinction procedures for the teacher. The teacher continued to collect data and compared treatment data with baseline data.

After several weeks, there was still no improvement in Ariel's aggressive behavior. The school psychologist observed plan implementation and determined that it was fully implemented. Close examination of plan procedures revealed that the items used as reinforcers were not being varied. Ariel was consistently rewarded only with crackers, and it appeared that she was satiating on them. So, the reinforcers were changed and varied, with a selection of different foods and activities used in place of just crackers. After the reinforcers were changed and varied, Ariel's behavior began to improve. By the end of the second month of plan implementation, her aggression was virtually eliminated.

Case 2

David was a 10-year-old boy with a learning disability and social skills deficits who engaged in high-frequency screaming in class. A consultant was brought in to design a behavior change plan for David with the help of his classroom staff. The functional assessment revealed that screaming served the functions of task avoidance, often obtaining for David extra attention and the presentation of more preferred tasks. The plan included a dense schedule of positive reinforcement as well as stimulus control procedures such as daily use of a written schedule.

The school system, however, decided not to provide the resources to implement David's plan. No reinforcers were purchased, and the teacher rarely remembered to provide David with a written schedule of his activities. The staff continued to present more preferred activities to him after he screamed, in order to quiet him down.

After one month of improperly implementing the written plan, the classroom teacher decided that positive reinforcement did not work. She and David, thus, had a very difficult semester. At mid-year, she was transferred to another school, and another teacher took over David's class. This teacher implemented his plan fully, and within one month, David was cooperating in his work. His screaming was virtually eliminated.

Case 3

Allen was a young man with autism and self-injury. A behavior change plan was designed for him that provided a DRO schedule for behavior other than self-injury. The reinforcer used was praise. No functional assessment of Allen's behavior had been done before development of his plan, and the reinforcement schedule was the plan's sole component. After two weeks of observing no change in Allen's behavior, the head of the school decided that positive procedures did not work and that punishment was necessary. A shock rod was used as the punisher. Each time Allen hit himself, he was given an electric shock.

Allen's case provides a not uncommon example of the inadequate use of behavior modification as justification for the use of aversive procedures to manage behavior.

Summary

Behavior modification is the systematic application of the principles of behavior. Once these principles are incorporated into a behavior change plan, sufficient planning, follow-through, and evaluation are needed if behavior change is to occur.

The plan must first be put into written form so that anyone who might need to use it can understand the procedures. Next, anyone who might need to implement the procedures must be thoroughly trained. Training should consist of general training on behavior modification and specific training on the individual behavior change plan. It should include follow-up monitoring to insure that the plan is being fully and accurately implemented. Parents, teachers, teacher assistants, job coaches, relatives, and any other individuals who might need to implement the plan should benefit from thorough training.

Following training, the plan can be implemented; and implementation should be complete from the outset. It can be problematic to implement a plan gradually. Several procedures might be designed to complement each other, such as positive reinforcement and extinction, and implementing one without the other can create problems and hamper progress. Follow-up monitoring must also be done, as well as ongoing evaluation of the effectiveness of the plan.

If the plan is successful, decisions must be made regarding its continued implementation. If progress does not occur, consideration must be given to a number of factors, such as the degree of implementation, the scope of the functional assessment, the sufficiency of the strategies, the potency of the reinforcers, and the purity of the extinction process. Pitfalls to avoid include failure to provide sufficient resources and resistance to change. Another very important pitfall to avoid is jumping to the unwarranted conclusion that positive procedures do not work and that punishment is therefore necessary.

Study Questions

1. Describe a typical training sequence for a behavior change plan prior to implementation in a classroom with one teacher and two aides.
2. What is the purpose of follow-up monitoring? How can it be done?
3. How can the effectiveness of a behavior change plan be evaluated in respect to baseline data? Describe three additional methods for assessing progress.
4. Describe five factors that might account for an individual's failure to progress with a behavior change plan.

Exercises

1. Joan was a 4-year-old girl who had frequent tantrums. A functional assessment revealed that the functions of her behavior were to obtain favorite toys and adult attention. A behavior change plan was then designed that included reinforcers about every 2 hours for cooperative behavior, extinction of the tantrums by ignoring them, and parent-structured play periods at least

once an hour. Write Joan's behavior change plan, incorporating these strategies.

2. Ellen is a 16-year-old girl who has mild mental retardation and a part-time job at the library sorting books. She has a behavior change plan for her refusal to work. Her plan consists of a fixed ratio reinforcement schedule: she is rewarded with a trip to the water fountain for every 40 books that she sorts. However, her plan is not working; she still refuses to work. What factors must be considered in evaluating the reasons for the plan's failure? What improvements could be made in it?

SELF-MANAGEMENT PROJECT

1. Evaluate the effects of your interventions by comparing baseline data to data during intervention. Is your plan working?
2. If your plan is not working, consider some reasons why it might not be working. What changes are needed in your plan? Make those changes.
3. If your plan is working, consider what you will do next. Will you fade, change, or terminate your interventions?
4. Continue to implement your interventions until you feel they are no longer needed or no longer working.
5. After terminating your plan, continue to collect data to determine whether any positive effects maintained following plan termination.

14

Ethics of Behavior Modification

Nancy R. Weiss

Donald attended a special-education program at a regular high school. His functional level was more limited than the levels of most of the other students in his class. His teachers viewed him as being unable to participate in the range of learning activities that they had designed for the other students. They therefore selected a few activities for Donald that they felt were geared toward his ability level. These included sorting nuts and bolts into two separate bins, putting together a puzzle, and matching squares of colored paper to the squares on a colored grid.

Donald was often reluctant to stay in his seat. He showed curiosity about the activities in which the other students in the room were taking part. These activities were frequently of a more active and participatory nature. He often refused to work on the activities assigned to him, sometimes throwing his materials on the floor. At these times, he frequently became aggressive, hitting and kicking his teachers and other students in his class. His actions led his teachers to ask for assistance in designing a behavior plan that would "help Donald control his temper." When asked what their goals for Donald would be, his teachers expressed hope that he would "learn to work quietly and independently on his assigned tasks and not disrupt the rest of the class."

Donald's case raises a number of ethical questions. These include whether the problem here lies with Donald or with his environment and how the goals for behavior change are selected. To know what to do in this situation requires much more information about Donald, the interactions between him and other people, and the functions of his behaviors. However, one might question whether it is fair to Donald to design a behavior plan that would teach him to be compliant in a situation that is likely inappropriate for him.

This chapter discusses the ethics of behavior modification. Whereas most of this book focuses on *how* to change behavior, this chapter examines decisions with regard to what is right and wrong. It also examines ethical factors related to the choice and application of behavioral principles.

The Random House Dictionary (1987) defines ethics as "a system of moral principles . . . the rules of conduct recognized in respect to a particular class of human actions . . . that branch of philosophy dealing with values relating to human conduct, with respect to the rightness and wrongness of certain actions. . . ." (p. 665). There are no clear answers regarding what is ethical and what is unethical. Skinner (1971) says the technology of behavior modification "is ethically neutral. It can be used by villain or saint. There is nothing in a methodology which determines the values governing its use" (p. 150). Individuals must decide for themselves what is right and what is wrong.[1] There are, however, some important concerns that need to be addressed when designing or implementing a behavior change plan. These include the following:

- concerns about control and the use of behavior modification
- concerns about opportunities to make choices
- concerns about the balance between safety and risk
- concerns about informed consent, due process, and least restrictive environments
- concerns about whether a problem lies with the individual or with the environment
- concerns about how goals for behavior change plans are selected
- concerns about how methods for behavior change plans are selected
- concerns about the use of aversive procedures
- concerns about the use of reinforcement
- concerns about the collection of baseline data
- concerns about safeguards to assure the ethical practice of behavior modification

The Issue of Control

Control is a primary concern in the use of behavior modification. There is an inherent imbalance of power between the person attempting to modify behavior and the person to whom the program is applied. A congressional study in 1974 expressed concern that behavioral technology poses a

[1]For an in-depth discussion of the process for evaluating the ethical issues inherent in the use of one aspect of behavior modification see Turnbull, H. R., & Guess, D. (1986). A model for analyzing the moral aspects of special education and behavioral interventions: The moral aspects of aversive procedures. In P. R. Dokecki & R. M. Zaner, *Ethics of dealing with persons with severe handicaps* (pp. 167–210). Baltimore: Paul H. Brookes Publishing Co.

serious threat to an individual's constitutional right to self-determination. The report stated that the gravest danger presented "by the technology of behavior modification is the power this technology gives one man to impose his views and values on another."

Behavior modification is a target for concerns about control, even though attempts to control or influence the behavior of other people are commonplace. For example, when an advertising agent designs a campaign to sell a product, when a parent or teacher disciplines a child, or when a political candidate makes a speech directed at attracting more voters, attempts are being made to influence the behavior of others. Even within the field of psychology, behavior modification is not unique in its effort to influence others' behavior. The goal of all forms of therapy is to change behavior.

Behavior modification is particularly susceptible to criticism and concern with regard to ethics. This is because behavior modification is a scientific, systematic approach to behavior change that is directed toward a specific person. It is an approach that often is not well understood. Control becomes an issue because behavior modification is frequently more effective than other forms of therapy in changing behavior and because the behavior change itself is more measurable.

Sometimes the level of concern about these issues of control rises to one of paranoia, with people using terms such as *mind control* and expressing concern about a society similar to the one described in George Orwell's *1984*. However, as one author states,

> All of us try continually to influence our own and others' behavior, so that individuals using behavior modification procedures are distinctive only in that they attempt to influence behavior more systematically. . . . to be opposed to behavior modification is to be opposed to the law of gravity. Rather, the key issue is what sort of care, caution, and control should be exercised when behavioral principles are applied precisely and systematically (Stolz, Wienckowski, & Brown, 1974, p. 1027).

In fact, not all of the concerns about the use of behavior modification are unfounded. The case example at the beginning of this chapter is an illustration of a way in which behavior modification could be used inappropriately. Because behavior modification is effective and has the potential to be misused, particular caution must be exercised with regard to the ethical application of behavior modification principles.

The Issue of Choice

Behavior modification has been used on a widespread basis with people with mental retardation. About 90,000 people with mental retardation continue to reside in large, impersonal, overcrowded institutions in the United States,[2] where we "permit them only limited social relationships, deprive them of freedom of movement and of opportunities for decision making, and forbid them most of the amenities they could enjoy outside" (Sidman, 1989, p. 218). People with even the most severe levels of mental retardation have fewer behavior problems when they are able to make choices, to have impact on their environment, to feel valued and empowered, to be productive, and to enjoy freedom of movement and a range of meaningful activities.

Many people with disabilities lead lives that are highly controlled. Not only people living in institutions but also children in schools and even people living in highly structured community settings have many everyday decisions made for them. These include when to wake up, whether to take a bath or a shower, what to wear, and when and what to eat. Individuals with disabilities are rarely given the opportunity to make choices about where and with whom to live, what work to perform or educational setting to attend, or how to spend their free time. Such pervasive control over major and minor aspects of people's lives may lead them to escalate their problem behavior in protest. The result is a cycle of control, as shown in Figure 14.1.

This cycle illustrates a power struggle that starts with an individual attempting to assert control over his or her life. This natural response is characteristic of all people who are made to feel powerless. The individual protests the degree of control imposed by behaving in ways that are challenging. Parents, residential staff, or teachers working with the individual apply additional restrictions to inhibit attempts at self-expression. The individual then escalates the behavior in a further attempt to assert control. This leads the caregivers to conclude that even more control measures must be needed, and the cycle continues. Such cycles of control are broken only when the function of the behavior is recognized as an attempt to assert control and when serious efforts are made to assist individuals to exercise their right to self-determination.

The Issues of Safety and Risk

When behavior modification techniques are used, there is often a need to balance the degree to which the safety of individuals will be assured against the amount of risk individuals will be allowed to experience. The following example illustrates this balance between safety and risk.

The principal of Paul's residential school reviewed the data on the program being implemented to address Paul's pica behavior, and it revealed consider-

[2]Braddock, D., Hemp, R., Fujiura, G., Bachelder, L., & Mitchell, D. (1990). The state of the states in developmental disabilities (p. 12). Baltimore: Paul H. Brooks Publishing Co.

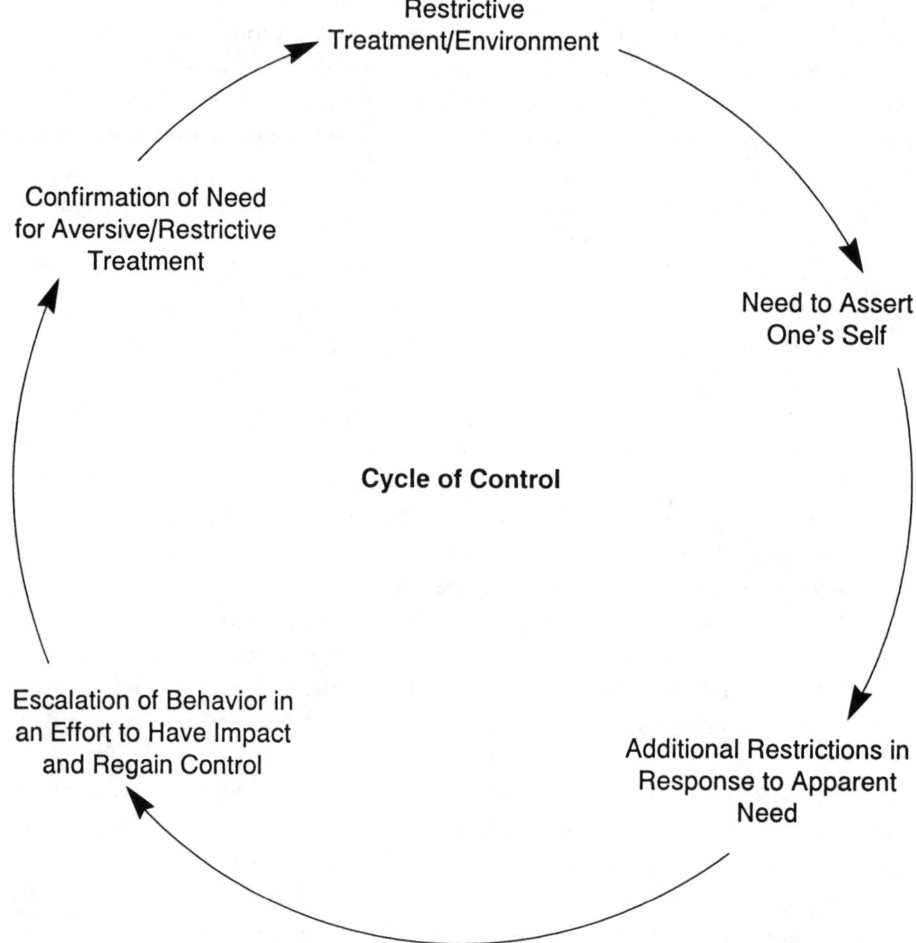

Figure 14.1 Cycle of control.

able success. Paul had an average of 24 incidents of pica per month prior to implementation of his program; in the three months since the program was implemented, he had only one incident. The principal then wrote a note to Paul's psychologist and to staff at the school congratulating them on their remarkable success. However, he should have done some further investigation before assuming that good behavioral programming had led to a decrease in problem behaviors.

Paul's behavior program consisted of several components. One was that he was moved to a locked unit that was kept free of any objects he could ingest. The unit had a sterile feel to it, and there were few activities or materials available in it to occupy Paul's time. Another aspect of the program was that Paul was put in arm splints, which prevented him from bending his arms at the elbow and putting anything in his mouth. In addition, the program instructed staff to praise Paul every hour for not eating anything he should not eat.

Although a significant reduction in such a serious behavior as pica is laudable, the success of Paul's program is not surprising given its restrictiveness. The benefits to Paul under such a restrictive program may be questioned.

There are many restrictive techniques that have been used in an effort to assure that problem behaviors do not occur. Typically, these techniques are used to enhance safety and reduce risk. Often, however, their use does not involve the systematic application of the principles of behavior modification. Examples of these techniques, which are often confused with applied behavior analysis, follow:

- *Mechanical restraints.* Arm splints or four-point restraints to keep an individual tied to a bed are examples of mechanical restraints. Although these can reduce behavior problems, lasting behavior change is unlikely. The behavior is likely to recur when the restraint is removed.
- *Medications.* Medications have an important use with many individuals. Sometimes, however, they are misused or overused to control behavior for the convenience of the staff, teacher, or family. When they are used as a substitute for behavioral programming or are overused, they can interfere with an individual's ability to benefit from behavioral programming.
- *Environmental adaptations.* The locked, sterile living unit already described is an example of an environmental adaptation. Other such changes include replacing glass windows with unbreakable plastic, prohibiting access to certain areas or objects, or replacing ordinary furniture with heavy, institutional furniture that cannot be thrown or otherwise present dangers.
- *Additional staff.* The number of staff is sometimes increased for the purpose of restraining or controlling the movements of an individual.

Only when one understands the specific circumstances related to an individual's behavior and environment can techniques such as these be determined as ethical or unethical. The use of restrictive techniques should always receive careful consideration. The fact that the data from a behavior program show that an individual has stopped breaking windows is less meaningful when it is known that all of the windows in the classroom have been replaced with unbreakable plastic. The individual might be making just as many attempts as before to break windows and, in another environment, would be successful. Thus, whenever restrictive techniques are recommended, it is most important that their necessity and the sacrifice that results in terms of individual freedom and choice be weighed carefully.

Such techniques as these represent behavior control in its most primitive form. Certainly if a child is physically or chemically prevented from performing a behavior, one could say the behavior is modified. However, these techniques are not rightfully classified as behavior modification procedures as defined and discussed in this book. Parents, teachers, and other professionals who work with individuals with behavior problems should be aware that when these techniques are used independent of a competently developed and applied behavior modification program, ethical standards almost certainly have been breached.

The Issue of Rights

Citizens of the United States with developmental disabilities have the same rights as citizens without handicapping conditions. In addition to these rights that are shared with all citizens, they have some specific rights that have been established through class action suits and federal legislation. Three rights that are pertinent to a discussion of the ethics of behavior modification are informed consent, due process, and least restrictive environments.

Informed consent is the ability of an individual to make informed decisions regarding treatment and services. It requires that the goals and methods of any formal behavior change plan be explained fully to the individual. It also requires that the individual have the ability to understand the information and the ability to make judgments. If the individual is judged incapable of giving informed consent, guardianship can be assigned by a court to a family member or another person to act on behalf of the individual with disabilities.

Particular care must be exercised when the recipient of a behavior change plan is a child, is an involuntary participant, or has mental retardation or another disability that may call into question the ability to give informed consent. Children with disabilities are under the guardianship of their parents unless a court has ruled otherwise.

Adults with disabilities are their own legal guardians unless a court has ruled them incompetent. Making such a ruling is a complex and time-consuming process. In addition, most courts are reluctant to remove guardianship from an individual unless there is a compelling reason to do so. As a result, the vast majority of adults with mental retardation or other disabilities are their own legal guardians and, therefore, responsible for providing informed consent for any formal behavior programs in which they may participate.

Professionals designing a formal behavior change plan have a responsibility to assess an individual's competence to make a decision with regard to participation in the plan. The goals, methods, and alternatives to the plan must be explained. When the individual's ability to make an informed decision is in question, additional safeguards must be employed. Efforts should be made to include a review by persons who are friends of the individual or advocates for the rights of the individual and who will represent the interests of the person with disabilities without compromise.

Individuals with developmental disabilities are vulnerable to the treatment decisions made by other people. Those served might be dependent on the professionals who work with them, not only for their education but, in the case of residential programs, for shelter, food, clothing, social contact, and all other aspects of their lives. In addition, families of individuals with disabilities may feel compelled to cooperate with whatever procedures are recommended. The professionals seeking consent from the individual or family members for participation in a behavior change plan must, therefore, be sensitive to the effect of this dependence on the consent process.

Due process is an established course of action designed to protect the rights of individuals. It is a protection guaranteed to all United States citizens under the Constitution. Professionals serving people with disabilities have a responsibility to assure due process through internal systems that assure protection of individuals' rights. Examples of internal due process systems include the explaining of grievance procedures to individuals with disabilities and their families and the reviewing of behavior programs by human rights or peer review committees.

Class action lawsuits have established the right of all persons with disabilities to services in the *least restrictive environment* (e.g., *Wyatt v. Stickney*, 1972). Under this doctrine, if a person's rights or freedoms are to be restricted in any way, it must first be demonstrated that all other possibilities for less restrictive treatment have been exhausted. In relation to behavioral programs, this means that restrictive techniques should never be used until it can be clearly demonstrated that well-designed, consistently implemented positive programs have not been successful.

The Issue of Establishing the Root of the Problem

An important ethical question is whether the individual or the environment is at the root of a behavior problem. It is ethically suspect to attempt to change a person's behavior in an effort to get the person to adapt to a situation that is inappropriate or oppressive. The following case provides an example of this ethical dilemma.

Laura was a child with profound mental retardation who attended a residential school program. Her teachers reported that she had few behavior problems at school, but the residential staff reported many incidents of her screaming, object throwing, property destruction, and aggression toward other people. The school provided a full schedule of interesting and challenging activities in which Laura could participate. In contrast, planned activities in the residential setting were rare; there were few toys or stimulating materials available. The television set was usually left on but Laura showed little interest in it.

It would be unethical to design a behavior change plan to assist Laura in conforming to an environment that does not meet her needs. The problem lies with the residential setting and the lack of stimulating opportunities provided there. Laura's behavior, in fact, can be viewed as an objective critique of how she is being treated. The behaviors she exhibits are certainly problematic. The solution, however, does not lie in applying a behavior program directed at getting her to conform to the residential environment but, rather, in focusing on a range of environmental changes.

It is important that individuals working in the field of behavior change do not equate nonconformity with noncompliance. Often, behaviors that are viewed as maladaptive should instead be viewed as highly adaptive responses to maladaptive environments. Therefore, suggesting environmental changes, or even a total change of setting, may be well within the role of the behavior modification professional.

The Issue of Goal Selection

The issue of how goals for behavioral intervention are selected is an important one. The following case provides an illustration.

Janet attended a school that prided itself on the degree to which its students looked and acted as if they did not have handicaps. She had a habit of rocking in her chair and moaning softly several times a week, usually for about 15 to 20 minutes each time. Afterward, she usually returned to her assigned task without prompting. Her teacher, who had designed a behavior change plan to address Janet's rocking and moaning behavior, told her that this behavior was not normal and that if she exhibited it in public, it would draw attention to her and perhaps subject her to ridicule.

Janet's teacher thought he was doing what was best for Janet by implementing a behavior change plan to address her rocking and moaning behavior. If Janet had been able to express herself verbally or if an attempt had been made to understand the behavior from Janet's perspective, her teacher may have come to a very different conclusion.

A functional assessment may have revealed that Janet's behavior served the function of achieving time alone, without demands. Although her rocking and moaning behavior took her away from more productive activities several times a week, the behavior did not last long and she willingly returned to her assigned tasks on her own. Janet's teacher could have regarded this behavior as a harmless, idiosyncratic activity. He could have viewed it as Janet's attempt to schedule a break for herself, rather than as a behavior that needed reduction.

Often people designing behavior change plans view the targeted behaviors from their own point of view. They tend to target behaviors for change based on what they would want for themselves, to meet the expectations of other people or of society in general.

Certain well-accepted ideologies tend to determine and justify the goals that are selected. For example, an accepted ideology in our culture is that people should work productively and support themselves to the degree to which they are capable. Within the field of disability services, such philosophies as normalization (assisting people to live in a manner as close to normal as possible) and the concept that people should be taught to function as independently as possible guide service delivery. Such ideologies are sometimes poorly translated into behavioral goals; for example, many people might think that Jason's behavior of talking too much should be modified to improve his chances of obtaining a competitive job. Jason, however, may not agree that this behavior is a problem for him. A better approach might be to locate a job for Jason in which his talking would not prove to be a problem.

Sometimes, the goals of an individual are selected by parents, staff at a residential or day program, or teachers. These goals might be selected for convenience rather than for the good of the individual. For example, a teacher may want to use behavioral programming to assure that the children in the class are quiet and cooperative; or, staff at a group home may ask that a behavior program be designed to reduce a certain individual's behavior of pacing the halls by getting that person to wash windows, thereby reducing staff responsibilities. When behavior modification techniques are used for compliance with an arbitrary set of expectations or for the convenience of other people, the ethical implications should be weighed carefully.

Stolz (1978) asks, "Have the psychologist and the client or the client's representative considered whether the goals selected are appropriate for this person? Are the goals realistic, explicit, and positive? Has the intervention been designed so the client is the one primarily benefitting from it?" (p. 112). In some of the previously mentioned examples, it is not clear whether the individual with disabilities is the person who will primarily benefit from the intervention.

Ideally, the designer and the recipient of a behavior change plan should decide on a mutually agreeable set of goals. This is not always possible, however, Sometimes the individual's disability prohibits full participation in such decision making. In addition, often there is conflict between the values and goals of the individual and the values and goals of society. An individual may have no interest in modifying aggressive behavior; however, other people in the environment have a right to be protected from harm.

Persons designing behavior change plans must consider whether they are acting as agents of an individual with a disability, as agents of society, or as agents of a specific group of individuals, such as family members or residential staff. While it may not always be possible to act purely as an agent of an individual, the person designing the plan has a responsibility to consider the view of that individual and to acknowledge when the program is being implemented in response to the needs or values of other people.

Persons who design behavioral change plans should use objective criteria to guide decision making about which behaviors are in need of change. Using a clear set of criteria helps to assure that the rights of an individual with disabilities are protected and that the plan will be in that individual's best interest. Before a plan is written to change a behavior, Weiss (1990) suggests that the following should be considered:

- Is the behavior potentially dangerous?
- Does the behavior interfere with the individual's ability to learn new skills?
- Does the behavior interfere with the individual's ability to participate in activities?
- Does the behavior diminish potential for community integration?
- Does the behavior result in increased dependence on caregivers or other support?
- Do the actions of the individual create a need for medications to manage inappropriate behavior or other restrictive strategies (e.g., time-out, physical restraint, etc.)?
- Does the individual, or the individual's family or advocate, when appropriate, agree that this is a problem behavior in need of change? (p. 63).

These criteria provide a standard against which the importance of changing a behavior can be measured. There are, in fact, ethical considerations in choosing *not* to implement a behavior program. Some behaviors are dangerous or destructive, or they severely limit an individual's ability to participate in educational or other activities. Denying people with such behaviors the best available behavioral technology is just as questionable as attempting to change behaviors that are neither dangerous nor disruptive.

The Issue of Method Selection

The methods used to change behavior must be not only effective but also ethical. It is not acceptable to select a behavior change method simply because it has worked with similar behavior problems in the past. Methods must be selected systematically, based on the needs of the individual involved. The only truly systematic approach to designing a formal behavior change plan is through the use of a functional assessment, discussed in detail in previous chapters. Methods selected for implementation should respond directly and logically to the identified functions of the behavior.

The individual who is the recipient of a behavior change program should be given the opportunity to participate in the selection of the methods used in the program and should understand the program and its purpose. If this individual is unable to participate effectively in this process, persons who can advocate for the individual's rights and interests should be sought and included in decision making.

An important consideration is whether the methods chosen for a program are effective in changing behavior. Their effectiveness must be continually assessed. No matter how benign the methods used are (and whenever restrictive methods are used), revisions in the design or implementation of a program must be made as soon as it is clear that the program is not working.

Staff or teachers sometimes develop a pride of ownership in programs that they have worked hard to design. They are reluctant to give up on them even when the data indicate that behavior change is not occurring. In the worst case, this can result in an increase in the restrictiveness of the program: since 10 minutes of time-out did not work, staff may modify the program to require 30 minutes of time-out. To assure that they are being ethical, people who design programs must be willing to abandon those that prove to be unsuccessful and to return to the functional assessment to learn more about the purpose the behavior may be serving for the individual with disabilities.

Ethics must be considered in the use of certain behavior change strategies. The use of procedures both with and without aversive components has ethical implications.

Ethical Issues Related to the Use of Aversive Procedures

The preceding chapters of this book focus on how to change behavior using positive approaches. Other approaches are sometime used that include the application of procedures that are painful, humiliating, or restrictive. These are known as aversive procedures. The following example illustrates some of the important ethical questions inherent in the use of aversive procedures.

Alan made a low grunting noise under his breath as he sat at his work carrel sorting objects. His teacher immediately walked behind him and shouted, "No inappropriate noises!" At the same time, the teacher grasped Alan's head and tipped it back so he could insert into Alan's nose the pointed tip of a plastic squeeze bottle containing ammonia. Several hours later, Alan glanced at some visitors who were there to observe him, and his teacher shouted, "Eyes on work!" The teacher then grabbed a hose, and as Alan raised his hands and blinked, he sprayed Alan's face until Alan was sputtering and his shirt was soaked. Without even pausing to wipe the water from his eyes, Alan then returned to the task in front of him.

The American Association on Mental Retardation states that aversive procedures have some or all of the following characteristics:

1. Obvious signs of physical pain experienced by the individual.
2. Potential or actual physical side effects, including tissue damage, physical illness, severe stress, and/or death.
3. Dehumanization of the individual, through means such as social degradation, social isolation, verbal abuse, techniques inappropriate for the individual's age, and treatment out of proportion to the target behavior (*News and Notes*, 1990, p. 1).

Aversive procedures used include the following:

- electric shock
- water spray to the face
- lemon juice, vinegar, or pepper sauce in the mouth
- forced exercise
- white noise at 95 decibels
- placement in a bath or shower of cold water
- slapping or pinching
- blindfolding
- ice to the cheeks or chin
- teeth brushed or face washed with an antiseptic solution
- prolonged physical restraint or isolation
- withholding of meals

Aversive techniques are used most often when the behavior in need of change is very dangerous to the individual with disabilities (e.g., severe self-injurious behavior) or to other people (e.g., severe aggression). However, the use of aversive techniques is not limited to attempts to change dangerous behaviors. These techniques are used also for other behaviors, including out-of-seat behavior, facial grimaces, off-task behavior, and noise making.

Many advocates of the use of aversive procedures justify their use by claiming that because a behavior problem is serious, it needs or requires punishment. There is simply no truth to this notion (Donnellan, LaVigna, & Negri-Shoultz, 1988). Many practitioners, who for ethical reasons began using nonaversive behavioral techniques, are now contributing to a "growing body of empirical data which demonstrates that non-aversive procedures are at least as effective and possibly more effective than intrusive interventions" (Knoll, 1987, p. 4).

Many people who defend the use of aversive procedures claim that they are more effective than positive approaches to behavior change. Few people would argue that aversive procedures are likely to have a measurable impact on the performance of the behaviors to which they are applied. However, LaVigna (1987) states that "while punitive procedures may produce rapid and sharp suppression of problematic behaviors, serious questions about the durability and generalization of treatment effects, side effects, and social validity suggest that present punishment technology has narrow utility and is of little if any value for true community and social integration" (invited address). Many studies report the initial suppression of behavior through the use of aversive procedures. However, as discussed in Chapter 9 on punishment, these techniques do not address the functions of the behaviors and do not leave the learner with new skills or enhanced adaptive behaviors.

Initial suppression of behavior is not the most important measure of efficacy. There is limited scientific evidence that aversive techniques are successful in achieving the maintenance of behavior change over a long period of time and in assuring generalization of the behavior change to other situations or environments.

Aversive procedures are not used universally. In fact, some states and countries, responding to the ethical and moral issues raised by the use of aversive procedures, have outlawed their use. Some federal and state regulations limit the use of aversive procedures, often by requiring that nonaversive techniques be tried before aversive techniques are used. This approach to protecting the rights of individuals with disabilities is insufficient. Often a poorly designed or overly simplified nonaversive approach is tried for a few days before it is dismissed and aversive techniques substituted.

People with disabilities comprise some of the most devalued members of our population. The techniques described above are not tolerated for use on the elderly, on prisoners, or even on animals. However, when told these techniques are being used to benefit individuals with disabilities, many people are willing to ignore the abuse. Kazdin (1980) did a study on the acceptability of treatments and found that college students viewed as acceptable a wider range of aversive procedures when the recipients were described as having more severe levels of mental retardation. The use of procedures that cause pain or are dehumanizing should not be tolerated by a society that bases its system of beliefs on the fair and ethical treatment of all of its citizens.

Guess, Helmstetter, Turnbull, and Knowlton (1987) state that "persons with disabling conditions, especially those with severe/profound mental retardation, comprise the minority group in America that has experienced the most systematic and long term application of aversive procedures to modify behavior perceived as deviant" (p. 32). The public's perception of all people with disabilities is compromised when the treatment used implies that these are dangerous, unpredictable people whose extraordinary behaviors need to be controlled through extraordinary means. In addition, when staff or teachers are asked to implement dehumanizing procedures, their ability to treat the individuals in a manner that values and respects them is severely compromised. Staff cannot be expected to use water spray or ammonia fumes on individuals and then convey to them that they are fully valued, respected members of society.

A reduction of dangerous or disruptive behavior can be achieved without sacrificing an individual's self-esteem, the development of relationships with other people, or the preservation of human dignity. Success should not be viewed simply as the reduction of a behavior, without considering the sacrifice to quality of life and well-being of the people who are subjected to aversive procedures.

Ethical Issues Related to the Use of Reinforcement

A person with a developmental disability once said, "I've figured it out. Don't tell them what you like or they'll make you earn it" (Henning, 1991, lecture). In speaking these words, that person eloquently described an ethical dilemma in the use of reinforcement techniques.

The ethical approach to choosing a reinforcer is to select something that the person likes but does not have access to usually. It is sometimes difficult to identify a reinforcer that is convenient to offer whenever it is earned yet does not require limiting access to something that, in the past, has been freely available. Often, the reinforcers that come to mind first are those things that the individual has been observed to choose and enjoy frequently. The following case provides a good example of this difficulty.

Joan had a behavior of destroying property. Her parents met with the school psychologist to design a program to address Joan's behavior. When asked to list those things that Joan liked best, they put music at the top of the list. Joan loved music. Each day when she returned home from school, she would turn on her cassette player to listen to her favorite music. Thus, it was decided that her parents would hold Joan's cassettes. When she did not destroy property during the day, she would be offered her choice of a cassette to listen to for a half hour before going to bed. The use of music is ethically problematic.

In another example, an individual may like coffee, but if there is free access to coffee, it would be a poor choice of a reinforcer. It is unlikely there would be motivation to change a behavior in order to earn something that is freely available. If access to coffee is restricted because staff know it would be a powerful reinforcer, serious ethical considerations arise.

Another concern with regard to the use of reinforcement is whether it is akin to bribery. There are major differences, however, between bribes and reinforcers. All employees work for pay, for example, but most would resent the implication that they are working for a bribe. Bribes are usually provided prior to a requested behavior; reinforcers are provided after the behavior is demonstrated. Additionally, bribery has an unsavory connotation. It is associated with the promotion of activities that are immoral or even illegal.

It is true, however, that the use of reinforcement creates a situation that may be less than natural. The least intrusive way to change behavior is to identify reinforcers that occur naturally within the environment. When one designs structured reinforcement schedules, the effort required to maintain the schedule and the intrusive nature of the strategy should be weighed against the anticipated effectiveness of the procedure. It is thus preferable to use more natural reinforcers whenever possible.

The Issue of Baseline Data Collection

A distinct advantage of the behavioral approach is that it allows for comparison between baseline data and treatment data. This comparison provides an objective measure of effectiveness. However, the amount of time needed to collect baseline data has ethical implications. Ethical concerns arise with regard to the effects of allowing the behavior to go untreated during the baseline period. Failure to collect baseline data, however, presents ethical dilemmas also, in terms of how to evaluate the program's effectiveness.

For example, Alex is an adolescent with mental retardation and severe aggression, including biting other people. Several teachers have required medical attention from Alex's bites. The psychologist has requested one month of baseline data prior to designing a behavior change plan for Alex. However, leaving Alex's biting behavior untreated for a full month raises ethical concerns.

The importance of collecting baseline data and the duration of this period must be weighed against the potential consequences of leaving the behavior untreated. Compromises may be required to balance the need to establish pretreatment measures against the need to protect the individual and other people from the effects of an untreated, dangerous behavior.

The Issue of Assuring Ethical Safeguards

Several safeguards should be considered to assure that behavior modification techniques are applied ethically. Adherence to the agreed upon goals and methods of behavior change programs must be monitored. Some agencies have human rights or peer review committees that are responsible for approving behavior change plans. These committees should seek to assure that the best interests of the recipients of the programs are served and that the least intrusive and restrictive methods are used.

Attention must be paid also to the qualifications and training of staff who are designing or implementing the programs. Rarely is the person who designs a program also responsible for implementing it. The persons responsible for implementation should understand fully the methods they are asked to apply. Occasionally, staff who lack sufficient training and supervised clinical practice are expected to design behavior programs. The complexity of program design must be recognized. Responsibility for program design should be limited to those persons with adequate credentials and experience.

Each profession has ethical standards that guide practice within it. Behavior change plans should be designed by qualified professionals. These professionals should then supervise implementation and provide ongoing training to the staff who are responsible for program implementation. In this way, ethical abuses can be avoided.

Summary

Ethics is the study of decision making with regard to what is right and wrong. Decisions are rarely black or white; they require careful consideration of a range of issues specific to each situation. Behavior modification raises significant ethical issues. A primary consideration is the degree of control the person designing or implementing behavioral programs has over the recipient of such programs. Control is of particular concern when behavior change plans are used with individuals with disabilities, who are often devalued by society and in settings in which opportunities for making choices are restricted. Such individuals are likely to protest the amount of control asserted over their lives by behaving in ways that are challenging.

Challenging behaviors often signify a problem with the environment rather than with the individual. Attempts to change a person's behavior to achieve adaptation to an environment that is inappropriate are ethically suspect.

Decisions as to behavioral goals and behavioral methods should be made with the participation of the individual being served, whenever possible. Not all individuals are able to participate effectively in these decisions. If they are not able to make informed decisions, objective advocates who can act on the individuals' behalf should be involved.

Some approaches to behavioral programming employ restrictive or aversive procedures. These procedures are often dehumanizing and are banned in a number of states. There are ethical considerations inherent in the use of reinforcement as well, most notably the restriction of access to previously freely available reinforcers. Finally, it is important that qualified professionals be involved in plan design, implementation, and evaluation.

Study Questions

1. Define *ethics* in your own words.
2. Discuss the ethical implications and some possible results of controlling many aspects of the lives of people with disabilities.
3. List three criteria that should be considered before a behavior is selected to be addressed by a behavior change plan.
4. Define *informed consent*. How does it apply to behavioral programming?
5. Describe a restrictive technique and discuss ethical considerations with regard to its use.
6. Define *aversive procedures*. Discuss ethical reasons why aversive procedures should be avoided.
7. Discuss an ethical issue that must be considered in selecting a reinforcer for an individual.

Exercises

1. Each afternoon when Mark returned to his residence after school, he enjoyed spending several hours snipping magazines into tiny pieces of paper. He kept his confetti in a shoe box and took pride in showing other children at the residence how much he had produced during his free time. His behavior of snipping paper was annoying to staff, however. They viewed it as unproductive and described it as not normal. With the residence's psychologist, they designed a behavior change plan to address Mark's behavior. The plan consisted of reinforcing Mark for participating in activities other than paper snipping. Discuss the ethical implications here.

2. Gary insisted on eating his lunch with a spoon, even though his teacher told him to eat with a fork. His teacher told him that table manners such as his would be unacceptable in a restaurant. She attempted to remove the spoon

from his hand and showed him that he had a fork with which to eat. Gary threw the fork, hitting another student, and swept his lunch onto the floor. His teacher told him that he needed to go to the time-out corner. Discuss how the *Cycle of Control* was operating here.

3. Wendy had a problem staying in her seat at school. During the baseline period, she left her seat an average of eight times daily. This behavior led Wendy's teacher to design a program that involved tying Wendy to her seat with a soft belt. Her teacher later pointed out proudly that the number of incidents of Wendy's out-of-seat behavior had dropped to zero after implementation of this program. Discuss the ethical implications here.

4. Karen had just arrived at a residential school. She had a problem of biting her wrist. This behavior was severe, causing her tissue damage that required medical attention. The psychologist at the school met with Karen and observed her wrist-biting behavior for about an hour in his office. During that time, she bit her wrist for over 20 minutes. The psychologist then wrote a behavior program that entailed spraying Karen with water and saying "No!" to her loudly whenever she bit her wrist. Discuss the ethical implications here.

5. Steve loved chocolate. When staff needed a reinforcer to offer Steve several times a day for completing assigned tasks, they agreed to make it chocolate. The instructions to staff were to never allow Steve chocolate other than as a reinforcer, for its power as a reinforcer would be weakened. Discuss the ethical implications here.

References

American Association on Mental Retardation. (1990). *News and Notes.* July/August, 3 (4).

Braddock, D., Hemp, R., Fujiura, G., Bachelder, L., & Mitchell, D. (1990). The state of the states in developmental disabilities. Baltimore: Paul H. Brookes Publishing Co.

Donnellan, A. M., LaVigna, G. W., Negri-Shoultz, N., & Fassbender, L. L. (1988). *Progress without punishment: Effective approaches for learners with behavior problems.* New York: Teachers College Press.

Guess, D., Helmstetter, E., Turnbull, H. R., & Knowlton, S. (1987). Use of aversive procedures with persons who are disabled: An historical review and critical analysis. *Monograph of the Association for Persons with Severe Handicaps, 2* (1), 32.

Henning, Dana. Lecture, sponsored by the Kennedy Institute. September 10, 1991. Baltimore, MD.

Kazdin, A. (1980). Acceptability of alternative treatments for deviant child behavior. *Journal of Applied Behavior Analysis, 13,* 259–273.

Knoll, J. A. (1987). *Review of revised regulations on intensive behavior management and other programs utilizing behavior modification techniques proposed by Maryland Department of Health and Mental Hygiene.* Syracuse, NY: Center on Human Policy.

LaVigna, G. W. (1987). The case against aversive stimuli: A review of the clinical and empirical evidence. An invited paper presented at the 13th annual convention of The Association for Behavior Analysis. May 1987, Nashville, TN.

The Random House dictionary of the English language, second edition, unabridged. (1987). New York: Random House, Inc.

Sidman, M. (1989). *Coercion and its fallout.* Boston, MA: Authors Cooperative, Inc.

Skinner, B. F. (1971). *Beyond freedom and dignity.* New York: Alfred A. Knopf, Inc.

Stolz, S. B. (1978). *Ethical issues in behavior modification.* Washington, DC: Jossey-Bass.

Stolz, S. B., Wienckowski, L. A., & Brown, B. S. (1975). Behavior modification: A perspective on critical issues. *American Psychologist,* 1027.

Subcommittee on Constitutional Rights of the Committee on the Judiciary (1974) United States Senate, Ninety-third Congress, second session. Individual rights and the federal role in behavior modification. Washington, DC: Government Printing Office.

Weiss, N. (1990). Positive behavioral programming. In J. F. Gardner & M. S. Chapman, *Program issues in developmental disabilities.* Baltimore: Paul H. Brookes Publishing Co.

Index

Note: Page numbers in *italics* indicate figures; page numbers followed by t indicate tables.